State College

at

Framingham

THE PROBLEMS OF
BIRDS AS PESTS

Chairmen of the Sessions

Sir LANDSBOROUGH THOMSON, c.b., o.b.e.
Air-marshal Sir PETER WYKEHAM, k.c.b., d.s.o., o.b.e., d.f.c., a.f.c.
R. K. CORNWALLIS
Professor V. C. WYNNE-EDWARDS, f.r.s.e.

THE PROBLEMS OF BIRDS AS PESTS

(Proceedings of a Symposium
held at the Royal Geographical Society,
London, on 28 and 29 September 1967)

Edited by

R. K. MURTON

and

E. N. WRIGHT

*Ministry of Agriculture, Fisheries and Food, Infestation
Control Laboratory, Worplesdon, Surrey, England*

1968

Published for the
INSTITUTE OF BIOLOGY
by
ACADEMIC PRESS
LONDON and NEW YORK

ACADEMIC PRESS INC. (LONDON) LTD.
Berkeley Square House
Berkeley Square
London, W.1

U.S. Edition published by
ACADEMIC PRESS INC.
111 Fifth Avenue
New York, New York 10003

Library of Congress Catalog Card Number: 68-17668

3 |70

PRINTED IN GREAT BRITAIN BY
W. S. COWELL LTD.
AT THE BUTTER MARKET, IPSWICH

Contributors

T. BROUGH, *Ministry of Agriculture, Fisheries and Food, Infestation Control Laboratory, Worplesdon, Surrey, England*

R. G. BUSNEL, *Institut National de la Recherche Agronomique, Laboratoire Physiologue Acoustique, Jouy-en-Josas, France*

J. H. CROOK, *Department of Psychology, University of Bristol, Bristol, England*

P. E. DAVIDSON, *Ministry of Agriculture, Fisheries and Food, Fisheries Research Laboratory, Conway, Wales*

G. M. DUNNET, *Culterty Field Station, University of Aberdeen, Scotland*

J. GIBAN, *Institut National de la Recherche Agronomique, Laboratoire Physiologie Acoustique, Jouy-en-Josas, France*

W. W. H. GUNN, *Canadian Wildlife Service, Ottawa, Canada*

R. K. MURTON, *Ministry of Agriculture, Fisheries and Food, Infestation Control Laboratory, Worplesdon, Surrey, England*

N. D. NEW, *Ministry of Technology, London, England*

*I. NEWTON, *Edward Grey Institute, Oxford University, Oxford, England*

I. J. PATTERSON, *Culterty Field Station, University of Aberdeen, Scotland*

G. SCHAEFER, *Loughborough University, Leicestershire, England*

V. E. SOLMAN, *Canadian Wildlife Service, Ottawa, Canada*

E. R. STABLES, *Ministry of Technology, London, England*

R. J. P. THEARLE, *Ministry of Agriculture, Fisheries and Food, Infestation Control Laboratory, Worplesdon, Surrey, England*

**P. WARD, *Department of Psychology, University of Bristol, Bristol, England*

E. N. WRIGHT, *Ministry of Agriculture, Fisheries and Food, Infestation Control Laboratory, Worplesdon, Surrey, England*

*Present address: The Nature Conservancy, Hope Terrace, Edinburgh, Scotland.
**Present address: Ministry of Overseas Development, Anti-Locust Research Centre, College House, Wrights Lane, London, England.

Participants in the Discussions

A. W. R. ALLCOCK, *Ministry of Technology, National Gas Turbine Establishment, Pyestock, Farnborough, Hampshire, England.*

W. R. P. BOURNE, *Scientific Adviser, Royal Air Force Ornithological Society, Shrodells Hospital, Vicarage Road, Watford, England*

W. B. BROUGHTON, *Sir John Cass College, Department of Botany and Zoology, Jewry Street, Aldgate, London, England*

J. G. W. BROWN, *British European Airways, Technical Office Aerodrome Services, Bealine House, Ruislip, Middlesex, England*

B. CAMPBELL, *Hordley, Woodstock, Oxfordshire, England*

P. CONDER, *Royal Society for the Protection of Birds, The Lodge, Sandy, Bedfordshire, England*

P. B. CORNWELL, *Rentokil Laboratories Ltd., East Grinstead, Sussex, England*

P. DARE, *Ministry of Agriculture, Fisheries and Food, Fisheries Experimental Station, Castle Bank, Conway, Caernarvon, Wales*

C. S. ELLIOTT, *National Institute of Agricultural Botany, Cambridge, England*

R. G. GIBBS, *Department of Agriculture and Forest Zoology, University College of North Wales, Bangor, Caernarvon, Wales*

J. J. D. GREENWOOD, *Department of Natural History, University of St. Andrews, Dundee, Scotland*

J. R. GULLIVER, *British Overseas Airways Corporation, Heathrow Airport, Hounslow, Middlesex, England*

H. J. HAMBURY, *Glamorgan County Naturalists' Trust, Gower Road, Sketty, Swansea, Wales*

C. J. O. HARRISON, *Bird Section, British Museum (Natural History), Cromwell Road, London, England*

G. S. HARTLEY, *Fisons Pest Control Ltd., Chesterford Park Research Station, Nr. Saffron Walden, Essex, England*

R. JARDINE, *Ministry of Technology, Abell House, London, England*

F. J. S. JONES, *Ministry of Agriculture, Fisheries and Food, Infestation Control Laboratory, Tangley Place, Worplesdon, Guildford, Surrey, England*

M. JONES, *Council for Nature, Zoological Gardens, Regents Park, London, England*

J. KEAR, *The Wildfowl Trust, Slimbridge, Gloucestershire, England*

J. D. LOCKIE, *Department of Forestry and Natural Resources, University of Edinburgh, Edinburgh, Scotland*

I. I. MCNAUGHTAN, *Ministry of Technology, Engineering Physics Department, Royal Aircraft Establishment, Farnborough, Hampshire, England*

K. MELLANBY, *The Nature Conservancy, Monks Wood Experimental Station, Abbots Ripton, Huntingdon, England*

P. LE S. MILSTEIN, *Transvaal Department of Nature Conservation, Barberspan Nature Reserve, P.O. Barberspan, Western Transvaal, Republic of South Africa*

J. D. NORRIS, *Ministry of Agriculture, Fisheries and Food, Government Buildings, Brooklands Avenue, Cambridge, England*

C. P. NORBURY, *Sherridge, Nr. Malvern, Worcestershire, England*

P. J. S. OLNEY, *Royal Society for the Protection of Birds, The Lodge, Sandy, Bedfordshire, England*

M. K. PALFREMAN, *Rentokil Laboratories Ltd., Chester Road, Manchester, Lancashire, England*

I. PRESTT, *The Nature Conservancy, Monks Wood Experimental Station, Abbots Ripton, Huntingdon, England*

J. L. SEUBERT, *United States Fish and Wildlife Service, Patuxent Research Station, Laurel, Maryland, U.S.A.*

J. SPARKS, *British Broadcasting Corporation, Broadcasting House, Whiteladies Road, Bristol, England*

D. D. B. SUMMERS, *Ministry of Agriculture, Fisheries and Food, Infestation Control Laboratory, Tangley Place, Worplesdon, Guildford, Surrey, England*

H. V. THOMPSON, *Ministry of Agriculture, Fisheries and Food, Infestation Control Laboratory, Tangley Place, Worplesdon, Guildford, Surrey, England*

J. E. THORPE, *Croftcarnoch, Killiecrankie, Perthshire, Scotland*

W. B. YAPP, *Department of Zoology and Comparative Physiology, The University, Birmingham, England*

Preface

During the latter half of the nineteenth century man was exploiting birds on a scale never seen before or since. Armed with the new breech loading shotgun he killed excessively for sport, for the pot, to fill a glass case with mounted specimens, or to adorn his womanfolk in egret and ostrich plumes and grebe furs. There was little chance for any species to be regarded as a serious pest for, even if some were harmful to agricultural production, a surfeit of cheap agricultural labour and the means and willingness to kill gave sufficient psychological relief to the farmer's frustrations. The excesses of these ruthless Victorians stimulated a minority to press for legislation to protect birds and their efforts resulted firstly in the Sea Bird Preservation Act of 1869 followed later by the more general Acts of 1880–96. No longer could the farmer slaughter any bird thought to be damaging his crops and the situation called for more critical study than had been the case hitherto. At the same time the demands of industry were causing a steady drift from the land to the cities, a condition that has hardly been checked since it began. This industrial society at first adopted a laissez-faire attitude towards country affairs but slowly, perhaps in protest against the environment of bricks and mortar, a new interest developed in wildlife. The violence, cruelty and hardship of two world wars produced an emotional backlash that has found an outlet in such pastimes as bird-watching and the subtle exploitation of this mood, through the press, radio and above all, television, has created a public that is highly sensitive to wildlife matters. It is against this background that present day bird problems must be viewed.

The second World War faced Britain with the need to be self-sufficient in her agricultural output; farming had slumped badly since the hey-day of the mid-nineteenth century, but now cereal and other production was boosted to an unprecedented level. Inevitably attention was focused on any animal liable to interfere with productivity and in response to requests from the Ministry of Agriculture, the Agricultural Research Council sponsored scientific enquiries into the agricultural status of the rook and wood-pigeon.

British farming has not looked back since these years and the pattern has been one of steadily increasing efficiency. Bird problems of agriculture were not unknown, as some of the authors have pointed out,

ix

but improved efficiency, low profit margins and a high degree of competition have increasingly focused attention on the pestiferous species and farmers have more and more clamoured for governmental action. It was in this climate of opinion that the MAFF began serious research into bird problems in agriculture in 1952. Sixteen years of work have done much to define and understand the problems but have produced little in the way of tangible answers. Much work has gone into the study of individual species and the knowledge obtained is fundamental to any advance in their management. An understanding of the population dynamics of the wood-pigeon led directly to the abandonment of costly but fruitless bounty schemes and this saving alone has justified the cost of research. Techniques for frightening and repelling birds have been investigated empirically and fundamentally to provide both immediate advice and a basis for long-term development. Humane and efficient methods of catching and killing birds have also been sought and although methods may be improved we have to admit that destruction of harmful birds shows little promise of solving the problems of crop damage. In Africa 100 million *Quelea* were killed in a year, but the subsequent population size was unaffected, likewise in Britain shooting wood-pigeons and rooks has not decreased their overall populations. Scaring remains the most effective way of protecting crops, although modern scarecrows often involve the broadcasting of recorded distress calls rather than the display of crucified carcases, while radar introduces a twentieth-century technique for detecting flocks of birds which might hazard aircraft in flight.

So it is that the ground work for future progress has been well prepared, yet the problems remain intractable; this for a very simple reason. Bird pests cannot be dealt with in scientific isolation, which has been the case with numerous entomological problems. Experience with organo-chlorine insecticides clearly demonstrated that the widescale application of poisonous chemicals to cereal seeds could reduce, if not eliminate, populations of birds. Fortunately the contamination of the environment with persistent and poisonous residues, ultimately dangerous to man himself, was halted in time – at least we hope in time – and we must be grateful that this experience has engendered a policy of utmost caution in all concerned. As a result, public sensitivity to the harmful effects of some agricultural chemicals on wildlife has made it increasingly difficult to contemplate the use of chemicals to control birds. Although safe in the sense of not leaving harmful residues or in having adverse secondary effects, these chemicals are not easily distinguished in the public mind from the general use of pesticides. Moreover, although cheap and effective methods of killing birds involving chemical

substances could be designed, they would inevitably lead to some protected birds being occasionally killed. It must be remembered that
protected species of birds, especially game birds, sometimes eat crops and
it is asking a lot to expect the scientist to develop species specific methods to kill one but not the other. Nevertheless this is the situation today.

Bird problems are therefore to a large extent political and not
scientific. Nowhere are the paradoxes more evident than in our towns
and cities. The conflict between birds as pets and birds as pests is
illustrated by the familiar town pigeon; on the one hand loved by a
bird-feeding public and on the other detested by the public health
authorities concerned at its fouling of buildings and its potential for
disease transmission.

A twentieth-century development is that man, the aeronaut, now
competes with birds for air space. Here the term pest is hardly appropriate for there is no dependence of bird populations on aircraft, the
two are merely incompatible and collisions between them have resulted
in both loss of human life and expensive repairs. For example, in 1960
an airliner at Boston, Mass., crashed with the loss of 62 lives after
flying into a flock of starlings and the Canadian Air Force has lost
7 starfighter aircraft, costing over 10 million dollars, through collisions
with birds, fortunately without loss of life. The problem has grown with
the development of the jet engine and ever increasing speeds of flight and
is now a matter of great concern to aviation authorities. As if to emphasize the importance of the problem the Symposium was honoured by
the presence of Merlyn Rees, M.P., Parliamentary Under Secretary of
State for Defence for the Royal Air Force, during the first session, and
through the acceptance by Air-marshal Sir Peter Wykeham, Deputy
Chief of Air Staff, of an invitation to take the Chair during the afternoon.
The devotion of the whole day to aviation bird problems seemed justified
by the safety aspect alone, quite apart from financial considerations, and
if the result is a greater contribution by biologists to the solution of the
problems involved it will have been well worthwhile.

Because economic ornithology provides such a good example of the
conflicts that may arise between biology and the conduct of human
affairs our Director, Dr. I. Thomas, recognized that this subject would
be ideal for a Symposium of the Institute of Biology and was instru-
mental in getting it inaugurated. It is fitting that this collection of
papers should be published in his year of retirement from a lifetime of
work devoted to Applied Biology.

July, 1968   R. K. Murton

                                                    E. N. Wright

Contents

Birds and Aircraft

Birds and Agriculture

Birds and Aircraft

Chairman's Introduction

SIR LANDSBOROUGH THOMSON

It is to be hoped that the title, "Problems of Birds as Pests", will not lead anyone to think that this symposium has been conceived in a spirit of hostility to bird-life. Most of those taking part are in fact ornithologists or conservationists, or both. The perspective in which the topic should be viewed is that control is an aspect of conservation, requiring study like any other. In an environment where the balance of nature has been greatly disturbed, mankind has a responsibility for wildlife management; this properly includes reasonable defence of human material interests.

Birds are to a large extent economically beneficial; they are also, of course, scientifically interesting and aesthetically delightful. Yet some species tend to be harmful, and others become pests when present in excessive numbers or in the wrong places. The task is, dispassionately and objectively, to determine the facts and consider what to do.

It may be noted, incidentally, that birds may be pests not only to mankind but to other species of birds and to wildlife generally. Another point is that control does not necessarily involve destruction. In respect of hazards to aviation, for instance, the remedy can scarcely lie in that direction. The bird-lover may also take comfort from the fact that investigation has often shown, in particular cases, that drastic forms of control are unnecessary, because the problem has been misunderstood; or that they are futile, because they fail to achieve their object.

The study of the control of bird pests may be regarded as a form of applied ornithology. It should draw freely on the general pool of scientific knowledge of birds—their distribution and migrations, their ecology and behaviour. But one also expects a return flow of information; as in other fields, the investigation of practical problems brings out new knowledge that is of interest in a wider context.

Birds and Aircraft : the Problems

E. R. STABLES and N. D. NEW

Ministry of Technology, London, England

This paper presents a brief survey of the subject, with special reference to the problems that affect aircraft designers, operators, and others concerned with the precautions that have to be taken to minimize the danger and damage caused by bird strikes.

A collision with a bird is an accident, and when we consider accidents to aircraft we are inclined to think, quite naturally, of danger to human life. The seriousness of a particular type of accident is often judged by the number of people killed or injured. Fortunately the bird hazard does not have to be regarded as a serious risk on this basis. In spite of the fact that aircraft have now spent millions of hours in the air carrying millions of people the number of reports of fatal accidents caused by bird strikes is very small. There seems no reason to doubt the accuracy of records in this respect, as major aircraft accidents are always investigated very thoroughly. Military as well as civil types have a low record of fatal accidents due to bird strikes, and, when one considers the damage that collision with birds can cause, it is remarkable that more human lives have not been lost. There have been, it seems, only two major disasters and one very near disaster:

In 1960 at Boston, U.S.A., an Electra took off with seventy-two persons on board, and soon after take-off flew into a flock of starlings. One engine failed immediately and the power of another two was substantially reduced for a short time, causing the aircraft to yaw, stall, and spin into the ground from 150 ft. Sixty-two persons on board were killed.

In 1962 in the state of Maryland, U.S.A., a Viscount collided with a flock of whistling swans at 6 000 ft altitude. Strikes on the tailplane caused the port side of it to break off and the aircraft to dive vertically to the ground. All seventeen persons on board were killed.

In 1962 at Turnhouse airport, Edinburgh, a Vanguard flew into a large flock of gulls immediately after take-off, at night and in poor weather. This was in spite of the fact that the airfield had been

3

inspected and declared free of birds 15 min before take-off. Number 1 engine failed immediately and the remaining three lost power. Number 2 engine also failed very soon afterwards, leaving the aircraft to fly on numbers 3 and 4 engines only, both on one side of the aircraft. Number 3 engine then became critical and the pilot kept it running beyond its limitations and managed just to maintain height, circle and make a successful landing, being airborne for half an hour with 76 persons on board. A marvellous performance, but an extremely "near miss". One hundred and twenty-five dead gulls were recovered after the incident.

Smaller aircraft do not appear to have suffered greatly in comparison with the larger types.

In 1962 at Lahore, Pakistan, a vulture struck the windscreen of a Dakota when on late finals of approach, killing the second pilot. Fortunately the first pilot was able to keep control and made a normal landing.

In 1964 at Newtownards, Northern Ireland, a little Turbulent private aircraft, whilst on late finals of approach to land, struck a bird a glancing blow on the windscreen, stalled and spun into the ground, killing the pilot. The perspex windscreen in this case was not broken and it can only be surmised that the shock of the strike caused the amateur pilot to allow the aircraft, which would at this stage of approach be flying slowly, to stall and the consequential incipient spin followed when there was insufficient height to recover.

The Royal Air Force and Royal Navy have a good fatal accident record with respect to bird strikes due to the efficiency of the British ejector seat which has saved air crews who would otherwise have been killed. In general it may be said that, compared with the loss of life caused by other kinds of aircraft accident, the risk of death or injury from bird strikes has so far proved small. Whether this will remain so in future is questionable.

Although the danger to human life has been slight, the amount of damage caused has been and continues to be very substantial (Plates 1 and 2). The bird strike problem is therefore largely one of the cost of repairs, replacement of damaged parts, delays to scheduled services, loss of operational use, reduction in aircraft efficiency due to built-in protection, and the cost of the various bird control schemes for reducing the risk of bird impact. It is not easy to assess the total monetary cost. But to give a rough idea we can say that the annual repair and replacement bills resulting from bird strikes in the Royal Air Force alone are

PLATE 1. Penetration of the pressure cabin of a Canberra by a large bird.

PLATE 2. A view inside the cockpit of the aircraft shown in Plate 3 showing damage to the forward side of the instrument panel. The navigator was only slightly injured in this case.

PLATE 3. Result of testing the centre windscreen of a passenger aircraft with the gun shown in Plate 4A firing a 4 lb bird at 272 m.p.h. during the course of development of the panel.

estimated to total about £1 million sterling a year. Several hundred strikes are recorded annually, and undoubtedly many go unrecorded. On the civil side, the cost of such repairs to BOAC and BEA, and the number of strikes experienced, appear to be very much less, and about one serious strike in twenty thousand flights seems to be the order of incidence. The difference between the military and civil experience is no doubt explained by a greater emphasis on low flying, including flying training, in the Services. Bird populations and habits, and consequently the hazards, vary in different countries. Local conditions naturally have a great effect and in some regions the problem is considerably more serious both to military and civil aircraft than it is in the United Kingdom. The difficulty of estimating or assessing overall costs increases the difficulty of determining very rationally all that ought to be done to reduce the incidence and minimize the effects of bird strikes.

The foregoing has dealt with the broad nature of the problem. How can or should it be tackled, and how is it being tackled? The methods to be considered fall under five headings.

(1) Reduce the number of birds.

(2) Make the birds get out of the way of the aeroplanes.

(3) Arrange for the aeroplanes to avoid the birds.

(4) Add physical protection to the aircraft.

(5) Endeavour to change to types of aircraft that are inherently safer with regard to bird strikes.

(1) To set about reducing the numbers of birds to an extent that would have an appreciable effect on the problem as a whole would seem highly undesirable. It would, of course, be for biologists to advise upon any attempts to tackle the problem on this basis, either on a small or large scale, but most people would be opposed in principle. If faced with the choice of which to eliminate—birds or aeroplanes—most of us would probably choose the latter.

(2) To make the birds get out of the way of the aeroplanes is the subject of much research and experiment which is dealt with by other contributors. Various devices have been tried and one adopted for regular use. But although they are helpful they are inadequate in the sense that none has so far proved satisfactory enough to be regarded as lessening the need for further research into means of combating the bird strike hazard. Most of the schemes for removing birds are expensive and public interest in what is done to birds has to be considered.

(3) Bird populations are so scattered over the surface of the world that it is virtually impossible for aircraft operators to adopt a policy of keeping to routes that are free or nearly free of them. In other words, it is generally impracticable to take avoiding action in a lateral direction. But with regard to altitude the picture is very different. Nearly all the birds spend most of their time near the ground, thus making avoiding action by means of height both possible and practicable. There are substantial economic advantages to be gained by flying civil airliners at altitudes higher than those achieved by birds. Although birds are occasionally seen at great heights, even above 20 000 ft, the majority fly for most of their time at what are regarded as low altitudes by aircraft standards. Records show that about 95% of bird strikes occur below 6 000 ft, and about 60% below 2 000 ft. Current long-distance airliners cruise at above 30 000 ft and the supersonic transports of the future are likely to cruise at about 50 000 ft. Only during part of the climb and descent does the bird hazard exist for these aircraft. This does not apply, however, to short range and military aircraft. To fly

low is a way of avoiding radar detection and is necessary for certain military operations, while to fly fast reduces the chance of successful enemy attack. Most flying training is also carried out at lower altitudes. Hence most strikes on military aircraft occur at lower altitudes than those on civil craft; in fact, about 95% of military bird strikes happen below 2 000 ft, and about 70% below 500 ft. To travel at high altitude is undoubtedly one of the best ways of dealing with the bird strike problem; but all aircraft pass through the regions of greatest bird density, and some must operate at these heights for long periods. So there is much scope for devices which will give warning of the presence and location of birds and enable flight times or routes to be modified accordingly.

(4) Because the risk of collision with birds appears very difficult to eliminate, aircraft designers naturally try to devise ways and means of minimizing the damage when collisions do occur, and look to other scientists and engineers to help them. The good designer will always pay special attention to the possibility of bird impact on the forward facing parts of the structure, and try to design them in such a way that a strike will not be catastrophic; the damage should be localized and not allowed to cause serious loss of structural strength or disrupt essential services or controls or produce a leakage of inflammable fluid.

The pilot's windscreen presents a particular problem; it has to be very thick, sometimes about $1\frac{1}{2}$ in., and heavy in order to minimize the risk of bird penetration and injury to the pilot. A typical panel may cost as much as £400. One method of construction (Fig. 1) involves placing a thick layer of polyvinyl butyral between the glass layers. In the event of a bird strike, after the glass has shattered, this "vinal" layer, being somewhat elastic, prevents complete penetration by the bird. Thus, although the panel struck is no longer transparent, air pressure is maintained within the cabin and the flight can continue with the first or second pilot seeing through the remaining windscreen panels. But for

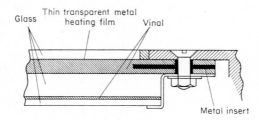

FIG. 1. This form of windscreen construction has been used to resist bird strikes.

the "vinal" to be effective and not too brittle when cold, it has to be kept at a temperature around 40°C. This is achieved with an exceedingly thin and transparent film of metal, often gold, applied to one of the layers of the windscreen, through which an electric current is passed. Other plastics are now replacing glass, resulting in a 50% or more saving in weight for a comparable strength.

In the modern gas turbine engine, containing many small blades rotating at very high speed between rows of stationary blades, it is difficult to localize damage in the event of a bird strike and the designer has to allow for loads which would not otherwise arise and which are not easy to estimate. Unlike the propeller, which is robust and rotates less fast and could thread its way through flocks of birds with comparative safety, the turbine engine has to take in huge quantities of air, and bird ingestion is a problem. Small birds can be passed through with little or no damage to the engine, but larger ones and flocks can cause serious damage or stoppage of air flow with partial or complete loss of power. It might be thought that a guard of some sort could be placed in front of the air intakes, but the disadvantages are quite appreciable, including a serious increase in fuel consumption and the creation of icing problems.

(5) It may be thought surprising that a metal skinned aircraft, weighing 100 tons or so, cannot withstand safely the impact of birds weighing a few ounces or a few pounds. It is not easy to gauge the disruptive effect of impact at high speed, so it may be helpful to translate the damaging power of a bird into something which can be more readily appreciated. If we imagine a ton weight, say a 2 ft 6 in. cube of concrete, suspended at about 22 ft above the ground, suddenly released and allowed to fall freely, the force of the impact with the ground (or more strictly the energy that has to be absorbed on impact) is the same as when a 4 lb bird strikes an aeroplane travelling at 600 miles/h. This case may also be compared with a motor car crashing into an aeroplane at 25 miles/h. It should be noted that in contrast to the block of concrete or the motor car, the bird's impact is concentrated on an area of only a few square inches and the disruptive effect is proportionately greater (Fig. 2). Let us now consider what is today reckoned an extremely low speed, namely 60 miles/h, attainable only on a few aircraft types. Here the energy will be one-hundredth of our high speed example, since energy varies as the square of velocity. One of the first things to note, therefore, about the bird strike hazard is that, other things being equal, the damage caused by birds increases greatly with speed, and it follows that much progress towards reduction of the problem would come from a reduction in aircraft speed, especially at low altitudes where most birds are to be

B*

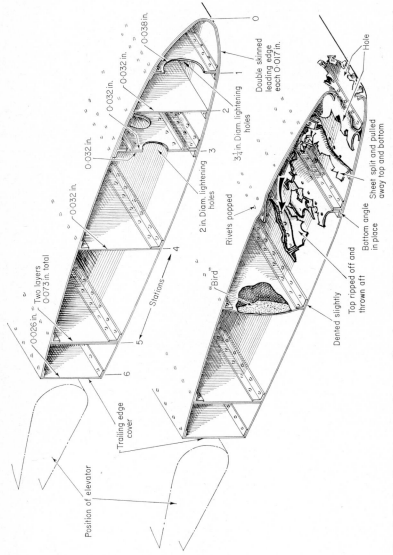

FIG. 2. Bird strike test on a tail plane. (Based on Field Note No. 44, issued by the Associate Committee on Bird Hazards to Aircraft, National Research Council, Canada).

found. However, to reduce the landing and take-off speeds of a conventional aircraft involves reducing its top and cruising speeds, so there seems little prospect of achieving this in the future. The advantages gained from high speed both in the military and civil uses are such as to give little hope of a general return to slower air travel, with lower landing and take-off speeds. It might be thought that Vertical and Short Take-Off and Landing aircraft and helicopters would provide an answer to the question of speed, but this is only partially true. V/STOL aircraft can fly at high speed when cruising, and a bird sucked into the engine while hovering could be disastrous, while the top speed of helicopter rotor blades can be as high as 500 miles/h. One method of reducing the high speed danger is fortuitous. The large impact forces that we have just considered depend upon the bird flying directly into the aircraft. If the bird does not penetrate but is merely deflected past the surface of the wing or fuselage the forces will be less. The swept back, thin wings of modern high speed aircraft are theoretically the right shapes for deflecting birds and should give less chance of penetration than did the rounded sections of the slower aircraft of the past. However, if the surface struck deforms appreciably on impact, as is likely to happen, the advantage of the angular contact may be lost.

Research workers at universities and government establishments give valuable help to the aircraft and engine designers in combating the bird hazard. At the Royal Aircraft Establishment and the National Gas Turbine Establishment tests are carried out to simulate as realistically as possible on the ground the impact of birds with windscreens and engines in flight. The experiments with windscreens were started during the second World War and the method then used was to suspend a dead bird and propel a windscreen into it. Nowadays special air guns are used to propel the bird into the object under test (Plates 3, 4A and B). Some firms as well as government establishments possess these devices, and work is now proceeding on the testing of typical aircraft structures to determine their resistance to bird impact. This kind of research and experiment is expensive and takes a long time. There are usually many variations of design and conditions to cover, and unfortunately not very much scientific manpower can be employed on the work owing to the cost and demands for effort in other fields.

Determination of official regulations governing the airworthiness of aircraft in respect of bird strikes is the responsibility of the Air Registration Board for civil aircraft, and the Ministries of Defence and Technology for military types. The Air Registration Board already requires windscreens and engines to be safe against birds of up to 4 lb

PLATE 4. A bird strike test facility showing (A) the bird gun and (B) the test specimen. The speed of the shot is controlled by the air pressure in the container at the breech of the gun and the actual speed achieved is measured electronically as the projectile breaks thin wires stretched across each end of the frame shown in front of the target.

weight at maximum aircraft speeds up to 8 000 ft altitude, and extension of these regulations to cover the whole aeroplane is now under
consideration. The reason for the choice of 4 lb for civil aircraft is
interesting. When numbers of bird strikes are plotted on a graph against
the weight of the birds involved, the resulting curve shows a marked
change of slope in the region of 4 lb (Fig. 3). By far the greatest number
of strikes occurs with birds of under 1 lb in weight. Between 1 and 3 lb
the number decreases appreciably, between 3 and 4 lb it becomes
relatively small, and above 4 lb quickly reaches very small proportions.
So the choice of 4 lb for civil aircraft is a logical one; it also happens to
fit in quite well with what has proved to be feasible in the practical problems of protecting the aircraft. To attempt to provide good protection
against birds weighing 6 or 8 lb would seriously handicap the aircraft
designer; to set a general standard of 20 lb or so would appear to be out
of the question—a swan-proof aeroplane would be so heavy as to be

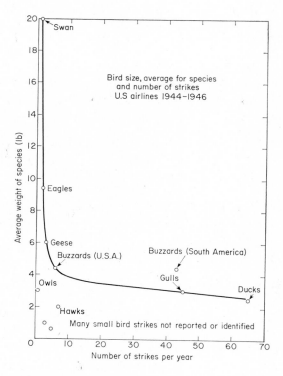

FIG. 3. Based on Field Note No. 42 issued by the Associate Committee on Bird Hazards
to Aircraft, National Research Council, Canada.

useless. A general rule such as that fixed by the Air Registration Board is not applied to military aircraft because of their many different roles; the required bird resistance is specified separately for each new aircraft type.

Committees and working parties drawn from government departments, research establishments and industry, meet periodically to discuss the bird hazard problem and endeavour to keep in touch with everything that is going on, and make recommendations on what ought to be done. They bring together the different specialists who can contribute: scientists, engineers, administrators and operators of aircraft both military and civil are represented on these committees, which now exist in the major European countries and in the Commonwealth and America. Special mention should perhaps be made of Canada's contribution where the Canadian National Research Council has taken a great interest in the problem. In Britain the Ministry of Technology has set up within one of its research and development branches a committee known as the Bird Impact Research and Development Committee which meets three times a year.

The problems that the birds set the invaders of their environment are not easily solved. The many variable factors involved make prediction of the incidence and effect of bird strikes difficult. It seems that experience may be the only reliable guide of what should be done, and of how priorities should be allocated. It is to be hoped that scientific studies will continue and that co-ordinated statistical records being kept will further a better appreciation of what needs to be done to keep the accident risks and the costs of bird strikes to a minimum.

SUMMARY

Considering the potentially serious damage to an aeroplane that a bird strike can do, it is surprising that the loss of life has not been greater.

The "force" of a strike is very great. With an aircraft flying at 600 m.p.h. a strike with a 4 lb bird can be likened to a one ton block of concrete, measuring 2 ft 6 in. cube, being dropped from a height of 22 ft, or a motor car crashing head on into a wall at 25 m.p.h., the "force" of the strike being concentrated into an area on the aeroplane of the size of the bird, say 3 in. to 4 in. diameter.

Very strong specially constructed windscreens are necessary to protect the pilot. Jet engines are very vulnerable, both to damage to the static and rotating blades of the compressor, which turn at very high speed, and to being "suffocated" by a number of birds being sucked into the intake and forming a screen across the front of the engine. Guards are not a practicable solution but engines incorporating recent design improvements are less vulnerable.

On civil aircraft provision has to be made against a strike with a 4 lb bird at the maximum speed likely to be flown below 8 000 ft. It is not practicable to make provision for strikes at very high speed or with heavier birds.

The density of birds is greatest near the ground and fortunately civil passenger aircraft fly most of their time at a height above where birds are expected to be found. The maximum strike probability therefore occurs during take-off and early climb, and approach and landing. Under these conditions the speed of the aircraft will be lower than when cruising at its operational height, so a strike on the airframe is unlikely to cause serious damage. Damage to engines is less closely related to the forward speed of the aircraft.

Military aircraft fly a greater proportion of their time at lower altitudes, and fly faster at these altitudes. Even so, the number of serious accidents is surprisingly small. The ejector seat has saved a number of lives. The total cost of repairs to aircraft after bird strikes is enormous and aircraft are put out of use while repairs are carried out or an engine changed. An engine change may cost as much as £75,000. When the pilot has ejected from a military aircraft, the aircraft is, of course, invariably a complete write-off after it has crashed and there is the danger to people and property on the ground.

Bird strike tests were formerly carried out by mounting the component of the aircraft on a sled and running it into a suspended dead bird at the appropriate speed. Tests are now carried out with a compressed air gun, having a barrel of about 6 in. bore and 50 ft long, which fires the dead bird, generally a chicken, at the test component which is mounted as a stationary target.

ACKNOWLEDGEMENTS

We wish to acknowledge the provision of information and assistance given us in the preparation of this paper and illustrations by Mr. R. Crick, English Electric Company (Luton); Mr. M. S. Kuhring, Chairman Associate Committee on Bird Hazards to Aircraft, National Research Council, Canada; Mr. H. S. Fowler, National Research Council, Canada; Mr. H. Bird, Air Canada; Mr. A. G. L. Huggins, Board of Trade; Mr. J. D. Harris, Air Registration Board; Mr. I. I. McNaughtan, Royal Aircraft Establishment; Mr. A. W. R. Allcock, National Gas Turbine Establishment; Squadron Leader P. F. Hart, Ministry of Defence;

Mr. R. Belton, British Overseas Airways Corporation; Messrs. Morgan, Burge, Kenwood, Searle and Brown, British European Airways; Mr. J. C. Reynolds, British United Airways; Captain J. Manning, British Eagle International Airlines Limited; and the loan of the films and slides from Anglia Television, English Electric Company (Luton) and the Royal Aircraft Establishment (Crown Copyright. Reproduced with the permission of the controller, Her Majesty's Stationery Office).

Prospective Considerations Concerning Bio-Acoustics in Relation to Bird-scaring Techniques

R. G. BUSNEL and J. GIBAN

Institut National de la Recherche Agronomique, Jouy-en-Josas, France

INTRODUCTION

Since the early work done by Frings (1955, 1958), Busnel, *et al.* (1957) and their co-workers on the use of acoustic distress calls to attract or repel certain species of gregarious birds, particularly *Laridae, Sturnidae* and *Corvidae,* a whole literature has grown up describing the development of these methods, the equipment and the exploitation of the results from the practical point of view, either in agriculture or on airfields. Papers on synthesis and reports of international symposia, mostly organized in France, have surveyed the question already. If it is now possible to look back and gauge the advantages of these methods in relation to the needs of our civilization, from the point of view of applied research, it seems necessary to see what theoretical aspects of this problem might enable us to launch out on further development, or change of methods.

The object of this report is to define certain points of scientific interest concerning these problems.

SYSTEM OF BEHAVIOUR AND HIERARCHY OF SIGNALS

The acoustic distress signal alone, with some strictly gregarious species of birds, provokes the now well-known type of reaction in which flight is followed by attraction to the source of sound and then finally by dispersal and temporary abandonment of the area. It has been demonstrated that in this behaviour this type of signal possesses a predominant hierarchical value. However, careful examination of the reaction with the species mentioned (*Laridae, Sturnidae, Corvidae*) shows that if, at long range, this signal has this dominant position, a second signal, valid at the level of the source of sound and of an optical nature, is certainly necessary for complete realization of the succession of phases of this behaviour. The distress cry is not generally emitted in objective, natural conditions of behaviour except when a bird is actually in a condition of distress, i.e. for instance, when struggling with a bird of prey. In fact, if the distress call has been artificially

17

replaced by a recording, it may be envisaged that the addition of an animated dummy at the level of the source of sound, for instance that of a bird of prey or a cat, would thus complete the series of stimuli which release the reactional behaviour associated with the distress signal. In these circumstances one would probably observe different and more formal behaviour, at least in the final stage.

The feeding call, has neither been specially used for practical applications on a large scale, nor been demonstrated experimentally except in the case of the *Laridae* (Frings *et al.* (1955)). If, however, such a call were followed by an automatic distribution of food at a localized point it would probably be possible to obtain a local settlement of birds. It would remain to be seen whether the competition between such distributed food and the natural sources of food would be valid from an economic point of view. One can imagine that this distribution of food could consist of bait containing poisons or sterilants, at least at certain times of the year, in order to diminish reproduction, or reduce local populations.

A few observations, although not fulfilling strict experimental conditions have been made on the use of fireworks to disperse flocks of birds. There is no doubt about the temporary scaring action they produce but, purely from the point of view of behaviour, it would appear much sounder if these pyrotechnics were associated with the acoustic distress signal. It may then be possible to obtain flight conditioning of local sedentary populations, by reinforcement of the effect of noise alone, through the use of a meaningful (biological) signal.

Finally, returning to the first case: the use of the distress signal alone holds good for agricultural situations or on airfields where the intensity of the signal can be of the order of 115 dB at 1 m from the loudspeaker, giving extensive acoustic cover of the order of 1 km². But close to dwellings this source of nuisance to human beings needs to be prohibited, and this brings about a restriction in the use of this method. The addition of an optical stimulus would probably enable the sound intensity to be reduced while keeping the same effectiveness of the acoustic signal. We are studying a device of this kind which it should be possible to use close to dwellings with sound levels in the order of 80 dB covering 100 m by 100 m and thus becoming tolerable for the neighbouring human populations.

To return to the behaviour as a whole one should stress the point of research with regard to other signals and their possible combination, based on the natural sequence. Thus alarm signals combined with distress signals deserve to be studied as they would make stronger reactions possible.

To sum up therefore, it is the whole series of possible signals which ought to be studied. Individual calls should not be isolated from the total context, as has been done hitherto with a view to simplification and because the distress signal alone has already proved effective, but be associated with each other according to the temporal process of their successive sequence.

The Informative Content of Acoustic Signals

Research into the physical parameters which support the information in acoustic signals is a subject of fundamental interest which is now accepted by a number of bio-acousticians; but studies in this field are still too few. Only about a dozen are known, on Insects, Amphibians and Mammals. On birds, the works of Bremond (1962, 1966) and Falls (1962) may be specially cited.

If the theory of this research is simple, technically it necessitates complicated equipment and considerable experimentation, the results of which must be statistically significant to be valid. Measures of redundancy, syntactic levels, variations of the decay rate, repetition rate of the frequencies occurring in some parts of a signal—are necessary, all of which is very time consuming. It does not seem necessary to refer here to the wiring systems which have to be employed using filters, modulators, speed adjusters, frequency and time transposers. But it should be made clear that only studies in this direction will make it possible to isolate the physical characteristic or characteristics of a sound signal which are the primary releasers of the reactions. It is worth recalling here that for instance a variation of 5% in the rise time of a single transient can alter the reaction of an insect by 50%. The object of this research is of course to succeed in isolating various effective characteristics and to regroup them in a single synthetic signal. It is, however, also desirable to obtain these with low cost electronic apparatus for practical applications and to envisage the realization both of "super-signals" and of interspecific synthetic signals.

This general problem of the analysis of the physical factors carrying the information then links up at theoretic level with that of the recognition of forms, which should, itself, lead to more effective models of stimulation than the natural signals. It is only in this way that one may hope to achieve "supersignals" which, entering directly into the innate behaviour reactions should lead to suppression of habituation, i.e. to true reflex reactions.

Everything we know at present about the quality of broadcasts of signals shows that recognition of the form, in the species studied, demands only a minimum of signal structure which is not composed of the instantaneous spectrum but of the envelope, the rise time and the variations in the amplitude of frequency modulations. But the relative importance of these elements is not yet known. It will of course vary with each species. The future of this research is linked to the availability of computers capable of measuring and extracting all the relative parameters, classifying them and finally synthetising artificial signals according to programmes which will be calculated by the machine. Figs. 1–5 illustrate the principle of the method using a computer-vocoder system. Examples are given for *Larus argentatus* and *Sturnus vulgaris*.

These calculated forms of signals will certainly still have to be tested on the birds and even then it will probably be necessary to consider a totally different method of approach from that used up to now, which consists in working with wild, free animals. The knowledge of the electrophysiological reactions of the higher nervous centres of isolated animals picked up with chronic electrodes for instance, like evoked potentials, and transmitted by telemetry, will enable us to develop this type of analysis. At present, the considerable expenditure of time taken by experiments in the field through chance encounters with wild animals, have greatly hampered such experimentation.

Analysis of the auditory memory of birds, both of the phosphorescent and the long term memory, will also be an essential stage in the effective perfection of the use of such signals, making possible a better analysis of the problem of conditioning.

INTERSPECIFICITY

What can be expected of the idea of interspecificity which we stated earlier on and which is now a well-established fact?

It is certain that interspecificity of the signal based on conditioning connected with an ecological and geographical situation of a particular kind can only be of general value, since it is too confined to particular situations. One must nevertheless think that its essential interest lies in the possibility of a bird reconstructing the acoustic form or forms which release this or that behaviour from elements which are physically very varied. Comparative analysis by calculation of the sound images, not by sonagrammes which only give a crude idea without easy mathematical correlation of the various elements, should make it possible to isolate these common criteria and thus to link up the ideas mentioned previously with a view to achieving a synthetic interspecific supersignal.

THE SIGNAL-NOISE RATIO

We recently demonstrated, with our British colleagues (Bremond, Brough, Gramet and Wright, 1968) that the use of a "high-fidelity" broadcast system is of definite advantage in cases where birds are subjected to a natural background noise at a high level. This type of research, which concerns the signal to noise ratio and which to our knowledge is the first of its kind, deserves to be developed. In fact this ratio is directly connected with the intelligibility of the informative parameters of the signal, some of which are deadened by surrounding low-frequency noises (the sound of waves breaking on the shore, the noise of wind, etc.) in field experiments. The auditory capacities of birds which are up to now only known through electrophysiological measurements must be studied again by behavioural methods; this must be done, not with pure frequency signals, but with natural signals which are of a complex structure, and here again the informative characteristics, which must be sought for independently, will be a key to the psycho-physiological reactions.

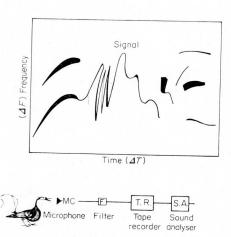

Fig.1. Recording system components of the bird-signal (MC: microphone; F: filter; T.R.: tape-recorder; S.A.: sound analyzer) and general pattern of a sonagram (ΔF: frequency in kHz; ΔT- time).

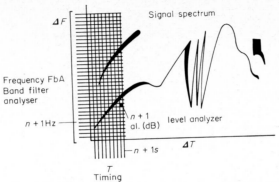

FIG. 2. The signal is analyzed by the vocoder, in different respects, separately:
  (a) The total time of the signal is cut in time fractions (T: timing). The time is chosen in relation to the thickness required and the detail needed ($n + 1\ s$).
  (b) The total frequency of the signal-spectrum is divided in frequency bands by pass-band filter (generally 1/3 of octave, or less).
  (c) The total amplitude of each unit related to the time-section and the frequency-band of the filter (section) is measured by a level analyzer with an arbitrary scale of amplitude, with unit of sound pressure each 4 or 2 dB [$n + 1$ al. (dB)].

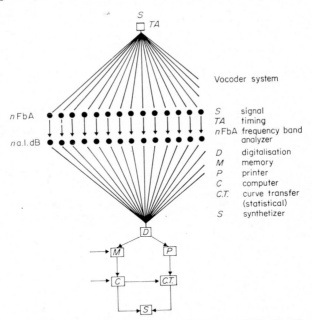

FIG. 3. This picture summarizes the detailed explanations of Fig. 2. After the different parameters (time, amplitude, level, and pass-band filter) are extracted from the signal (S), all the information is digitalized and sent on two tracks. One is on a printer (P) which writes the value of the different parameters (see Figs. 4a and 5b). This printer can be followed by a curve-tracer which makes a scale curve of the values of the digitalization. By the other track, all the data are recorded on a computer memory (M) and are analyzed statistically by the computer (C). The results can be injected to the curve-tracer ($C.T.$), to obtain some statistical curves. Both tracks can be connected with an inverse-vocoder, which gives a synthetic signal with the parameters extracted from the natural one, or from artificial values injected at the level of the digitalization system.

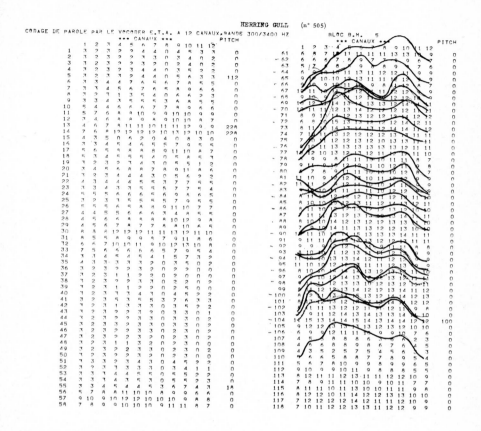

FIG. 4(a). Example of some records for a herring-gull *Larus argentatus*, obtained at the end of the printing machine, after the digitalization. Vertical lines: each one corresponds at one filter pass-band the total range of the frequency is 8 kHz, and this scale of 8 000 Hz is cut in 12 band-filters (780, 940, 1 160, 1 360, 1 600, 2 000, 2 400, 3 000, 3 600, 4 000, 5 400, 6 600 Hz). The time section between two horizontal lines is 1/100th of a second. On the horizontal line the values printed, for each filter, are the arbitrary amplitude value for an artificial amplitude level of 4 dB (with ± 2 dB of precision). The scale is with 16 levels (range 64 dB). On the right-part of the printing obtained from the printing-machine, some of the curves given by the curve-tracing device, and corresponding at different times. The sums of these curves are not normally made, but we give this example here for general information. See also fig. 4(b) which is the sonagram of the same natural signal.

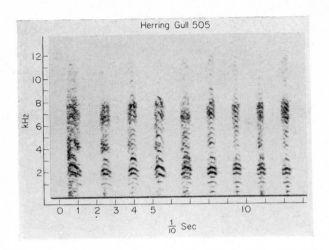

Fig. 4(b). Sonagram of Herring Gull No. 505.

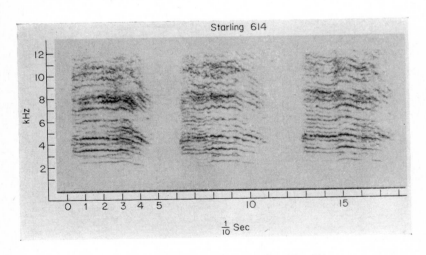

Fig. 5(a). Sonagram of the Starling No. 614.

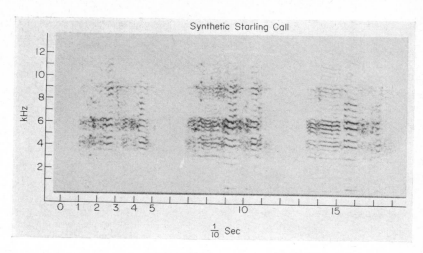

Fig. 5(b). Synthetic signal produced by the vocoder with the information extracted from the natural signal.

SUMMARY

In order to improve the effectiveness of acoustic bird-scaring techniques several fundamental approaches may be defined:

1. Addition of optical signals.

2. Measurement and analysis of acoustic signals other than the so-called distress signals: such as awakening, alarm, flight, and food-finding calls.

3. Investigation of the physical parameters of signals supporting the information so as to define the criteria for recognition of forms and study the correlation of these various parameters in different species from a statistical point of view.

This kind of research can only be envisaged at the present time with computers, since the sonagraphic method does not permit this type of analysis, although it has been, and remains, useful.

4. Investigation of a method of studying the reactions of captive birds; it has been suggested that this should deal with the evoked potentials in order to permit deep research in relatively constant psychophysiological conditions which would be less burdensome than working in nature with erratic animals.

These methods of approach should make it possible to obtain inter-specific supersignals which would be more effective for the objects proposed.

ACKNOWLEDGEMENTS

We wish to thank the Acoustical Laboratory of the C.N.E.T., (Lannion), its head G. Ferrieu and his co-workers, for the common discussions and work with the vocoder of their own; and A.-J. Andrieu and Mrs. M.-J. Eucher for the sound-spectrograms and the recordings of the different signals.

REFERENCES

Brémond, J.-C. (1962). Paramètres physiques du chant de défense territoriale du rouge-gorge (*Erithacus rubecula*). *C.r. hebd. Séanc. Acad. Sci., Paris,* **254**, 2072–2074.

Brémond, J.-C. (1966). Recherches sur la semantique et les éléments physiques déclencheurs de comportements dans les signaux acoustiques du rouge-gorge (*Erithacus rubecula*). Thesis C.N.R.S. A.O.1120 Paris.

Brémond, J.-C., Brough, T., Gramet, Ph. and Wright, E. N. (1968). A comparison of some broadcasting equipment and recorded distress calls for scaring birds. *J. appl. Ecol.* (In press.)

Busnel, R. G., Giban, J., Gramet, Ph., Frings, H., Frings, M. and Jumber, J. (1957). Interspecificité des signaux acoustiques ayant une valeur sémantique pour des Corvidés européens et nord-americains. *C.r. hebd. Séanc. Acad. Sci., Paris* **245**, 105–108.

Falls, J. B. (1962). Properties of bird song eliciting responses from territorial males. *Proc. XIII Int. orn. Congr., Ithaca* **I**, 259–271.

Frings, H., Frings, M., Jumber, J., Busnel, R. G., Giban, J. and Gramet, Ph. (1958). Reactions of American and French species of *Corvus* and *Larus* to recorded communication signals tested reciprocally. *Ecology* **39**, 126–131.

Frings, H., Frings, M., Cox, B. and Peissner, L. (1955). Recorded calls of herring gulls (*Larus argentatus*) as repellents and attractants. *Science, N.Y.* **121**, 340–341.

BIBLIOGRAPHY

GENERAL WORKS

Busnel, R. G. and Giban, J. (1958). Colloque sur "La Protection Acoustique des Cultures et Autres Moyens d'Effarouchement des Oiseaux". *C.r. Réun. Lab. Physiol. Acoust.* Jouy-en-Josas (26–7 Nov.). Also *I.N.R.A.* (1960). 1–246.

Busnel, R. G. (1963). "Acoustic Behaviour of Animals" 3–933. Elsevier, Amsterdam.

Busnel, R. G. and Giban, J. (1963). Colloque sur "Le Problème des Oiseaux sur les Aérodromes". *C.r. Réun.* Nice (25–7 Nov.). Also *I.N.R.A.* (1965). 3–326.

Brémond, J.-C. (1966). Thèse sur "Recherches sur la sémantique et les éléments physiques déclencheurs de comportements dans les signaux acoustique du rouge-gorge (*Erithacus rubecula* L.)" *Thes. pres. Fac. Sci., Paris* (18 Nov.). 1–112.

Giban, J. (1961). Colloque sur "Les Moyens de Protection contre les Espèces d'Oiseaux Comettant les Dégats en Agriculture. *C.r. Réun. C.N.R.A.* Versailles (9–11 Oct.). Also *Annls Epiphyt.* (1962). 1st series. **13**, 3–258.

SPECIALIZED ARTICLES

Brémond, J.-C. (1962). Paramètres physiques du chant de défense territoriale du rouge-gorge (*Erithacus rubecula*). *C. r. hebd. Séanc. Acad. Sci., Paris.* **254**, 2072–2074.

Brémond, J.-C. (1962). Etude sur certains signaux acoustiques provoquant le rassemblement et la dispersion des Pies (*Pica pica*). *Angew. Ornithol.* **I**, H.2, 49–63.

Brémond, J.-C. (1963). Acoustic behaviour of birds. *In* "Acoustic Behaviour of Animals". 709–750. Elsevier, Amsterdam.

Brémond, J.-C. (1964). Sur quelques propriétés réactogènes du motif du signal acoustique de défense territoriale du rouge-gorge (*Erithacus rubecula*). *C. r.hebd. Séanc. Acad. Sci., Paris.* **259**, 3365–3366.

Brémond, J.-C. (1965). Valeur réactogène de fréquences acoustiques dans le signal de défense territoriale du rouge-gorge (*Erithacus rubecula*). *C. r. hebd. Séanc. Acad. Sci., Paris.* **260**, 2910–2913.

Busnel, R. G. (1955). Mise en évidence d'un caractère physique réactogène essentiel de signaux acoustiques synthétiques déclenchant les phonotropismes dans le règne animal. *C. r. hebd. Séanc, Acad. Sci., Paris.* 240, 1477–1479.

Busnel, R. G. (1956). Etude de l'un des caractères physiques essentiels des signaux acoustiques réactogènes artificiels sur les Orthoptères et d'autres groupes d'Insectes. *Insectes soc.* **III**, (I), 11–16.

Busnel, R. G. and Brémond J.-C. (1961). Etude préliminaire du décodage des informations contenues dans le signal acoustique territorial du rouge-gorge (*Erithacus rubecula* L.). *C. r. hebd. Séanc. Acad. Sci., Paris.* **252**, 608–610.

Busnel, R. G. and Brémond, J.-C. (1962). Recherche du support de l'information dans le signal acoustique de défense territoriale du rouge-gorge (*Erithacus rubecula*). *C. r. hebd. Séanc. Acad. Sci., Paris.* **254**, 2236–2238.

Busnel, R. G. and Giban, J. (1966). Réactions d'une population de *Larus Argentatus Atlantis* de l'Ile de Madère à des signaux acoustiques de détresse d'oiseaux européens. *Bocagiana* (II), 1–9.

Busnel, R. G., Giban, J., Gramet, Ph. and Frings, H. (1957). Interspécifité de signaux acoustiques ayant une valeur sémantique pour des Corvidés européens et nord-américains. *C. r. hebd. Séanc. Acad. Sci., Paris.* **245**, 105–108.

Busnel, R. G., Giban, J., Gramet, Ph. and Pasquinelly, F. (1955). Observations préliminaires de la phonotaxie négative des Corbeaux à des signaux acoustiques naturels ou artificiels. *C. r. hebd. Séanc. Acad. Sci., Paris.* **241**, 1846–1849.

Falls, J. B. (1962). Properties of bird song eliciting responses from territorial males. *Proc. XIII Int. orn. Congr., Ithaca* **I**, 259–271.

Frings, H. (1954). Controlling pest birds with sound. *Proc. natn. Shade Tree Conf.*, 108–112.

Frings, H. (1962). Observations on acoustical control of Starlings. *Annls. Epiphyt.* **13**, 1st series, 87–94.

Frings, H. (1963). Bringing you up-to-date on birds control. *Am. Fruit Grow. Mag.* **83**, (6) 14, 16, 29.

Frings, H. (1964). Sound in vertebrate pest control. *2nd Vert. Pest Control Conf.*, Anaheim, Calif., 50–56.

Frings, H. (1964). Study of sonic stimuli on flying albatrosses. Univ. Hawaii, AD-431 285, 7 pp.

Frings, H. and Boudreau, G. W. (1963). Studies on effects of sonic stimuli on flying albatrosses at Midway Island. Final Report, Contract NBy 53155, 18 pp.

Frings, H. and Cook, B. (1964). The upper frequency limits of hearing in the European starling. *Condor*, **66**, (I), 56–60.

Frings, H. and Frings, M. (1959). The language of crows. *Scient. Am.*, **201**, 119–131.

Frings, H. and Frings, M. (1959). The intensity factor in comparative studies on phonoreception. *Anat. Rec.*, **134**, (3), 566.

Frings, H. and Frings, M. (1962). Bio-acoustics and pest control. *Bio-Acoustics Bull.*, **2**, (4), 21–24.

Frings, H. and Frings, M. (1962). Pest control with sound. Part I: Possibilities with invertebrates. *Sound*, **I**, (6), 13–20.

Frings, H. and Frings, M. (1963). Pest control with sound. Part II: The problem with vertebrates. *Sound*, **2**, (I), 39–45.

Frings, H. and Frings, M. (1963). Sound: A better way to control pests. *Electronics*, 36, (2), 24–26.

Frings, H., Frings, M., Cox, B. and Peissner, L. (1954). Auditory and visual communication in the Herring Gull, *Larus argentatus*. *Anat. Rec.*, **120**, (3), 734.

Frings, H., Frings, M., Cox, B. and Peissner, L. (1955). Auditory and visual mechanisms in food-finding behaviour of the herring gull. *Wilson Bull.*, **67**, (3), 155–170.

Frings, H., Frings, M., Cox, B. and Peissner, L. (1955). Recorded calls of herring gulls (*Larus argentatus*) as repellent and attractants. *Science, N.Y.*, **121**, No. 3140, 340–341.

Frings, H., Frings, M., Jumber, J. and Busnel, R.-G. (1958). Reactions of American and French species of *Corvus* and *Larus* to recorded communication signals tested reciprocally. *Ecology*, **39**, (I), 126–131.

Frings, H. and Jumber, J. (1959). Preliminary studies on the use of a specific sound to repel starlings (*Sturnus vulgaris*) from objectional roosts. *Science, N.Y.*, (1954), **119**, No. 3088, 318–319.

Frings, H., Jumber, J. and Frings, M. (1955). Studies on the repellent properties of the distress call of the European Starling (*Sturnus vulgaris*). Occasional papers, Dept. Zool. and Entomol., Pennsylvania State Univ., No. 55, I.

Frings, H. and Slocum, B. (1958). Hearing ranges for several species of birds. *Auk*, **75**, 99–100.

Recent Developments in Bird Scaring on Airfields

T. BROUGH

Ministry of Agriculture, Fisheries and Food,
Infestation Control Laboratory, Worplesdon, Surrey, England

Birds frequent airfields to seek food, to rest and sometimes to breed and their presence, especially when in flocks, constitutes a hazard to aircraft. British airfields are typically large open spaces with extensive areas of short cut grass which provide a wealth of both plant and invertebrate animal foods utilized by a number of bird species. The flat ground permits good visibility all around and is an ideal resting place for gulls (Laridae) and lapwings, *Vanellus vanellus*, which do not discriminate between the safe grassy areas and the dangerous runways. The fact that birds are often virtually the sole occupants of some air-fields, for example at weekends when no flying may take place, and that during the working week they are generally undisturbed by humans who rarely appear in person but travel about in planes or vehicles along distinct pathways, enables birds to become accustomed to airfield con-ditions despite the noise. Birds may be so little disturbed on airfields that they rear young; lapwings commonly do so, their greatest hazard being the mowing machine. Oystercatchers, *Haematopus ostralegus*, black-headed gulls, *Larus ridibundus*, and common gulls, *L. canus* are other species that are known to breed on some airfields in Britain.

If the very size of airfields, where runways may be 1–2 miles long, favours the presence of birds, equally it makes effective bird scaring measures more difficult to apply. Devices which might have some use in a small garden would be insignificant on an airfield and the cost of providing sufficient devices to protect such a large area is excessive. Scarecrows, often in the form of colourful cut-out models of a man with a gun, and meteorological balloons tethered to fly a few feet above the ground, are in this category. Their useful range is limited and they are best sited to protect the most vulnerable parts of the airfield. Even so, their effectiveness soon diminishes and re-siting provides only a tem-porary renewal of effect. The widespread application of chemicals as bird repellents on a large scale may also be uneconomic, and trials have not revealed any chemical repellent suitable for general use.

29

Perhaps because the problem of birds on airfields has never had a ready solution, many diverse ways of scaring birds have from time to time been suggested, tried and have generally been found wanting: for example the use of maleic hydrazide to make grass "purple", this colour supposedly being disliked by birds; the erection of rows of low stakes to interrupt the line of sight and thereby create uneasiness in birds because ground predators might lurk undetected nearby, and the "buzzing" of birds with radio-controlled model aircraft.

It sometimes happens that a method found to be unsatisfactory by one user is acceptable to another. For example, the flying of trained falcons is undoubtedly the most effective visual scaring method used on airfields and possibly the most specialized, because few people are adept in the art of flying these birds. The Royal Air Force in 1947 (Adams, 1949), and the Canadians very recently (Solman, 1965), experimented with falcons for bird control on airfields but abandoned the idea as impracticable for general use. The peregrine falcons, *Falco peregrinus*, are very difficult to obtain and the supply is insufficient for all airfields; both birds and handlers need specialized training and the technique cannot be used by the average serviceman. Once trained, the falcons may be lost in action, especially in wooded areas, or through sickness and occasionally some are shot. A serious disadvantage is that they cannot be flown at night or in adverse weather conditions such as fog, strong winds or heavy rain. Regardless of these many drawbacks the Royal Navy, through considerable effort and keenness, appears to have put the method to good use and reduced the bird strike incidence on one of its airfields. It seems unlikely, however, that many other airfields will follow this example.

Noise-making gadgets, especially those producing sudden explosive bangs, have for years been used to scare birds, and automatic acetylene guns commonly used by farmers still find a place on some airfields where they are effective for a time, if moved about periodically. Birds eventually grow accustomed to them, however, as indeed they do to the nearby roar of jet engines. Shooting is probably more efficient but less convenient, and shotgun patrols are rare on airfields in Britain where some of the troublesome species are protected by law. Not infrequently Very cartridges, normally used for signalling purposes, may be used to scare birds, but the greatest development along these lines has been the evolution of the "shellcracker" which takes different forms in different parts of the world. In Britain, Very pistols have been modified by the simple addition of a liner in the barrel in order to accommodate 12-bore shellcracker cartridges. The latter project an explosive charge which detonates about 100 yd from the pistol and which can be directed at the birds. This relatively simple and readily available device, with its element of surprise, is proving most successful.

Another type of noise having some inherent meaning for the birds and therefore more likely to be effective is the artificial reproduction of bird calls. This so-called bio-acoustic technique, supplemented where necessary by the firing of shellcrackers, is the method which is currently favoured in Britain.

The bio-acoustic method of bird control appears to have been first expounded by Frings and Jumber in 1954 in the United States but since that time it has been developed in a number of countries largely for crop protection (Busnel and Giban, 1960, 1965). Frings and Jumber found that starlings, *Sturnus vulgaris*, caught by man or a predator uttered "distress" or alarm calls which, when recorded on magnetic tape and then broadcast over loudspeakers to starling flocks, caused the birds to fly away. This technique has now been applied to a number of different species of birds. Some, such as wood-pigeons, *Columba palumbus*, and oystercatchers, are not known to have distress calls, but the majority of birds which gather in flocks on British airfields, i.e. gulls, corvids, lapwings and starlings, do have these calls and can be dispersed by broadcasts.

A brief description of the usual reactions of gulls to broadcast distress calls will give some idea of the kind of behaviour observed. On hearing the calls the birds become alert, pause and then fly up, perhaps circling once or twice before flying towards the loudspeaker in front of or over which they circle persistently. In general the recordings, which are usually repetitive, are not broadcast for longer than $1\frac{1}{2}$–2 min which is time enough to elicit the above behaviour. When the broadcast ends, or occasionally sooner, the birds begin gradually to disperse, either flying away directly in ones or twos or forming spiralling movements in thermals and thus departing rather slowly. After a few minutes all the birds will have gone. When scaring birds from airfields it is the final dispersal stage which is desired and, when using distress calls, the early orientation movements and subsequent investigational flights in the vicinity of the sound source can be an embarrassment. Operators of acoustic equipment on airfields are advised, because there is no known way of obviating these intermediate stages, to allow sufficient time to enable the birds to depart before the next aircraft movement.

The behaviour of corvids on hearing their distress calls is not unlike that of gulls. Lapwings, however, are more variable in their behaviour in that they do not always approach the sound source and starlings usually fly directly away. Many factors condition the behaviour observed in any one species. To mention a few, it is generally relatively easy to disperse roosting or resting flocks but difficult to scare away established breeding birds; feeding birds are more difficult to repel when food is scarce than when plentiful. In any one species some individuals may have distress calls which, subjectively, sound more intense than others and may produce an enhanced scaring effect. The most successful dispersals are usually brought about by playing the call of the species to be moved. There is, however, some interspecificity especially among closely related species; for instance, broadcasts of herring gull calls will disperse black-headed and common gulls and vice versa. In practice, flocks of birds on airfields are often of mixed species and broadcasts of the calls of any of these is likely to cause all species to fly. It may be that some of these birds respond to the flight behaviour of their neighbours rather than to the call itself, nonetheless the reaction is beneficial for scaring purposes.

The occurrence of interspecificity in the behavioural response to distress calls appears to contradict the popularly held belief that dialect differences prevent birds in one area from "understanding" conspecific calls from some other region because it seems unlikely that related species should "understand" the calls of one species more easily than members of that species itself, even if these conspecifics do live in relative isolation from one another. It has been suggested that dialect differences might account for a failure to disperse starlings in England with recordings of an American starling. Also Hardenberg in Holland was unable to disperse herring gulls, *L. argentatus*, with the recording of an American representative of this species although subsequently he was successful with recordings of Dutch gulls (Busnel and Giban, 1960). These dialect differences, if they exist at all in distress calls, do not appear to be of general significance because recordings of herring gulls from the United States, herring and black-headed gulls, rooks, *Corvus frugilegus*, jackdaws, *C. monedula*, and starlings from France and herring, black-headed and common gulls, starlings and lapwings from Holland have all elicited normal response patterns when played to the appropriate species in Britain.

The early experimental applications of the bio-acoustic technique on British airfields were designed to make the operation of the method as simple as possible. A number of loudspeakers, fixed at suitable intervals alongside the runways, broadcast the calls played by the air traffic control personnel from the control tower. When birds were located on the airfield it was only necessary to place the appropriate recording on the tape deck and select the circuit activating the loudspeakers in the vicinity of the birds. Only two or three such installations were ever constructed because for various reasons they proved unsatisfactory.

One obvious disadvantage was the expense of the large amplifiers and the many loudspeakers and the necessity to bury all cables on the airfield. Accidental fractures of these cables in the course of other airfield maintenance work were a common occurrence and frequently put the system out of action for long periods. In addition the whole arrangement was perhaps too easy to use; there was little incentive to leave the control tower to investigate a malfunction, and in fact a large proportion of the loudspeakers on an airfield have been known to become unserviceable through neglect before outside advice was sought as to why the birds were no longer being repelled.

The shortcomings of the static installation led to the development of the less expensive "mobile" equipment which is generally carried on a vehicle. It consists of a tape deck with a 30 W amplifier feeding three loudspeakers which are mounted on the cab roof (Plates 1 and 2). Power is supplied by a 12 V battery which may be that of the transporting vehicle. Recordings are provided in continuous loop cassettes which at $3\frac{3}{4}$ in/sec play for approximately $1\frac{1}{2}$ min before repeating themselves.

PLATE 1. Tape deck and amplifier of a bio-acoustic bird-scaring equipment mounted behind the driver's seat in an airfield fire-fighting vehicle. (Crown copyright)

PLATE 2. Loudspeakers on the cab roof. (Crown copyright)

Experience has shown that better results are obtained with mobile equipment than with the static system. This is probably because the operator is more personally involved in the task at hand; he can hear whether or not the speakers are functioning; he is more interested in actively seeking and scaring birds in a vehicle as opposed to merely selecting appropriate tapes and pressing the right button in the control tower, and if the broadcasts should not be effective he is present at the spot and able to carry out alternative or supplementary measures, such as firing shellcrackers.

Even the mobile system has shortcomings, however, and perhaps the most serious is the difficulty of obtaining consistently good results when the equipment is used by different people some of whom, through lack of enthusiasm, may allow it to deteriorate. Those sets which have been used on civil airfields for several years with varying success have often been manned by air traffic control staff for whom bird scaring duties are of secondary importance. When aircraft flights are frequent, these people often cannot afford the time to scare away birds. This situation has recently been improved considerably at some airfields by transferring the responsibility of actually scaring birds from the air traffic staff to that of the station fire service. Firemen are on duty at all operational airfields, their main function being to stand by in case of emergencies. The kinds of work which firemen can do without detracting from their primary function are rather limited, but bird scaring duties on the airfield would seem to be perfectly suitable and consistent with the fireman's role of accident prevention. With this arrangement, if air traffic control officers require birds to be moved they call on the firemen to carry out the task.

The use of firemen in this way has been pioneered by the Royal Air Force whose requirements for an effective method of keeping birds off airfields initiated most of the experimental work with the bio-acoustic technique of bird scaring carried out by the Ministry of Technology (formerly Aviation) and the Ministry of Agriculture, Fisheries and Food. As there was at first some doubt as to the practicability of this rather sophisticated method in the hands of servicemen and of its efficiency in daily use, the Royal Air Force arranged for a trial to be carried out on five of its airfields which were all issued with the appropriate mobile loudspeaker equipments. It was decided that station firemen would be responsible for actually handling the apparatus and accordingly they all received instruction in its use and also on the relevant aspects of bird recognition and behaviour. The trial, which began in June 1965, lasted for just over one year and during this time each of the stations was visited periodically to ensure that correct procedures were maintained and to investigate any problems that arose.

The trial was evaluated by analysis of report forms which were completed by the operators on each occasion a scaring operation was carried out. The forms carried details of time, place and the prevailing weather conditions, the species of birds involved, their numbers, distance from loudspeaker and location, the kind of call broadcast and the general effect produced.

The use of the broadcast distress calls was supplemented where necessary with the firing of shellcrackers and, although it was not intended to compare the relative effectiveness of these two measures, some information on this point was obtained. The results of individual dispersal attempts can be conveniently grouped into three categories, viz. "good", "moderate" and "poor" depending largely on the proportion of birds reacting and whether or not they left the danger area. The frequency with which these different results occurred for each of the major bird groups encountered and for different scaring techniques is shown in Table I where the results from all stations have been combined.

Irrespective of the method employed, "good" results were clearly in the majority; the best and most consistent were obtained with the combination of tape and cracker regardless of bird species. Compared with these, the use of tape alone was equally successful against corvids but diminished to 57% "good" results for starlings. However, over half the total starling results, and nearly all the unsuccessful ones, originated from one airfield, implying some local factor was responsible because the other four airfields had 80% "good" results for tape alone. Nevertheless these figures hardly suggest that starlings responded consistently well to distress calls, as Saul (1967) finds in New Zealand. Indeed it appears that shellcrackers alone were more successful than distress calls against starlings, but more data on this point are desirable.

TABLE I

The combined results from five airfields of attempts to disperse birds

Birds	Treatment	Total number of tests	Percentages of:		
			Good	Moderate	Poor
Gulls	Tape alone	202	85	6	9
	Tape and cracker	153	92	6	2
	Cracker alone	50	62	26	12
Corvids	Tape alone	181	93	5	2
	Tape and cracker	115	94	6	0
	Cracker alone	21	86	14	0
Lapwings	Tape alone	97	71	14	15
	Tape and cracker	20	90	5	5
	Cracker alone	34	73	18	9
Starlings	Tape alone	118	57	11	32
	Tape and cracker	18	94	6	0
	Cracker alone	15	93	7	0

In contrast, shellcrackers on their own were not nearly so successful as distress calls when used against gulls. There appears, therefore, to be some variability in reactions depending on the species. A number of factors could account for this, for example the different behavioural response of different species and the possible use of better recordings for one group than another. It is clear that the results obtained, although not 100% successful, were on the whole most beneficial. It was also shown that the technique could be managed by Service personnel and the Royal Air Force are therefore considering equipping a large number of their airfields with the requisite bird scaring apparatus.

A most important concomitant of this decision to invest in the bio-acoustic technique is the need to train firemen in bird identification and methods of bird control. The basic training programme of Service firemen in Britain now includes such instruction and this, it is hoped, will help to increase the efficiency of bird scaring on airfields by making firemen more aware of the situation and by improving their knowledge of birds and the appropriate control techniques.

Summary

The large size of airfields makes it difficult to keep them clear of birds which occur there, often in great numbers, to feed, rest or even breed. The practice of falconry to disperse flocks of birds has proved of value in isolated instances but cannot be recommended as a suitable method generally. Shellcrackers fired from modified Very pistols have proved very successful and are used to supplement the bio-acoustic method of bird scaring which is currently favoured in Britain.

Broadcast calls can be used to disperse all the major hazard species on British airfields with the exception of wood-pigeons and oystercatchers. There is some variability in response depending on species, the activities of the birds at the time of broadcast and the kind of call played but this does not seriously curtail the usefulness of the technique.

Early experimental apparatus comprising several loudspeakers alongside runways with buried cables leading to the tape deck and large amplifiers in the control tower has been abandoned as too expensive and impracticable. Instead, portable battery-operated equipment carried in a vehicle with loudspeakers mounted on the roof has been adopted and is in use on a number of civil airfields. A trial lasting one year at five Royal Air Force stations has demonstrated the effectiveness of such apparatus when operated by Service firemen and, as a result, a large number of military airfields are to be supplied with distress call equipments. Adequate instruction in the identification of hazardous species and in the measures to scare them is necessary and is now incorporated in the basic training of all firemen in the Royal Air Force.

Acknowledgements

Much of the work dealt with in this paper has involved the co-operative efforts of the Ministry of Defence, the Ministry of Technology and the Ministry of Agriculture, Fisheries and Food and I should like to acknowledge the assistance, financial or otherwise, made available by these departments. In particular I would like to thank Squadron Leader P. F. Hart, Ministry of Defence, for the supply of photographs and my colleague Mr. C. J. Bridgman for his supervision of the R.A.F. bio-acoustics trial.

References

Adams, F. R. (1949). Experiments in clearing birds from airfields. Ministry of Civil Aviation ORS/MCA Report No. 7.

Busnel, R. G. and Giban, J. (1960). Colloque sur la protection acoustique des cultures. Institut National de la Recherche Agronomique, Paris.

Busnel, R. G. and Giban, J. (1965). Colloque sur le problème des oiseaux sur les aerodromes. Institut National de la Recherche Agronomique, Paris.

Frings, H. and Jumber, J. (1954). Preliminary studies on the use of a specific sound to repel starlings (*Sturnus vulgaris*) from objectionable roosts. *Science, N.Y.* **119**, 318–319.

Saul, E. K. (1967). Birds and aircraft: a problem at Auckland's new international airport. *Jl. R. aeronaut. Soc.* **71** (677), 366–376.

Solman, V. E. F. (1965). Use of falcons for airport bird control. Associate Committee on Bird Hazards to Aircraft, National Research Council, Canada, Field note 33.

Discussion

THOMPSON: One of the main hazards of bird strikes to aircraft lies in the disablement of a jet engine, or engines. Without regressing to propeller aircraft, would it not be possible to have a rotating blade in front of the jet engine intake, to prevent bird entry?

NEW: The latest generation of the bigger jet engines that are just coming into service have blades that are so robust that they are much less liable to damage. On some engines the forward row of compressor blades, instead of being stationary, rotate, and in effect constitute such a device.

LANDSBOROUGH THOMSON: You mentioned several incidents in which lives have been lost as a result of bird collisions with aircraft but did not mention one involving the tragic death of a biologist. In a postscript to the English translation of "The Serengeti Shall Not Die" by Bernard and Michael Grzimek (1960), it is recorded that the latter (son of the former) was killed on the 10th January, 1959, when the light plane in which he was flying solo crashed in the Serengeti National Park in Tanganyika (as it then was).

It is stated that the plane was seen by an Englishman to dive suddenly when flying at about 600 feet above the ground. Also that "British air officials" investigated the cause of the accident and found that a griffon vulture *Gyps fulvus* had collided with the right wing and bent it, blocking the rudder-cables and causing the machine to dive in a steep right-hand curve.

Several species of vultures as well as other large birds are common in the area.

WRIGHT: When Monsieur Busnel has identified the significant parts of the bird call by the type of analysis described, does he envisage the super-call being constructed from a combination of elements of the natural call or from purely synthetic sounds?

BUSNEL: The experience that has been acquired in my laboratory in the treatment of insect, amphibian and certain bird calls permits me to think that we can look forward, with some degree of confidence, to the construction of purely synthetic signals. The use of computers, moreover, makes possible the use of fragments of natural signals and of signals synthesized from experimental curves. I do not think there will be a real problem, the stock of recorded natural signals allows one to have a reserve of elements if one wishes, and for synthetic signals one can make practically all one will need.

SPARKS: Have you any information about the ways in which birds react to these synthetic calls as opposed to the homologous natural calls?

BUSNEL: I have no experimental data concerning the signals described in my paper because the work has only just been done and is in a preliminary stage. These experiments will be done during 1968. But what I can say, based on the long experience I mentioned previously on diverse zoological groups which my colleagues and I have studied since 1950, is that, with a little luck, one can obtain synthetic super-signals that will be more effective than natural signals. For example, as in the case of female insects which prefer to go to a loudspeaker diffusing such signals rather than to males of their own species emitting their natural call. For birds which are likewise animals having a well developed brain, the induced behaviour will perhaps be less formal but I shall not be surprised, in view of the reaction of certain species to decoy calls, which generate synthetic signals without electronics, if excellent results are obtained.

Dr. SCHAEFER asked M. BUSNEL if he could please tell him something of the background to this work. How long had he been working with birds?

BUSNEL: This work is the logical continuation of the technological evolution of animal bio-acoustics made possible by the development of vocoders and computers which permit special analyses of signals utilized especially in talking machines, dictation-typewriters and translation machines. The origins of the spirit of this work are to be found in the very first publications which I made in 1951 on synthetic signals concerning insects.

As for the work on birds, I think that I began about 1952 and since then my colleagues and I have published two or three books and about 40 papers on this theme.

You are probably right to be worried about my background. It worries me too. The only criterion that seems to me remotely valid is that, in the field of Natural Science, my colleagues have successively elected me President of the French Société de Zoologie and of the French Société de Biologie, and that, in the field of physics, I am at the moment also President of the Groupement des Acousticiens de Langue Française. As for bio-acoustics, I think I was one of the founders of the Comité International de Bio-acoustique, and my first publication in this field must have been given at the International Congress on Ultrasonics at Rome in 1948. I gained my doctorate at the Faculty of Science, Paris, in 1939 and this year I was the one guest of honour of the British Acoustical Society.

This array of titles, I know, has only a relative and indicative value; these are my feathers and one recognizes a bird, you know, by his song and his plumage, to quote La Fontaine.

DUNNET: Mr. Brough indicated that after being disturbed by the broadcast distress calls, gulls commonly circle in a flock near the source of the calls and then disperse in all directions. It is conceivable that this could result in a greater risk of damage to aircraft, especially in the vicinity of airfields, and I would be interested to know if any research has been directed at the possibility of keeping birds down on the ground where they would certainly not present any hazard to aircraft.

BROUGH: When distress calls are broadcast on airfields, sufficient time is allowed to enable gulls to disperse before the next aircraft movement takes place. If the birds are very slow in departing they can be hastened by firing shellcrackers. Experience on an airfield soon reveals the best course of action to be taken and often those birds which are on the airfield, but not in a dangerous position, may be left undisturbed.

No research that I know of has been undertaken to devise means of keeping birds on the ground in the vicinity of airfields. Such means would need to be more than transitory in effect. They should not attract additional birds to the area and must be capable of overcoming the conflicting stimuli of noise and fast-moving aircraft which incite the birds to flee.

NORBURY: As a fruit grower I am interested in the devices you have mentioned. Can you give me some idea of the cost?

BROUGH: I believe a portable broadcasting equipment suitable for mounting in a vehicle costs about £175. A mains-operated system with permanently fixed loudspeakers would be more expensive and I can only refer you to the manufacturers for details (Ultra Electronics, Western Avenue, London).

Mr. NORBURY asked whether ultrasonics could be used to scare birds and Mr. BROUGH said that the equipment was expensive and that there was no evidence that it did frighten birds.

BUSNEL: There was a paper about this by two research workers, Thiessen and Shaw (1957), both of the Canadian National Research Council, who made a remarkable ultrasonic siren intended to frighten ducks which, in some areas of that country, constitute a danger to aircraft. Besides the large amount of energy required to work the siren, and therefore its high operating cost, the noise produced was totally ineffective. This was for two reasons. The first physical, because of the poor propagation of ultrasonics in air, the second biological because animals habituate very quickly to these sounds and no longer react because they have no significance in their behaviour. A sound is devoid of meaning for an animal unless it is built into the behaviour of the animal (for example the characteristic sound of a predator or prey). From then on it loses its title of "sound" and merits that of "signal".

SPARKS: Is it known why gulls congregate on runways?

BROUGH: Apart from the well-known fact that gulls prefer the relative safety of large open spaces on which to rest, it is not known why gulls congregate on runways. There is speculation that slight temperature differences between the grassy areas and runways may govern their choice but we have no evidence to support this.

JARDINE: The first paper this morning drew attention to the fact that very few accidents involving loss of life have been attributed to collisions with birds. But what of the future? Is there not a danger of underestimating the increased hazard due to a greater volume of air traffic and the use of large aircraft in which a single accident might result in the death of 500 people?

STABLES: It is very difficult to estimate future trends. Larger aircraft may lead to a reduction in number of movements and as their bigger engines are likely to be less susceptible to damage, the danger may actually be less than at present.

GULLIVER: In the light of millions of hours of jet operation we in the British Overseas Airways Corporation are convinced that the aerodynamics of the aircraft and engine position have an effect on the bird strike probability.

In our experience of operations with three pure jet types, the Comet 4, with engines buried in the wing root, has the worst record, especially with regard to engine strikes. The Boeing 707, with pod mounted engines shows a considerable improvement over the Comet but the VC 10 with rear mounted engines has a relatively good record. For example in 1966 B.O.A.C. suffered a total of 69 bird strikes on Boeing 707 aircraft including 12 involving engines, and 28 strikes on the VC 10 of which two involved engines. Of this total of 97 bird strikes only 13 caused damage to the aircraft. All three aircraft types have operated a similar route pattern except that the VC 10 does not operate in the Pacific or Australasia.

We consider that design has an effect on the vulnerability of engines to bird strike damage and from our experience and observing other operators we believe that fan engines of the JT3D type, with a front fan exhausting directly into the airflow, have a centrifuging effect in that the bird is thrown outwards by the fan and is exhausted with the fan air stream and so does not pass through the gas generator. It is probable that the new generation of engines with very large fans will be even more effective in this respect.

STABLES: Perhaps Mr. Allcock of the National Gas Turbine Establishment and Mr. McNaughtan of the Royal Aircraft Establishment would care to comment.

ALLCOCK: On the general question put by Mr. Jardine it seems to me that future types of large civil aircraft may well prove to be less vulnerable to bird strikes. This is particularly true of the engines, which will tend to have much larger blades because of the trend to very high bypass-ratio fans. The speeds reached at heights below 8 000 ft are unlikely to be significantly different from present values, so the overall risk is likely to be somewhat reduced. These remarks do not apply to supersonic transports which may well suffer greater bird strike damage, mainly as a result of higher speeds below 8 000 ft.

On Mr. Gulliver's point I agree that the positioning of the engines has some effect on the statistical probability of a strike, rear engines showing a small advantage. However, the damage produced by a given strike is not affected by engine position, except for engines which are very close together. In such cases an engine may be damaged by ingesting debris from a neighbouring engine damaged by a bird.

The damage to a given engine by a given bird at a given impact velocity is unfortunately not quantifiable by any simple law, such as the V^3 law for windscreens. The rotating machinery contains hundreds of blades which can strike the bird in an infinite number of different ways, leading to widely different damage in separate incidents. It is not even certain whether increasing impact speed and/or bird weight will increase or reduce damage, although in general a big, heavy bird causes more damage than a small, light one, and a much higher impact speed will increase damage. The research at the engine companies and the National Gas Turbine Establishment has been aimed at defining the mechanism of impact and the resulting damage so that the worst possible cases and the worth of protective measures can be defined.

It seems worth pointing out that the real problem is with military aircraft. Civil aircraft spend only a few minutes per flight near the ground, always at low speeds, but current military techniques demand long flights at low level and very high speed. Also all normal passenger-carrying aircraft are safe to fly after an engine failure, but this is not true of military types.

BRIDGMAN: Some of the most expensive birdstrikes suffered by the R.A.F. have been on the engines of a particular type of aircraft and always during take-off. I attribute the absence of any similar occurrence during landing to the "nose-up" attitude of this aircraft during the approach phase.

McNAUGHTAN: The damage done in bird impact is a function of bird mass and speed. Since damage results from the absorption of the kinetic energy of the bird it would be expected to increase linearly with increase in mass and also to be proportional to the square of the impact speed. It is, however, very difficult to assess damage in a quantitative manner and it is therefore not possible to relate precisely the variation of damage with speed and mass except for specific cases such as penetration of a structure or windscreen. In such cases it has been found experimentally that the product of a bird mass (M) and the cube of the impact speed (V^3) is constant

i.e. $$MV^3 = K.$$

This relationship can be derived theoretically if failure or penetration is assumed to be due to punching shear and it is also assumed that the linear dimensions of the bird are related to the cube root of the mass.

i.e. $$M = \rho D^3$$

where D is a linear dimension such as bird girth.

Considering the bird impacting on a windscreen, the load per unit length around the impact periphery will be:

$$
\begin{aligned}
L \quad &\propto MV^2/D \\
&\propto MV^2/M^{\frac{1}{3}} \\
&\propto MV^3
\end{aligned}
$$

Thus for penetration MV^3 = Constant, but the size of the hole will be greater with a larger size of bird. This relationship has been proved experimentally for the penetration of windscreens and wing structures.

There was some discussion between Mr. Gulliver and Mr. Allcock as to whether a small bird could pass straight through an engine without causing damage. This brought Dr. Seubert of the U.S. Fish and Wildlife Service to his feet.

SEUBERT: Based upon the results of bird ingestion tests that the Federal Aviation Administration has been conducting in the U.S., I think we must consider the total mass of protoplasm involved. It is not just the size of an individual bird that always is critical, it is often the number of birds involved. I think this is particularly so in turbo-prop engines. The FAA has found that several starlings ingested at the same time will cause a very significant loss of power in the engine used in the Electra and in another smaller turbo-prop engine that recently has been evaluated.

BROWN: I must disagree with the first speaker's inference that because accident investigations show few lives lost from bird-strikes it cannot be regarded as a serious risk, and the problem is really one of cost of repair and inconvenience. Safety is only achieved by taking preventative measures. British European Airways bird-strike reports for the past four months June–September show 11, 6, 9, 11 strikes respectively, many of which were multiple strikes and a potential hazard to the safety of the aircraft, particularly so in the flight-phase of landing or take-off.

The most dangerous bird-strike is ingestion by the jet engine; this can cause loss of engine power instantly, and any appreciable restriction to the airflow passing through the engine will quickly cause overheating and complete failure of that engine. I should like to know where the first speaker and the member in the audience from B.O.A.C. obtained the knowledge that small birds can pass through a jet engine without doing or receiving damage? Some time ago when in discussion with an engine manufacturer on another aspect of engine ingestion problems, we were informed that a $\frac{3}{16}$-in. sized object is possibly the largest object that could pass through a jet engine without doing damage.

SOLMAN: The engines on executive jet and turbo-prop aircraft are generally smaller than those on commercial carriers. As such the compressor blades are usually smaller and more easily damaged by ingested birds. Our records show that an executive jet aircraft had to have an engine changed after a strike on a ring-billed gull, *Larus delawarensis* in Canada. A turbine-powered helicopter made an unscheduled landing because of power loss following ingestion of a swamp sparrow *Melospiza georgiana* which damaged the engine.

BOURNE: Although no longer in the Service, I am here as the representative of the growing number of birdwatchers in the R.A.F. The first essential surely is the collection of precise data on what is happening, and its circulation to all the people capable of interpreting it, especially the people who understand the most inflexible element in the situation, the birds. Yet it seems conspicuous in the first paper in particular that although much research is being given to the aircraft side of the problem and committees are being set up to study it, in this country at least the main body of ornithologists are not being brought into the discussion, or provided with the data on the basis of which they might be able to help formulate answers to the bird-strike problem.

I am aware that a restricted group, the ethologists preoccupied with the study of animal behaviour, who occupy a position in biology rather like that occupied by psychiatrists in medicine, have been consulted expensively at length, and have come up with the bird-scaring devices which we have been told about in the second two papers, in keeping with their general analysis of the world in terms of mechanical stimulus and response. But since they started to pursue their enquiries into how brains work to the point of vivi-section there are some of us who have begun to feel that they increasingly lie beyond the pale of proper ornithology, and that it is time for a return to broader concepts of behaviour study, of the sort which have been con-spicuously lacking throughout this session. Before this symposium I made particular enquiries in likely quarters as to the extent to which the authorities had attempted to consult general ornithologists over their problems in this country, and while everyone is very vague on this issue, in general it appears that approaches have usually been restricted to occasional impromptu telephone calls or interviews. This is not the way to deal with a hazard in-creasingly affecting all aircraft in all countries, already costing the R.A.F. alone a million pounds a year, and risking lives.

To return to an analysis of the ornithological aspect of the problem, ornithologists certainly would not agree that, as suggested by the authors of the first paper, bird hazards are randomly distributed in space and time in all respects except altitude. To us, the opposite is the case, so that there should be no difficulty at all in arranging for aircraft to avoid bird hazards with sufficient success at least to make the attempt worth while. However, the problem is a complex one involving many different factors, so that it is easy to see why the authorities have had difficulty in arriving at simple answers to it. None the less, there are certain points which are likely to occur to most ornithologists.

In the first place, the ordinary large or sociable birds of the countryside such as gulls, corvids and starlings, all have regular daily and seasonal rou-tines which cause them to present bird-strike risks at certain particular points. They present a moderate one when dispersing from their roosts at dawn, which becomes serious if the flight-lines cross airfields, and perhaps a rather greater one when they soar in flocks while looking round for food during the day. They may come down on airfields to feed or to rest. Coastal species are also liable to go to airfields to rest at high tide. They present an increased risk again when flighting in to their roosts in flocks at dusk, and a particularly severe risk when they gather in dense flocks to perform evolutions just before going to roost, either at high tide or at dusk. Some shore and water birds which feed at night may also present a risk when carrying out feeding flights at dusk and dawn and when the tide turns.

Second, many birds may present an increased bird-strike hazard on migra-tion, though the hazard may often have been over-estimated because many species do not flock on migration and most movement occurs on a broad front. There are possibly three main risks arising from migration; first, the birds usually fly higher then; second, the main movements tend to occur at certain restricted times of day at particular seasons, and third, large numbers of foreign birds may pass through an area and increase the general level of risk there. Though this last hazard is not particularly serious in Britain, we do have enough wildfowl in particular going through the area for both the East and especially the Northwest to deserve consideration.

Third, all bird behaviour is greatly modified by the weather, both the regular diurnal movements of the birds of the countryside and migration. Most birds tend to keep low when the wind is strong against them, while soaring species tend to go highest when they can find updraughts due to the effect of topography on the wind or especially the development of thermals in the middle of the day. Migrants clearly prefer to move in fine weather with the wind behind them, and the density of movement may be greatly influenced by the preceding weather.

All these factors taken together are liable to lead to a great variation in the number of birds in the upper air at different times, and especially the ceiling at which the general level of bird-strike risk over the country at large starts to fall off. There may also be particular places where risks are high, due to the occurrence of local concentrations of soaring birds around estuaries and inland waters or places of regular updraught or where they become concentrated on migration (usually in attempts to avoid long sea passages), or to the occurrence of regular movements to and from roosts. It should usually be possible to predict times and areas of increased risk through consideration of a combination of past experience, the weather, and the season and time of day, and confirm their occurrence with radar. Yet so far as I know, except where hazards are obvious around airfields and recently with low cross-country routes, little attempt has been made to allow for them. If pilots were warned of them it should surely reduce the hazards that they face.

The irregular distribution of bird-strike hazards is surely also of the first importance in the consideration of the location of airfields; and yet so far as I know until now this factor has never been considered until after they were built. As an ornithologist it is my impression that so far aviators have been extraordinarily lucky; points of high risk are often extremely limited in area, and at one airfield after another obvious hazards have been missed through chance by the narrowest of margins. As a boy I used to watch all the shore-birds from Chichester Harbour roost at high tide on a marsh right off the end of the runway at Thorney Island, but luckily the main flightpaths do not seem to have crossed those of the aircraft. At London Airport the authorities seem to have been equally lucky in that Staines and neighbouring reservoirs draw birds away from the airport rather than otherwise. Likewise the runway at Gibraltar luckily lies a couple of miles aside from the main flightpath by which most of the large soaring birds leave western Europe, while that at Akrotiri points exactly between two patches of bare ground which give rise to thermals by which a fairly high proportion of the big soaring migrants leave Cyprus. Something over 95% of the large migrants recorded in Cyprus have been seen within a mile of the runway at Akrotiri, though without a strike problem that I know of. But this sort of luck cannot last.

It is an interesting speculation where the luck will run out. At the present moment it seems likely that the most risky situation of all is where seabirds from vast areas gather to breed on oceanic islands. As far as I know it first became serious when the Americans built an airstrip across the centre of a Sooty Tern colony on Ascension during the period while the birds were away in 1942 (Chapin, 1954). They formed an intractable nuisance when they came back, but they are not very large, and eventually it was found that if their eggs were broken they would go away. The same technique was tried again when the Americans decided to extend the airfield on Midway in 1955, and got rid of the Sooty Terns (*Sterna fuscata*), but as reported in his paper by Mr. Wright it just made the albatrosses (*Diomedea Spp.*) fly around, and even the best brains in the U.S. Fish and Wildlife Department have failed to solve the bird-strike problem there. According to H. I. Fisher (1966) this may be because the runway was built between the main albatross colony and deep water, so that a high proportion of all the birds on the island tend to cross it on the way to and from their nests, regardless of local measures in its immediate vicinity.

Our own authorities now seem headed for even worse trouble on Aldabra, which has the largest breeding colony of Frigate-birds (*Fregata Spp.*) in the Indian Ocean in the immediate vicinity of the proposed runway. According to Marshal of the R.A.F. Sir Dermot Boyle (*The Times*, August 11th, 1967) the R.A.F. feel that they have considerable experience dealing with such hazards because they "overcame a challenge of this kind at Christmas Island". I have made enquiries of a number of people who have been to Christmas Island, and the two situations do not really seem comparable; Christmas Island is a much larger island, with many fewer Frigates; the colonies are said to number up to 500 there, as opposed to the swarms of tens of thousands, like midges, on Aldabra. On Christmas Island the birds also nest on the east side of the lagoon, near the centre of the island, and soar in thermals there, well away from the airfields at opposite extremities of the island, where they are not often seen, and indeed my informants did not know that there was a bird-strike problem at all with the piston-engined aircraft used to supply that base. On the other hand, on Aldabra it is proposed to build a runway for jets right in the centre of the south-east part of South Island where the birds are said to gather to soar in thermals. It is difficult for ornithologists to assess the full extent of this hazard, but it seems frightening; what seems even more frightening is the impression that the development is about to go ahead though it seems doubtful whether the authorities can assess the risk any better either.

Among other points raised, the Dutch have also tried shooting birds with the exhibition of corpses and trapping to reinforce other scaring methods which might help reduce the rate at which birds become habituated with other forms of scaring (De Jong and Blokpoel, 1966). Another important consideration is surely the provision of a more attractive alternative for birds which take to visiting airfields to rest; the grass might be kept short for them in some out of the way area, as well as being grown long to discourage them near the runways. It might be unwise to try and bait them away from places where they were a nuisance with food, as this could lead to an increase in the total population, but it has been found with wildfowl that dummies, call-birds, or broadcast calls are often extremely effective in causing birds to go where they are wanted (the latter so much so that they have had to be banned by law in many places) and there seems no reason why the same methods should not work with other species; indeed, we have been told that gull distress calls attract them in the first instance already. To try and scare birds away without giving them an alternative resort, and then armour aircraft against them when the method fails, seems a very negative proceeding.

WRIGHT: Whilst agreeing with much of what Dr. Bourne has said I feel he underestimates the problems involved in the introduction of biological thought into what is traditionally regarded as a technological field. It is necessary to bridge the gulf between the biologist and the engineer and much time needs to be spent in understanding each other's problems. This symposium was partly conceived with this in mind and the presence of so many engineers and representatives of the aviation industry shows their willingness to listen to what biologists have to say. As Dr. Bourne has rightly pointed out, many of the problems are complex and their solution requires further objective research both by biologists and engineers and the final integration of the results in a contribution to flight safety. All research costs money, and as bird strikes are only one of the hazards to aircraft safety the question of priorities inevitably arises. It would seem that, rightly or wrongly, the bird hazard has not received a very high rating and I think what we feel, as biologists, is that a great deal more could be done at comparatively little cost. Very often it is not a question of research, many airfields have bird problems that can be clearly identified and would probably be overcome if a mechanism existed for putting even simple anti-bird measures into operation. In my view the action taken by the R.A.F. in making the firemen responsible for bird scaring is a step in the right direction because it recognizes birds on the airfield as a potential hazard and places responsibility for action with the section concerned with safety. It therefore becomes a primary task and not something to be done if they are not otherwise occupied. The firemen receive training in bird recognition and dispersal methods and I should like to see something similar introduced on all civil airfields.

I cannot accept the allegation that aviation authorities have not consulted ornithologists, I happen to know that Dr. Tinbergen was at one time retained as an adviser by the (then) Ministry of Aviation and a representative of that department visited Dr. Lack and the Wildfowl Trust. Recently a senior member of the Directorate of Flight Safety paid a personal visit to Tring to follow up earlier contacts with the British Trust for Ornithology on the subject of bird migration. The two people concerned are unfortunately not present today but if Dr. Bourne remains in any doubt I can provide details later. The inference to be drawn from Dr. Bourne's remarks is that if only ornithologists had been asked they would have provided solutions to many of the outstanding problems and I wonder if he is not altogether too sanguine about the state of ornithological knowledge.

I do not question the vast amount of information, both published and privately cherished, that is available about birds but in my experience this is usually too general in nature to provide the answers to specific questions.

(Dr. BOURNE pressed his point further and made reference to the failure of radar display controllers to recognize and interpret bird echoes. He said he understood that radar film examined after the Electra crash at Boston in 1960, showed the aircraft flying into the flock of starlings. If the radar controllers had understood what was on their screens the accident might have been avoided.)

SEUBERT: Last year I participated in pre-trial legal procedures regarding the Boston Electra crash, and I heard nothing to indicate the existence of radar film showing the starlings that were involved in the crash. We are of the opinion, which is shared by some ornithologists, that people who do not have any particular interest in birds can be looking right at a flock of birds and not see them.

JONES: I should like to ask Mr. Brough if he has investigated inter-specific responses to alarm calls amongst species occurring together naturally as a means of avoiding habituation during scaring operations? Do you think, for instance, that it might be possible to use the alarm call of the fieldfare to scare starlings in winter?

BROUGH: The use of inter-specific calls within families is an accepted practice. Should habituation occur to specific calls, e.g. common gull calls can be broadcast to herring gulls. The success achieved so far with starling calls has not necessitated the investigation of inter-specific alternatives although it is quite possible that fieldfare calls might prove effective. The converse would not appear likely, however, because most thrushes in the vicinity of starling roosts are not unduly disturbed by the broadcasts of starling calls.

BROUGHTON: A simpler and less costly method than the deployment of whole vehicles about the airfield might be the use of remote-controlled models of ground predators, which could be moved as close as might be needed to put up the flock. This would also combine the advantage of operation from a comfortable control centre with freedom from cable-cutting troubles, and equally with the ensuring of proper supervision of the effectiveness of the transmitted instructions.

BOURNE: A remote controlled predator could be a sheep-dog. Really is not the answer to provide the birds with alternative sites that suit their requirements?

MURTON: The suggestion of providing alternative sites to attract birds away from places where they are causing damage raises an interesting principle also applicable to the theme of the discussions tomorrow. In general terms, there is the very real risk that the provision of what amounts to extra-habitat will simply lead to an increase in numbers of the problem bird. For instance, the provision of a specially planted and attractive crop adjacent to a vulnerable one could lead to a new population moving in rather than the resident one changing its feeding ground and, moreover, might result in particularly severe damage if the decoy crop became exhausted before the one at risk. It will, of course, depend to what extent the birds are limited or restricted by their chosen feeding ground, resting place and so on, and each case ought to be considered on its own merits.

SCHAEFER: I should like to suggest research into the use of lasers on air-craft, for confusing or burning birds in the direct line of flight. A medium power gas laser working in the visible range could be modulated at flicker frequencies corresponding to central nervous frequencies. Would this confuse birds into diving, escaping or stunned motions, when used at say 1 000 yd? The power level could be chosen so that no retinal damage would result, to birds or humans. The very narrow angle of the laser beam is required for this application.

Should these signalling methods fail, as a last resort a higher power laser working in the infra-red (to avoid damage to distant personnel behind aircraft windows) could burn off or wither the flight feathers of birds in the immediate track of climbing or level-flying craft. Our laboratory experiments on feathers show that about 5 J./cm² is required. This low value results from the very low density of feathers, and makes the method feasible, even at 500 yd.

Detection and control could be provided by forward-pointing aircraft radar, using echoes with signals below a given threshold at a given range. The flicker-type experiments would be easy to perform with ground-based tracking radar.

REFERENCES

Chapin, J. P. (1954). The Calendar of Wideawake Fair. *Auk* **71**(1).

De Jong, A. P. and Blokpoel, H. (1966). Hard Facts about Soft Feathers. *Shell Aviat. News* **342**(2), 2–7.

Fisher, H. I. (1966). Airplane–Albatross Collisions on Midway Atoll. *Condor* **68**, 229–242.

Grzimek, B. and Grzimek, M. (1960). "The Serengeti Shall Not Die." Collins, London, England.

Theissen, G. J. and Shaw, E. A. G. (1957). Acoustic irritation threshold of ring-billed gulls. *J. acoust. Soc. Am.* **29**, 1307.

Theissen, G. J., Shaw, E. A. G., Harris, R. D., Gollop, J. B. and Webster, H. R. (1957). Acoustic irritation threshold of Peking ducks and other domestic and wild fowls. *J. acoust. Soc. Am.* **29**, 1301.

Exhibit:
Bird Impact Testing of Aircraft Structure and Components

I. I. McNAUGHTAN

Ministry of Technology, Royal Aircraft Establishment, Farnborough

McNaughtan: The design requirements for Civil Transport Aircraft require that the windscreen shall resist the impact of a 4 lb bird at the operating speed of the aircraft below an altitude of 8 000 ft and also that the structure of the aircraft shall not suffer catastrophic damage from such an impact. To provide the designer with the necessary basic data to allow him to design bird-resistant aircraft and also to prove the integrity of specific designs, bird impact testing of aircraft structure and components is required. Two test methods are used: the sledge test and gun test.

The sledge test consists of mounting the test specimen on a rocket-propelled sledge and firing it down a rocket track to impact on a dead bird suspended above the track. The sledge is then decelerated either by retrorockets, or an arrester gear of hydraulic braking devices. This method of test is expensive, rocket tracks are limited in number (3 in the U.K.) and are in such demand for test work of various descriptions that occupation time on them is not readily available.

The gun method consists of firing a bird projectile from a compressed air gun at a stationary target. A gun test facility is not very expensive and is cheap to operate. A number of such guns (see Stables and New, plates 4A and 4B) are in use in the U.K. (at Rolls Royce, Bristol Siddeley Engines, Hawker Siddeley Aviation, British Aircraft Corporation, National Gas Turbine Establishment and Royal Aircraft Establishment) and they vary in style from single-bore guns firing a single projectile at high speed to multibarrel guns firing a flock of birds at low speed. Dead birds are normally used as projectiles and vary in size from small birds weighing a few ounces up to 4 lb chickens. Synthetic "birds" are used occasionally.

At high speed the aerodynamic loads on the bird projectile are too great for its structure and the feathers, wings and legs are ripped off, whilst at very high speed the bird disintegrates completely before impacting on the target. To avoid this the bird is put into a light nylon bag before loading into the gun. The analysis of high speed cine films has shown that the bag ruptures on impact and does not impede the flow of bird debris over the target.

The need for synthetic "birds" was mainly for reasons of hygiene in tests of rotating engine assemblies because of the difficulty in cleansing the test apparatus mechanisms of the widely distributed bird debris.

Examination of the results of sledge and gun tests have shown no significant differences and it is generally accepted that both methods give acceptable simulation of the actual collision case.

The R.A.E. Bird Gun, a model of which was exhibited, has a barrel of 6 in. bore and 50 ft length. With working air pressure of 20 to 200 lb/in² it can fire bird projectiles up to 4 lb in weight at speeds from 200 to 1 000 ft/sec (140 to 700 m.p.h.). To protect the bird during its acceleration down the barrel and to achieve uniformity in the impact speed/firing pressure ratio the bird is backed with a light foamed plastic plug. For birds less than 2 lb in weight this plastic plug is formed in the shape of a hollow split sabot into which the bagged bird is fitted. The gun is fired electrically (to allow synchronization with high speed cine photography) using a double bursting diaphragm system. Impact speed is obtained by measuring the time interval between the breakage by the projectile of two fine wires spaced five feet apart immediately ahead of the target.

Windscreen test specimens were exhibited to show the degree of damage which can result from high speed bird impact and the large amount of energy which is involved (see Stables and New, Plate 3).

Bird Recognition by Radar
A Study in Quantitative Radar Ornithology

GLEN W. SCHAEFER

Biophysics Research Unit,
University of Technology, Loughborough, Leicestershire, England

INTRODUCTION

"Point angels" are a common feature of the radar screen. Since the early days of World War II it has been known that large sea birds and groups of smaller birds can produce observable echoes. Sutter (1957) and Harper (1957) brought forward strong evidence, including some visual confirmations, that displays of angels are due to birds in flight, and this hypothesis has been followed, often uncritically, by subsequent research in radar ornithology. Data on bird migration have been derived largely from photographic records of plan-position (PPI) and range-height (RHI) indicators of medium- to high-power surveillance radars working at low angles of elevation. The quantitative features of these data are angel ground speed, direction of movement, approximate height and time of occurrence. The air speeds of the targets may be calculated from a knowledge of the wind velocity given approximately in aerological reports. The evidence used by Sutter and Harper in drawing their conclusion was the similarity of the calculated angel air speeds to bird flight speeds, the directions of the movements and the annual and daily rhythm of angel number densities.

Although these radar studies have thrown much light on the subject of bird migration, the limitations of the method are well known. The decomposition of an angel into species and individual numbers is impossible; indeed there are several types of situations where the quantitative features referred to above are insufficient to type the angel as avian, part-avian or non-avian. The number of angels is often unmeasurable, particularly on radars of low resolving power, designed to detect aircraft and weather.

The PPI or RHI records only the presence of echoes, and supresses the wide variety of quantitative information contained in each echo signal. This deprives the ornithologist of much of the potential power of radar as an analytical tool. An echo may be described in terms of signal strength and modulation pattern. These shall be called its "signature".

53

This paper presents some preliminary theoretical and experimental results concerning the main characteristics of the signatures of birds in flight. It discusses the relationships between these signatures and bird body size, shape, aspect, wing-beat, flocking and radar polarization. It indicates the limits within which it should be possible to identify species and count individuals. It gives a brief synopsis of the relevance of this research to the problem of the hazard of birds to aircraft.

Previous research on bird signatures has been carried out chiefly by Houghton (1964) and Eastwood and Rider (1966), and has been summarized in Eastwood (1967). This research will be reviewed in later Sections (pp. 69, 72, and 78).

According to the findings of radar ornithology, only a small proportion of angels are non-avian. Here a word of caution is advisable. Radar meteorologists and others have had long experience with signature analysis and high-resolution radar, and have concluded that there are three main scattering mechanisms—atmospheric refractive index gradients, insects and birds. In his review of "dot angel" phenomena, Atlas (1964) reiterated a long-held view that the majority of targets are meteorological, the caps of rising convective bubbles being a favoured mechanism. The commonest angels are said to be windborne, with a coherent signature. By contrast, Crawford (1949) gave convincing evidence that nocturnal point angels were due to insects, and Goldstein (1951) in his classical review favoured the view that insects predominate. This school has regained popularity during the past few years, particularly through the work of Hardy, Atlas and Glover (1966). Their conclusion was based mainly on the wave-length dependence of the echo intensities. Most of their angels had small air speeds below 15 m.p.h., a coherent signature, and were absent in winter.

These schools stand in apparent disagreement, particularly since some of the studies were conducted in the same general area over a similar period of time. The writer believes that the disagreement is less than it would appear to be for two reasons. First, as is often the case, the catch is determined by the catching net. The large mesh of the surveillance radar tends to catch the larger bird lumps at considerable ranges, while the high-resolution, generally vertically-pointing meteorological radars working at closer ranges tend to miss the relatively lower density bird movements but favour the often higher density smaller targets. Second, mistaken angel identity is probably not uncommon; signature analysis is a young science, targets are of a wide variety and researchers tend to be specialized in one subject. For example, the meteorologist Ottersten (1964) observed that most echoes were not steady but had "neat periodic variations", which he suggested might be explained in terms of expanding blobs of air, while the present writer believes that the illustrated echo signals are good examples, and probably the only published examples, of bird wing-beat patterns, in this case of individual night migrants.

The literature contains conflicting criteria for distinguishing the classes of angels. These criteria will be compared with the findings of the present research in the Section on page 79.

It is hoped that the contents of this paper will stimulate discussion between disciplines.

CHOICE OF RADAR

To achieve a quantitative analysis of the bird migrants within a given volume of space, in terms of number, species, velocity, flock size, etc., certain radar parameters must be chosen carefully. Radar resolving power should be maximized. Bearing in mind that the time required for scanning the volume increases with increasing resolution, that it is technically unfeasible at present to resolve individual members of flocks, and that during high-density, broad-front migration the angel density, summed over all heights, has been found by several authors to be of the order of 200 per square mile, a suitable resolution cell would have all three dimensions of the order of 100 yards. This is considerably smaller than that generally used by radar ornithologists, and larger than used in many meteorological applications.

Radar sensitivity must be sufficient to detect any bird at any viewing angle. An optimum wavelength is in the region of 10 cm in the S-band (Section 5v), where the minimum bird radar cross-section is expected to be about 0.2 cm^2 (Section on p. 69). A multi-wavelength installation appears to have some extra advantage for bird hazard studies (See Section on p. 81).

It is most important to the study of echo signatures that the frequency response of the radar be essentially flat from zero frequency to well above the conical-scanning or wing-beat frequencies. The design of the A.G.C. circuit is often contrary to this, and this may be a cause of the failure of previous research to detect wing-beat patterns, etc. For some purposes, the gain of the radar should be linearized.

The siting of the radar affects critically the detection of birds at low angles of elevation. Ground clutter can be reduced greatly if the radar is set in a shallow hollow, or if a carefully designed radar screening fence is erected.

Signature analysis is done best by tracking radar, which has the added advantage of producing precision co-ordinates for the study of speed of flight, navigational accuracy, height stability, and so forth. A number of ex-service tracking radars are available which are suitable for medium-range bird study. The results reported herein were obtained on a privately-owned A.A., No. 3, Mk 7 radar (S-band, 200 kW peak pulse power, 1 500 c/s p.r.f., 0·55 μsec. pulse length, 4·8° beam width, conical scan tracking), now part of Loughborough University of Technology's radar station at Bruntingthorpe, Leicestershire. Using a modified head amplifier and a modern crystal mixer (14 dB improvement), the smallest bird may be tracked to 3·5 miles, a flock of ducks to 15 miles.

The radar, sited in a depression, is shown in Plate 1. The PPI screen in Plate 2 shows a low-density October nocturnal migration, with six bird angels and one small patch of ground clutter in the west. These echoes from single birds (see below) show the radar resolution. The modulation is due to conical scan. The range ring represents a radius of two miles.

RADAR CROSS-SECTION

It will be helpful to define various concepts relating to radar echoes. The fundamental "radar equation" is

PLATE 1. The A.A. No. 3, Mk 7 Radar.

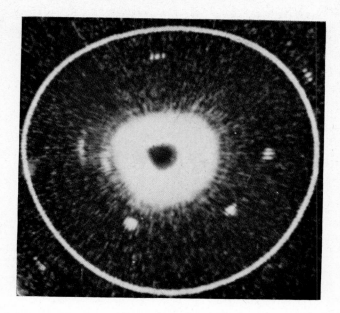

PLATE 2. Radar PPI, showing six single bird echoes, during a low-density October nocturnal migration. Ring radius is two miles.

$$P_r = P_t A^2 \sigma / 4\pi \lambda^2 r^4,$$

where P_r is the power received by the radar, P_t the power transmitted, A the area of the antenna, λ the wavelength, and r the range of the target. The radar cross-section of the target, σ, is a measure of the size of the target as seen by the radar, and has the dimensions of an area (cm²). It is defined as

$$\sigma = \frac{\text{power reflected towards source/unit solid angle}}{\text{incident power density}/4\pi}.$$

Its variation with time, $\sigma(t)$, is the echo signature. It may be calculated for targets of simple shape, or measured on a calibrated radar.

In the present study the radar was calibrated by tracking a silver-painted ping-pong ball ($\sigma = 36 \cdot 5$ cm²) carried by a balloon. This cheap target has a trackable range of $9 \cdot 0$ miles, and a corresponding altitude of about 20 000 ft. The local winds were measured simultaneously.

The radar cross-section of any target depends on five parameters: the dielectric constants of the target material, target size relative to λ, shape, the aspect presented to the radar and radar polarization. The bird target will be discussed under these headings in the following sections. Only monostatic (common transmitting and receiving antenna) radar with linear polarization is considered. A plane wave is said to be linearly polarized when the electric force vector, which always lies in the plane perpendicular to the axis of propagation, does not rotate about this axis, but has a constant direction, termed the direction of polarization.

The Dielectric Properties of the Avian Anatomy

In setting out a theory of the backscattering of radar waves from a bird, the first task is to look at a bird's anatomy in electromagnetic terms.

The propagation of radio waves within a homogeneous (non-magnetic) medium depends on only two parameters, the refractive index, n, and the absorption constant, k; or, alternatively, on the complex dielectric constant, $e - ie' = (n - ik)^2 . (i^2 = -1)$. Here e is the inductive capacity, and e' is a measure of electrical conductivity. These constants depend upon temperature and wavelength. Scattering occurs when the wave meets an interface with a medium having different dielectric constants. The amount of scattering increases with the dissimilarity. A useful guide to the importance of any medium as an echoing agent is the value of the reflection coefficient, R, for waves meeting perpendicularly the interface between that medium and vacuum: $R = [(n - 1)^2 + k^2]/[(n + 1)^2 + k^2]$. R increases with n or k. Another useful parameter is the attenuation of the wave amplitude in one centimeter, $A = e^{-2\pi k/\lambda}$. Here λ is the wavelength in vacuum.

The dielectric properties of bird feathers have been measured by Coultas and Houghton (1959). Unfortunately, no other avian data exist. However, a number of human tissues have been measured by Cook (1951), Cook and Roberts (1952) and Schwan and Li (1953). Table I gives the dielectric constants for a range of relevant substances. The entries refer to a wavelength of 10 cm and a temperature of 37°C. This is the experimental temperature nearest to the body temperature (44°C) of a flying bird. Values of R and A are also given in the table. It is seen that metals are nearly perfect reflectors because of their high conductivity, arising from a high free electron density. On the other hand, water is a good reflector because of its high inductive capacity, due to the strong polarizability of the "free" water molecule. The relatively large value of e for some biological substances is due to a high proportion of "free" water mixed with low capacity ($e = 2$) protein, fatty compounds and bound water, while the conductivity of these substances is increased over distilled water by the presence of cell ions.

TABLE I

Electromagnetic properties (37°C, 10 cm)

Substance	e	e'	n	k	R	A
Air	1·00	0·00	1·00	0·00	0·00	1·00
Metal	—	very large			1·00	0·00
High free water content						
Distilled water	73	8	8·5	0·47	0·62	0·74
Human blood	55·8	15·8	7·6	1·0	0·59	0·53
Human pectoral muscle and kidney	51	18	7·3	1·2	0·58	0·47
Low free water content						
Human bone	8	1·3	2·9	0·2	0·24	0·88
Human fat tissue (approx.)	4	1·2	2·0	0·3	0·11	0·83
Fatty and protein compounds, bound water, wood	2	very small	1·4	very small	0·03	1·00
Bird feathers	1·25	0·0	1·1	0·0	0·003	1·00
Bird bone (estimated)	2	0·3	1·5	0·1	0·04	0·94

The entries for bird bone are based on the assumption that it has one quarter of the density of human bone.

The dielectric properties for wavelengths between X- and L-bands are similar to those in Table I, the main characteristic being that k has a minimum at about 9 cm. This gives S-band the least absorption and the maximum "resonance scattering" (p. 62 (iv)).

The next task is to determine the approximate composition of birds in terms of these various types of substances. A linnet (*Acanthis cannabina*) and wood pigeon (*Columba palumbus*) in breeding condition were dissected. The approximate weight per cent in each of five regions of the body is presented in Table II. The value for the plumage was

TABLE II

Approximate composition and dielectric properties of the bird body (37°C, 10 cm)

Region	Weight %	e	e'	n	k	R	A
1. Plumage	9	1·25	0·0	1·1	0·0	0·003	1·00
2. Bones of wings and lower legs	3·5	2·0	0·3	1·5	0·1	0·04	0·94
3. Blood and muscles of wings	4·5	52	17	7·3	1·2	0·58	0·47
4. Bare head and neck	8	44	14	6·7	1·0	0·54	0·53
5. Thorax, abdomen, upper legs	75	44	14	6·7	1·0	0·54	0·53

taken from the survey by Turcek (1958). The dielectric properties are also listed, assuming for regions 3–5 that human and bird organs have the same values. In regions 4 and 5, 83% of the weight was in organs of high water content with an average dielectric constant of $52-17i$, while 17% came from fat tissue, bone, etc., with an average of $3-1i$, giving finally an overall average of $44-14i$. This averaging procedure is partly justified by the similarity of the dielectric constants for the majority of the body constituents, and by the relatively small size of any one constituent when compared with λ.

Several important conclusions may be drawn from the values of R and weight percentage. The plumage should contribute a negligible amount to the echo. This is confirmed by the experimental work of Edwards and Houghton (1959). The bones of the wings and legs may be neglected also. The watery wing stubs may contribute a small echo, although when investigated by Edwards and Houghton (1959) and by Blacksmith and Mack (1965), their presence was undetectable in the bird echo (Section on p. 72). We may safely conclude that the bird echo arises predominantly from the spheriodal body (thorax, abdomen and pulled-in thighs), and to a much lesser extent from the bare head-neck. These regions are so reflective that they give about half the echo they would if they were metal-coated! It should be noted that the value of A implies that any wave energy transmitted into the interior of a bird will be largely absorbed, and converted to heat.

THE RADAR ECHO FROM A SPHERICAL BIRD

The next stage in the theory is the calculation of the radar cross-section of a target with $n = 6 \cdot 7$, $k = 1 \cdot 0$ (assuming S-band) and a body-head-neck shape. Unfortunately, this shape is beyond the range of mathematical manipulation at present, and we must settle for a soluble model having as many birdlike features as possible. A useful starting point is the sphere. The bird, represented by region 5 above, is modelled as a unit density sphere. For a bird of weight $W(g)$, the equivalent sphere radius is $b = 0 \cdot 564 \ W^{\frac{1}{3}}$(cm). Because of spherical symmetry, σ does not depend upon viewing aspect or polarization, but only upon the ratio of circumference to wavelength, $x = 2\pi b/\lambda$. Figure 1 shows the dimensionless radar cross-section $\sum = \sigma/(\lambda/10)^2$ for metal-coated and "bird" spheres, plotted against the dimensionless weight $w = W/(\lambda/10)^3$. (Normalization has been chosen arbitrarily at $\lambda = 10$ cm.) The cross-sections for w less than 300 were specially computed by Lord (1967, private communication) from the first three terms of the well-known Mie series, while the metal sphere results for large w were computed from the leading term (called the E_1 term below) of the asymptotic series as given by Senior (1964). We shall give now a general physical interpretation of these results. A helpful reference is van der Hulst (1957).

(i) In the "optical region" of very large spheres, with w greater than 10^4 say, the echo is mainly produced by a backward specular reflection from the centre of the illuminated face, and σ has its geometrical optics limit, $R\pi b^2$. This is a special case of the general rule that for large smooth non-re-entrant bodies $\sigma = R\pi b_1 b_2$, where b_1 and b_2 are the principle radii of curvature at the point of back-reflection. For the sphere σ happens to be R times the silhouette area. These limiting values for metal and "bird" are shown by the dashed lines in Fig. 1.

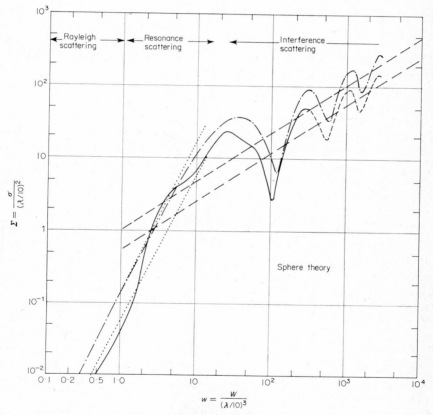

FIG. 1. Dimensionless radar cross-section of metal $(-\cdot-)$ and dielectric "bird" (---) spheres, with optical $(--)$ and Rayleigh $(\cdots\cdots)$ limits, versus dimensionless weight of sphere. (Section on p. 60)

(ii) As the sphere decreases in size we enter the "Mie, fluctuation or interference region", which extends down to about $w = 50$, and where a second type of back-scattered wave occurs. This is the "creeping wave" which arrives tangentially at the boundary between the lit and shadow faces, is diffracted around the sphere, making 1, 2 or more revolutions before setting off tangentially in the radar direction, at which time it joins the specular reflection. Their mutual interference produces the fluctuations in σ. Only that creeping wave component is important which makes one trip around the sphere and is polarized with its electric vector perpendicular to the surface. We shall call this the E_1 wave, and the approximate theory which considers only the specular and E_1 waves, the "E_1-theory". The "bird" spheres differ from the metal spheres in three ways: the specular reflection is reduced by a factor R due to transmission into the interior, the creeping waves are more attenuated because they may now refract into the interior, and the creeping waves have a small phase shift. Fortuitously, this extra attenuation in the case of "watery" spheres is approximately R, as may be seen from the computed values for w between 50 and 300, or from the similar computations of Aden (1951) and Stratton (1948). Therefore, throughout the Mie region the "bird" sphere cross-section is about R times the metal sphere cross-section. The "bird" values of Fig. 1 have been extended above $w = 300$ by this approximation. Fluctuations decrease with increasing sphere size because the creeping waves have a longer path over which to radiate away their energy, even though the path curvature is decreasing. The fluctuations are often mistakenly called resonances.

(iii) The "Rayleigh region" occurs for small spheres with $x < 0\cdot4$ or $w < 1$ approximately. Then $\sigma = fW^2/\lambda^4$, with f equal to $0\cdot141$ and $0\cdot055$ for metal and "bird" spheres respectively. These limiting values are shown as dotted lines in Fig. 1. Even in this region the "bird" to metal ratio differs little from R. It is known that any small target behaves like a dipole for Rayleigh scattering, with the cross-section varying approximately as W^2/λ^4. Surface roughness is unimportant.

(iv) For some types of targets there is a "resonance region" lying between the Rayleigh and Mie regions. This happens when the refractive index (n) is large and the absorption (k) is small. The "bird" sphere graph shows the presence of a moderate size (dipole) resonance near $w = 3$ and a second small resonance near $w = 24$. The explanation of this phenomenon is that some of the incident energy is transmitted into the interior where it sets up standing waves which are contained because of the high internal reflection. The resonances are only moderate for $\lambda = 10$ cm because of the fairly high internal absorption ($A = 0\cdot53$).

(As noted above, absorption is least for S-band; X- and L-band resonances are about 80% as large.) Resonance occurs when the sphere diameter is a multiple of the internal wavelength, λ/n. In the first resonance of the "bird" sphere the echo is three times stronger than a Rayleigh scatterer. A metal sphere exhibits no resonance (large k), and in the vicinity of $w = 3$ gives an echo actually smaller than the "bird" sphere!

(v) The sphere model may be used to predict an optimum radar wavelength λ for the detection of birds. Suppose that the smallest bird likely to appear on the radar screen has a weight $W = 5$ g. (In Britain this would be the goldcrest *Regulus regulus*.) Then the "bird" sphere results in Fig. 1 may be used to predict the minimum cross-section σ_{min} for all birds, for different values of λ. The resulting graph, Fig. 2,

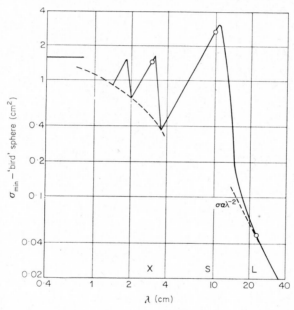

Fig. 2. Minimum cross-section for "bird" spheres weighing 5 g or over, versus radar wavelength.

shows that "birds" are most visible at $\lambda = 11$ cm, with a σ_{min} of 3 cm². The most commonly used radars operate in the X-, S- or L-bands at approximately 3, 10 or 23 cm wavelengths respectively. We may infer that S-band is to be preferred for visibility of "bird" targets. In this band the smaller birds lie in the resonance region, and the large birds in the lower Mie region where maximum interference effects occur.

We shall see that these are important regions for identification. Only the largest insects would be readily detectable as S-band. Although X-band is good for visibility of birds and insects, all bird species lie in the middle to upper Mie region, where interference effects are small. On the other hand, L-band is exceptionally poor for the detection of small birds and all insects. The minute cross-sections of many passerine birds at L-band are undoubtedly responsible for the flickering type of PPI display observed by Drury and Kieth (1962) and Eastwood and Rider (1966).

The "bird" sphere has been considered at length because many of the essential features of actual bird echoes may be understood in terms of it. However, spherical symmetry eliminates two important diagnostic features, the effects of the viewing angle (aspect) and the effects of radar beam polarization.

THE RADAR ECHO FROM A SPHEROIDAL BIRD

The simplest model which includes these features and is more realistic than a sphere is the prolate spheroid (ellipsoid of revolution about the long axis). As before we begin by neglecting the contribution from the head-neck, and represent the bird body cavity (region 5) as a unit density spheroid containing $0 \cdot 75$ W g of dielectric material with $n = 6 \cdot 7$, $k = 1 \cdot 0$ (assuming S-band). The length of the major axis, $2c$, is taken to be the distance from the anterior of the bird's thorax to the posterior of the abdominal cavity. Measurements of this length were made on freshly dead specimens of nine species of birds ranging in weight from 20–2 000 g. To within the measuring error, $c = 0 \cdot 89$ $W^{\frac{1}{3}}$ cm, or equivalently, $c = 1 \cdot 59b$. These measurements imply that the unit density spheroid should have an axis ratio $c/a = 1/e = 2 \cdot 00/1$. Happily, the measured maximum girths of the featherless bodies were all close to πc, so that the spheroid model is a consistent first approximation.

Having specified the dielectric constants and shape, the radar cross-section depends only upon three parameters: the dimensionless circumference to wavelength ratio $2\pi a/\lambda$, or alternatively, the weight ratio $w = W/(\lambda/10)^3$; the aspect, θ, the angle between the major axis and the viewing direction, with the convention that the "head-on" view is $\theta = 0$; and the polarization angle β. Because of the axial symmetry, we may define the "horizontal" $x - y$ plane as the plane containing the major axis and the viewing direction vector passing through the spheroid centre, with the "vertical" z-axis perpendicular to this plane. Then β is defined as the angle between the z-axis and the electric vector of the plane wave travelling along the viewing direction.

The exact calculation of $\sigma(w,\ \theta,\ \beta)$ is difficult, whether the infinite Mie series in terms of spheroidal functions or the asymptotic series is used. Very few results exist and these are almost exclusively for the metal spheroid at end-on ($\theta = 0$) incidence. The mathematical details of the new theory given below will be published elsewhere. The different scattering regions are discussed in turn.

(i) In the optical region, the calculations are straightforward. Applying the general rule of (i), p. 61 $\sigma = R\pi b_h b_v$. The horizontal and vertical radii of curvature at different aspects are given by

$$b_h = a^2c^2/p^3, \quad b_v = a^2/p, \quad p^2 = c^2\cos^2\theta + a^2\sin^2\theta,$$

so that

$$\sigma = R\pi c^2 e^4/(\cos^2\theta + e^2\sin^2\theta)^2, \tag{1}$$

where $R = 0.54$ for the "bird" spheroid. It is seen that σ is independent of the polarization angle β. When viewed from the side, $\sigma_s = 0.54\pi c^2$, which is very nearly πac, the side silhouette area of the body cavity. This is a very useful guide to bird radar cross-section. σ_s is plotted versus w as line O_s (long dashes) in Fig. 3. The end-view cross-section, $\sigma_e = \sigma_s/16$, is shown as O_e (short dashes) on the same graph. σ_e is about eight times smaller than the end-view silhouette area! A "polar diagram" is defined in general as the variation of σ with θ for fixed w and β. The normalized "optical" polar diagram is plotted in Fig. 4(c). The spheroid grows faint rapidly when turned from side-view.

(ii) In the fluctuation region, from about $w = 50$ to 10^4, it is very difficult to get numerical values from the mathematical theory. It is expected that the dominant contribution to the scattering is from a specular reflection and an "E_1" creeping wave. The theory presented here assumes that both of these are R times their corresponding values for a metal spheroid, as in the sphere case. We shall consider only the side-view, with vertical (V_s) and horizontal (H_s) polarizations, and the end-view (E). The principle of stationary path length is used as a guide to judge which of the possible paths around the spheroid the E_1 waves will take. This leads to the conclusion that for the side-view, vertically polarized creeping waves will travel around the circular boundary of the spheroid in the plane of the minor axes, while horizontally polarized waves will creep around the elliptic periphery in the mid-horizontal plane. The magnitude and phase of these E_1 waves were determined from the theory of Franz and Klante (1959) for the diffraction of waves on metal surfaces of variable curvature, while the diffraction coefficients were deduced from the (corrected) theory of the spheroid given by Levy and Keller (1960) and Senior's (1964) sphere equations. The results of

D

these calculations are shown in Fig. 3. The E curve was extended below $w = 50$ by interpolation between the 1·25:1 metal spheroid results of Mushiake (1956) and the 10:1 metal spheroid results of Siegel *et al.* (1955). It should be noted that the E curve is in excellent agreement with the corresponding 2:1 metal spheroid computations of Kennaugh and Moffat (1964), which were based on another method, and which came to the author's notice after Fig. 3 had been produced.

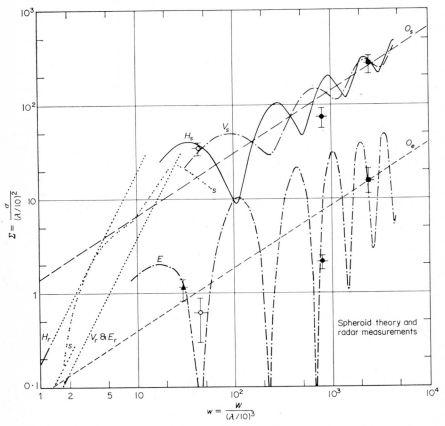

FIG. 3. Dimensionless radar cross-section of dielectric 2 : 1 "bird" spheroids, versus dimensionless weight. H_s, V_s: horizontal and vertical polarization at side-view. E, symmetric end-view. O_s, O_e: optical limits at side- and end-views. H_r, V_r, E_r: Rayleigh limits, for horizontal and vertical polarization at side-view, and symmetric end-view. S: "bird" sphere. Experimental points: *Passer domesticus*, 10 cm (triangle); *Apus apus*, 10 cm (open circles); *Passer domesticus*, 3·2 cm (closed circles); *Sturnus vulgaris*, 3·2 cm (squares). (Section on p. 64)

(iii) The Rayleigh region is easily dealt with by using the first term of the ellipsoid theory given by Stevenson (1953). The general form of the solution for a dielectric spheroid is

$$\sigma = 4\pi c^2 (2\pi a/\lambda)^4 |(F_1\cos^2\theta + F_3\sin^2\theta)\sin^2\beta + F_1\cos^2\beta|^2. \qquad (2)$$

For the "bird" spheroid, $F_1 = 0{\cdot}760 - 0{\cdot}011i$, $F_3 = 1{\cdot}71 - 0{\cdot}062i$. Equation (2) should be a good approximation for $w < 1$. The side-view cross-sections for the two polarizations are plotted as the (dotted) lines H_r and V_r in Fig. 3, while the end-on cross-section, labelled E_r, is identical with V_r. The Rayleigh polar diagram is shown in Fig. 4(a). Note the large difference between H and V.

(iv) The very interesting "resonance region", lying approximately between $w = 1$ and 10, has not been studied, although it should be calculable with only moderate difficulty. The "bird" sphere cross-section is repeated in Fig. 3 as the (double-dotted) curve S, to give an indication of the expected results. The position of the resonance may now depend on polarization and aspect. It is anticipated that the first resonance will be shifted to the neighbourhood of $w = 6$ for V_s and E, and to near $w = 1$ for H_s. X- and L-bands will again have smaller resonances.

(v) The conclusion from the sphere theory, that "birds" are most visible at S-band, needs some qualification. For the side-view, H or V, it is as valid as before, with σ_{min} increased now to about 10 cm². At end-view the situation is not clear, because the theory cannot predict

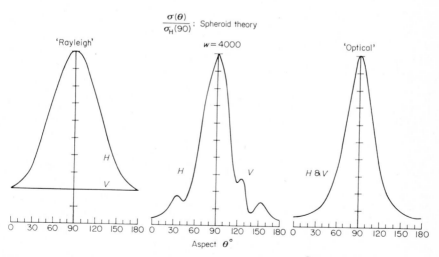

Fig. 4. Theoretical polar diagrams of the "bird" spheroid in the Rayleigh, interference and optical regions, with horizontal and vertical polarizations.

accurately the values of the minima of the first few deep fluctuations (see p. 70 i(d)). However, it should be safe to conclude as before that L-band has a much smaller σ_{min}.

(vi) The Rayleigh and optical polar diagrams have been discussed already. The only other theoretical polar diagram for a 2:1 spheroid known to the author is that of Andreasen (1966) for a metal spheroid with $2\pi a/\lambda = 4\cdot45$ or $w = 4\cdot10^3$. This is shown in Fig. 4(b). Clearly, it is composed of an optical (specular) wave and a small E_1 wave. This is typical of the fluctuation region. In this region the number of oscillations or lobes (L) in the polar diagram between head- and side-views may be found from the E_1-theory from the phase difference between the side and end waves. The result is

$$L_h = 0\cdot10 + 0\cdot30(2\pi a/\lambda), \quad L_v = 0\cdot10 + 0\cdot58(2\pi a/\lambda). \tag{3}$$

This prediction is confirmed by Andreasen's calculation in Fig. 4(b). It is a useful guide for a qualitative understanding of polar diagrams (but see p. 70 (ii) for its limitations).

(vii) Regarding polarization effects, that is, the dependence of σ on β, it is known that for any given body at a fixed aspect the cross-section may be expressed in terms of five parameters: the two values σ_h, σ_v for horizontal and vertical polarization, the phase γ between the H and V reflected waves, and two cross-polarization parameters. It is rigorously true that in the optical region of large spheroids (equation 1) and the Rayleigh region of small spheroids (equation 2) the cross-polarization is zero. This is also true for the E_1-theory as we have formulated it for the fluctuation region. We may safely assume that the neglect of cross-polarization is a good approximation in general. Turning to γ, it is zero for optical scattering, minute for Rayleigh spheroids (equation 2), and small throughout the fluctuation region according to the E_1-theory. Therefore, we may assume that cos γ, the only function in which γ appears, is unity. Within these approximations, the cross-section may be written in the form

$$\sigma = (\sigma_h^{\frac{1}{2}}\sin^2\beta + \sigma_v^{\frac{1}{2}}\cos^2\beta)^2. \tag{4}$$

Clearly, σ has two extremes, σ_h and σ_v. There are no polarization effects when these extremes coincide, as at end-view or in the optical region. As a general rule polarization effects decrease as target size increases relative to the wavelength, although for some target sizes and aspects the H and V echoes may be equal, as may be seen in Figs 3 and 4. We shall take

$$P = |\sigma_h - \sigma_v|/(\sigma_h\sigma_v)^{\frac{1}{2}} \tag{5}$$

as a measure of these effects. Throughout $w - \theta$ space, σ will have local islands of large P. The polar diagram between $0°$ and $90°$ should have approximately $L_v + L_h$ regions of large P, which may be visualized for the spheroid depicted in Fig. 4(b) by reflecting the H curve through the vertical axis to lie on top of the V curve.

The value of P should be a useful parameter in the identification of targets. It is easily measured on radars which have rotating dipole aerials, such as conical scan tracking radars, because the echo is then modulated between σ_h and σ_v at twice the dipole rotation frequency.

COMPARISON OF THEORY AND EXPERIMENT

It would appear to be difficult to take the theory beyond the spheroid stage, although it would be interesting to vary the $a:c$ ratio. We shall now test the usefulness and accuracy of the present theory against the few available radar cross-section measurements of known species of birds.

(i) Maximum and minimum magnitude:

(a) Edwards and Houghton (1959) measured σ_h between $\theta = 18°$ and $162°$ at $\lambda = 3\cdot2$ cm for the house sparrow *Passer domesticus*, starling *Sturnus vulgaris* and wood pigeon. No weights are given, but these are approximately $W = 27$, 80 and 500 g ($w = 800$, 2 400 and 15 000) respectively. The maximum σ, which always occurred at or near the side-view, was 7, 25 and 100 cm² respectively. These might be under-estimates because the experimenters state that their apparatus had a time constant which would tend to smooth the polar diagram. The measured minima were approximately $0\cdot2$, $1\cdot5$ and $1\cdot0$ cm² respectively. The results for the two smaller birds are shown on Fig. 3. The agreement for all three birds is reasonably good, considering the uncertainty in the phase of the fluctuations.

(b) LaGrone, Deam and Walker (1964), using the M-33 X-band radar, measured and published the echo from a soaring turkey vulture (*Cathartes aura*). This species weighs about 2 400 gm ($w = 72\,000$). The maximum and minimum σ were 250 and 25 cm². The theoretical prediction of 240 and 15 cm² is in good agreement.

(c) Blacksmith and Mack (1965) measured the end-view head and tail cross-sections of a chicken and two ducks ($W = 3\,300$; 5 500 and 10^4 g) using V radiation at $\lambda = 75$ cm. The corresponding values of w are $7\cdot8$, $13\cdot0$ and $23\cdot6$. These values straddle the first maximum in the end-view (E) graph shown in Fig. 3, and give rise to relative cross-sections which agree reasonably well with the experimenter's general findings that the largest and smallest birds had about one half of the echo of the medium-size bird, although this effect was attributed to a resonance. The measured average cross-section for the largest bird for the head-end was

600 cm², for the tail-end, 24 cm². The measurements depended critically on the position of the neck, as is to be expected with such a long wavelength for which the bird reflects like a dipole, particularly as the vertical neck was aligned with the vertical polarization. (This sensitivity is not likely to occur at S- or X-band. The head-neck echo is not studied in this paper.) The theoretical prediction for the large duck is 101 cm², which is approximately the geometric mean of the experimental head and tail values.

(d) Figure 7 of this paper shows the echo from what is almost certainly a gyrating swift (*Apus apus*) recorded by the author at dusk on June 21, 1967, at a range of 2 100 yards and an altitude of 1 800 feet, in the vicinity of many other almost stationary echoes of the same type. Over a period of several minutes the recorded maximum σ was 34 ± 5 cm², while the minimum is shown in the illustration. The zero line is drawn at the level of average noise. It is difficult to measure the minimum σ, but it has been estimated as $0\cdot6 \pm 0\cdot3$ cm². These results are shown in Fig. 3, positioned at the average swifts' summer weight of 45 g. Agreement with theory is good, particularly since the deep fluctuations of the spheroid echoes are unlikely to occur for a more irregular shape having a head-neck protuberance, and the first minimum may be shifted slightly by a more accurate spheroid theory. The theory certainly accounts for the very large ratio of "side" to "end" cross-sections. The end-view echo of a swift must be one of the smallest possible for birds at S-band. It is probable that the absolute minimum σ for birds occurs in this first minimum, and is not less than $0\cdot2$ cm².

(e) The author has begun radar cross-section measurements of dead birds suspended from balloons. In this way the minimum σ of a house sparrow was found to be $1\cdot1$ cm². This value is plotted in Fig. 3 at the specimen weight of 30 g. Agreement is good.

(f) A few other statements have been published, but to the author's knowledge they are only rough estimates for "gulls" and "large sea birds".

(ii) Polar diagram:

(a) Edwards and Houghton (1959) have produced the only published work. Their measured σ_h at X-band for the sparrow and starling are reproduced in Fig. 5. The angular variation has some resemblances to the spheroid polar diagram of Fig. 4(b). The theory would have predicted the number of lobes correctly if the experimental polarization had been vertical, but, as it stands, the measured curve has about twice as many lobes. It is thought that this discrepancy is due to the neglect of the head-neck in the model. At X-band these finer details are more important. More study is called for in this important area.

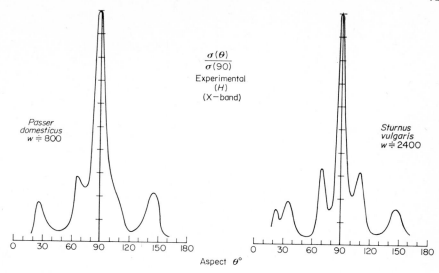

$$\frac{\sigma(\theta)}{\sigma(90)}$$
Experimental
(H)
(X—band)

Passer domesticus $w \doteqdot 800$

Sturnus vulgaris $w \doteqdot 2400$

Aspect $\theta°$

FIG. 5. Experimental polar diagrams for *Passer domesticus* and *Sturnus vulgaris* at 3·2 cm and horizontal polarization. (Edwards and Houghton, 1959)

(iii) Polarization:

(a) It appears that the only published reference to this topic is Houghton (1964). Referring presumably to the experiments of Edwards and Houghton (1959), he states that "the study of radar cross-sections made so far indicates that these cross-sections tend to have spherical symmetry, and so will probably reflect circularly polarized signals". The spheroid theory predicts [p. 64 (vii)] that cross-sections do not have spherical symmetry in general. This prediction may not contradict the above statement when it is remembered that at X-band (large w) polarization effects tend to be small, being often of the order of the experimental error ($\pm$ 1dB). To show up these effects a longer wavelength, like S- or L-band, should be used. It should be noted that a sphere reflects the mirror polarization of that received.

(b) Referring to Fig. 3, the theory predicts that for the swift there should be (1) negligible P at side-view and (2) at end-view, with (3) one zone of appreciable P about half-way between these. Figure 7 shows a short excerpt from the recorded echo of a swift. The presence of polarization effects would show up as areas of rapid oscillation (72 cycles/sec or 3 per scale division) due to the rotating dipole aerial. All three theoretical predictions are confirmed, with a band of large P ($P \doteqdot 2$·5) occurring between 3 and 15 cm² throughout the entire recording.

We may conclude from this section that the spheroid model exhibits the qualitative features of bird echoes, and may be used for some quantitative predictions, although much further theoretical and experimental research is required.

WING-BEAT PATTERN (WBP)

During a wing-beat cycle the unsteady aerodynamic forces exerted on, and the unsteady muscle forces exerted by, the bird amount to an appreciable fraction of the bird's weight. These forces should cause pitching oscillations (aspect changes) and changes in the body cavity shape, which, together with the motion of the muscles and blood in the wings, should cause echo modulations in rhythm with the wing-beat pattern (WBP).

The Mk. 7 radar displays the echoes in the beam direction as shown in Fig. 12. From the beginning of this study in 1964 it was observed that many of the night angels displayed in this way fluctuated rhythmically in amplitude. When they were selected and displayed on an oscilloscope with a slow time base, most of them showed strong beating patterns similar to those illustrated in Figs. 7 and 8. The frequency, v, of these oscillations varied from several to twenty or more per second, thus spanning the range of bird wing-beat frequencies. The implication seems clear. These are echoes from single birds, modulated with the WBP. However obvious this conclusion may appear, proof is difficult. The main features of the evidence offered here are: (1) the modulation frequency (8·2) and the lengths of the "flapping" and "gliding" periods of the echo from a (presumed) twilight swift, shown in Fig. 7, agree closely with the flight characteristics of day-flying swifts as recorded by cine film; (2) the leaping type of WBP of many small birds is often observed; (3) the steady beating characteristic of continuously flapping birds is common, and is illustrated in Fig. 8 (the pause seen at the right occurs rarely in this type). Recordings of signatures of types (2) and (3) have been reproduced in Eastwood (1967).

There are only two references known to the author to signatures of single birds in flight. (1) Houghton (1964) says of S-band studies that "no wing-beat modulations were detected in the film signal record from any of the birds under observation". (2) Eastwood and Rider (1966), using vertically-pointing X-band radar, observed echoes of angels passing through the beam. In summarizing, Eastwood (1967) states, "It was found that the pulse amplitudes were approximately constant and showed none of the rapid irregular fluctuations of the L-band angel echoes. It was to be expected that the X-band radar would see only single birds . . . but it was valuable to have direct confirmation of the fact by means of signature analysis". Why these two studies should not have detected WBP is not understood. It might have to do with radar frequency response mentioned in the Section on p.55. In the X-band case, it may be the reason given below.

If we accept the WBP interpretation of the evidence, we may ask which, if any, of the three mechanisms listed at the beginning of this section is the main cause. Edwards and Houghton (1959), working at $\lambda = 3 \cdot 2$ cm, side-view and large w (10^4), could find no measurable difference in bird echoes when the wings were closed or open. The same observation was made by Blacksmith and Mack (1965), who used $\lambda = 75$ cm, end-view, and w near to 20. This latter value is not very different from the w for a swift, and yet the beats of the swift are pronounced at all aspects, including end-view. (In fact the WBP modulation in many bird echoes is close to 100%.) On this laboratory evidence, the wing stubs are an unlikely cause. On theoretical grounds, the contribution from a long thin cylinder resembling the wing stub, and having the dielectric properties listed in Table II, could be detectable when the signal from the body is minimum, as at end-view, but probably could not give the large modulations observed often at these aspects.

If pitching aspect changes were the main factor, there would be little or no modulation at side-view. Unfortunately, Fig. 7 does not provide good evidence on this point, but on several occasions in the remainder of this recording, quite large beats occurred at side-view. This has been noticed also for many other echoes. The Research Unit has made high-speed cine films of birds of many species in level flight. Analysis is far from complete, but it appears that pitching oscillations, although usually present, are generally small and less than several degrees. This magnitude, when combined with the spheroid polar diagrams, implies smaller WBP modulations than are often observed.

These considerations incline the author to the view that body shape changes are the major cause of the WBP. The extension and contraction of the large pectoral muscles, the associated flexing and bending of the rib cage, and the probable enlarging and contracting of the abdominal cavity under the influence of the abdominal air sacs, are all contributory. In terms of the theoretical model, the length of the major axis, c, would remain nearly constant, while the minor axes would oscillate in magnitude. Thus the optical cross-section, $R\pi c^2$, arising from the specular reflection, would remain fixed, but the magnitude, and more importantly the phase, of the creeping waves would alter, giving rise to (often dramatically) modified polar diagrams. A 10% variation in the minor axes would appear to be quite adequate to account for the observed

D*

effects. A deduction would be that the percentage modulation should be largest in general on the steep parts of the polar diagram between side- and end-views, which is certainly the case in Fig. 7. Also, the WBP should be least observable at large w, which may account in part for the nearly steady echoes observed at X-band by Eastwood and Rider. In the author's opinion this is another good reason for avoiding short wavelengths for ornithological studies.

SPECIES IDENTIFICATION FROM WBP

The question arises as to whether it is possible to recognize species from the observed WBP. An experienced field observer can differentiate many species by a mere glance at a distant fluctuating silhouette, but he finds it difficult to say in many cases what the distinguishing features are. It is the author's opinion that the radar ornithologist should be able to take identification further than the field observer, because flight signatures may be recorded and analysed electronically.

From a preliminary study (Schaefer, 1967) of 45 species of migrating birds, based on high-speed cine photography in the field, it would appear that each species may be characterized by three basic flight parameters: wing-beat frequency, ν; the average duration of flapping periods; and the average duration of the quiescent (leaping, gliding or soaring) periods. The relative duration of the up-beat to the down-beat is often characteristic, but is too difficult to extract from the radar signature. These parameters vary somewhat with the mode of flight, so that it is essential to record only those individuals on long-duration (level) flight.

The frequency is the most distinctive feature. Greenewalt (1962) has collected all the published data. Much of it is of doubtful accuracy, being subject to the illusions of the unaided eye or obtained from birds in unknown modes of flight. For this reason it was decided to build up a library of wing-beat frequencies, etc., from slow-motion films, to include about eighty "radar species" that are thought to occur regularly over central England. Figure 6 shows the preliminary values of ν for 41 of these species, divided into abundant (A), common (C) and regular (R) species. The evidence indicates that ν varies by about 10% for any one species; this is indicated by the magnitude $\Delta\nu/\nu$ on the graph. It has been found that there is a strong correlation between ν and wing length, and between the product of these and air speed (V). These correlations have been used to predict the frequency for the remaining 39 "radar species", and these are shown as a, c and r in Fig. 6. It is seen that frequencies span more or less uniformly the logarithmic scale from about 2·8 to 30, allotting on average about four species per unit $\Delta\nu/\nu$. This is the predicted resolution of species by frequency alone.

The duration of the quiescent period is also characteristic. It is minutes for experts in soaring, seconds for gliders like the swift, fractions of a second for "leaping" species like small passerines and thrushes, and nil for birds like waders which flap continuously. Wagtails (*Motacilla sp.*) are readily separated from Finches (*Fringillidae*), etc. It appears from preliminary experiments that carriage of migrating fat shortens the leaping period, and allowance must be made for this.

The duration of the flapping period has less diagnostic value, although it appears that some Warbler species may be separated by this parameter (Griffiths, 1967, private communication).

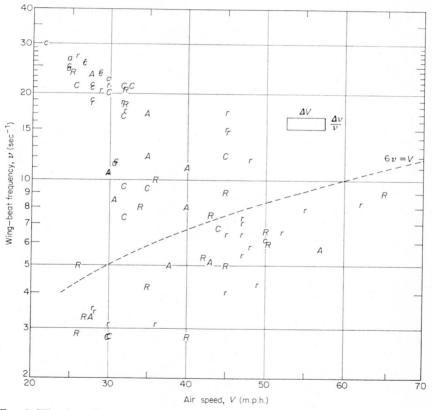

FIG. 6. Wing-beat frequency versus air speed for eighty "radar species" in level flight. $\Delta V, \Delta\nu/\nu$: typical variation in a species' air speed and wing-beat frequency. Measured and predicted values respectively for abundant (A,a), common (C,c) and regular (R,r) species.

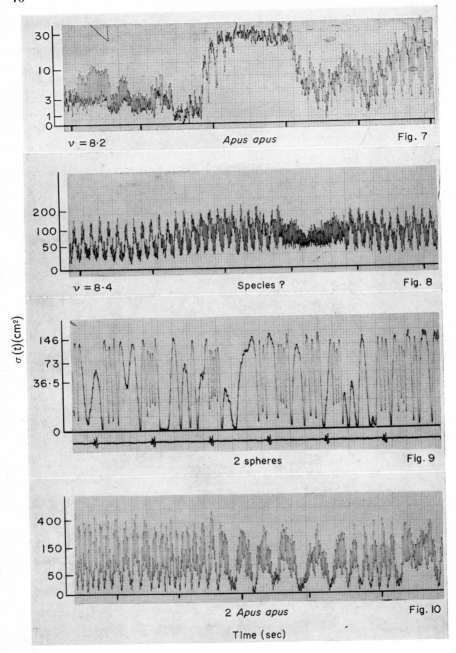

FIGS. 7–10. Examples of echo cross-sections versus time, for single and compound targets.

The photographic study of these flight characteristics is being continued as a full-time project.

Species Identification from Air Speed

The air speed of an angel is an important feature for distinguishing avian from non-avian targets, and as an aid to species recognition. Unfortunately, measurements are generally of ground speed, whether by field observation or radar, and determination of the simultaneous wind velocity is often problematic. The daily weather reports should not be relied upon for this purpose, because data are given only at widely separated space and time points. Ground level winds are often of little value in predicting upper winds, even for low altitudes. Most radar estimations of angel air speeds and directions should be treated with caution, unless supported by simultaneous balloon wind measurements. Flight speed varies with the mode of flight, and field studies of bird speeds should be confined to persistent long-distance flights of the type most likely to occur on radar.

Very few studies have met these requirements. The most reliable is the comprehensive review by Meinertzhagen (1955), but even here only a few dozen species have been documented sufficiently to produce a tentative average migration speed. It would appear from his study that a species has a characteristic migration speed, V, with a spread, ΔV, of about 5 m.p.h., and that migration speeds are higher than everyday flight speeds. Using these data, it has been found that the air speeds of allied species are closely correlated with wing-loading. Combining the data with the correlation, air speeds have been estimated for the 80 "radar species", and are shown, together with ΔV, in Fig. 6. Air speeds range from 22 to 65 m.p.h., or about eight units of ΔV. The distribution of species over this range is illustrated in Fig. 11. It is noteworthy that Harper (1958), as a result of measuring the air speeds of scores of angels over central England with wind-finding radar, found an almost identical distribution. Much more research is required into this interesting subject.

From the above discussion we may conclude that air speed, although a helpful additional parameter, does not have the diagnostic power of the flight pattern parameters, and is more difficult to measure. In summary, combining flight pattern, air speed and their uncertainties, it should be possible in the near future to identify any single bird target as one of three or four species, and in a number of cases, uniquely. Radar cross-section, polar diagram and polarization should provide further discrimination.

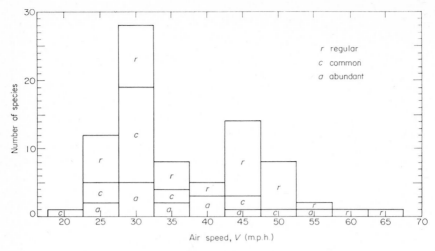

Fɪɢ. 11. Air speed distribution for eighty "radar species".

SIGNATURES OF BIRD GROUPS

So far we have been considering echoes from individual birds, readily distinguished as such by a clearly defined WBP modulation, as in Figs. 7 and 8. The echo from a collection of birds will be compounded of the individual echo amplitudes, each with its own phase, the latter being determined by the position of the individual in the group. If all individuals are in phase, the cross-section is maximum, and equal to the square of the sum of amplitudes. On other occasions, the phases may be such as to reduce the echo to zero. A simple example of this is shown by the recorded echo (Fig. 9) from two silver-painted ping-pong balls fastened about 15 in. apart on a thread tied to a hydrogen balloon. Due to atmospheric turbulence, the two spheres swing relative to each other, and the cross-section oscillates between zero and four times (2^2) the cross-section of a single sphere (36·5 cm²). (It will be noted that the radar frequency response is not flat, so that oscillations at 30 cycles/sec have about half of the full amplitude. This is the case for all the echoes presented in this paper.) Another example (Fig. 10) is the signature of the angel adjacent to the one which produced Fig. 7. It is thought to be from two swifts gyrating relative to each other within the beam resolution volume, since the echo appears to be compounded of two similar amplitudes with intermittent relative phasing, causing the cross-section to fluctuate with variable frequency between zero and about four times the amplitude for a single swift. The WBP is barely discernible.

In general, a compound echo will vary irregularly between the two extreme levels. This type of signature is important because of its frequent occurrence. Our sampling of echoes during the past few years has provided direct evidence that the majority of nocturnal angels are single birds, although diurnal angels give mainly complex signatures. Harper (1958), using a similar type of medium-range radar and an aligned telescope, saw flocks of birds on nearly all occasions during day-time tracking. Eastwood and Rider (1966) confirmed the expectation that the low-resolving-power long-range radars generally employed by radar ornithologists usually detect collections of birds with randomly fluctuating echoes, even though the majority of nocturnal migrants may be flying singly.

The author has developed a method for analysing complex signatures which gives species identification with an accuracy comparable to that for single birds, a good estimate of the number of birds in a flock, and an estimate of the mean distance between individuals. Unfortunately, the theoretical and experimental results are too lengthy to be given here, and will be published elsewhere. The reader is referred to Houghton (1964) and Eastwood (1967) for a background discussion of the subject.

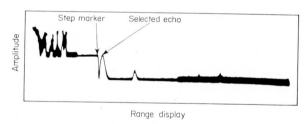

Fig. 12. Typical echoes in a radial direction as displayed on the Mk. 7 A-scope, with a step marker for selecting an echo for automatic tracking.

METEOROLOGICAL POINT ANGELS, INSECTS AND BIRDS.

A COMPARISON

As pointed out in the Introduction, each school of thought tends to discount the alternative types of targets. Oversimplified criteria are sometimes used for this purpose. We shall now examine the most important criteria in the light of the present paper. The situation is more complex than is generally realized.

(1) Air speed (m.p.h.): meteorological, nil; insects, small to 20 (Meinertzhagen, 1955; Hardy et al., 1966); birds in straight flight, 20 to

65. This is probably the best single criterion, but wind velocity must be measured accurately, and stationary (circling, thermal soaring, sea-breeze soaring, courting, etc.) birds and insects must be identified independently. Note that the faster insects and slower birds may over-lap. (See Section on p. 77 and Fig. 11.)

(2) Radar cross-section: meteorologists tend to believe that birds are distinguishable from the other types of targets by having considerably larger cross-section. For example, Hardy *et al.* (1966) incorrectly quote Houghton (1964) as stating that bird cross-sections are always greater than one cm². We have concluded in this paper that it is likely that the minimum bird cross-section at S-band is about 0·2 cm², with consider-ably smaller minima at X- and L-band. These values overlap appre-ciably with the larger meteorological and insect echoes, which vary up to 10 cm² (Atlas, 1964; Hardy *et al.*, 1966; Glover *et al.*, 1966; Hajovsky, Deam and LaGrone, 1966).

(3) Echo modulation and coherence: Atlas (1964) states in his review that (meteorological) echoes are remarkably coherent and steady (although he describes signatures obtained by Borchardt which are sometimes modulated with a well-defined period!), and, following the custom of many radar meteorologists and entomologists, refers to the conclusion of Roelofs (1963) that "bird echoes are easily distinguished both by periodic fluctuations in the echo intensity and erratic oscilla-tions in the tracking error signals". However, Hardy *et al.* (1966) found (meteorological) echoes that were characteristically incoherent and un-steady, and which were easily separated from the more numerous steady coherent (insect) echoes. By contrast again, Glover *et al.* (1966) found that free-flying insects dropped from aircraft often showed large ampli-tude fluctuations and well-defined small scale oscillations. Eastwood and Rider (1966) found that (bird) echoes observed at long-range were incoherent and unsteady, and concluded that these were from groups of birds. It has been shown in this paper that an echo from an individual bird is characteristically coherent with a definite modulation pattern. (It would appear that Roelof's incoherent echoes were from bird groups.) Thus all three types of targets may exhibit similar types of modulation. Much more research is needed in this complex subject.

The author believes that it is possible to classify insect signatures in a similar way to bird signatures in terms of cross-section, polar diagram, polarization and WBP, and to explain the cross-section data of Hajovsky *et al.* (1966) in terms of a model spheroid. The wing-beat frequencies of the larger insects will overlap those of the smaller birds, but the flap-ping patterns will be different in general. Following these lines it should be possible to distinguish many of the varieties of animal targets from each other and from atmospheric phenomena.

APPLICATION TO THE BIRD HAZARD PROBLEM

In the writer's opinion, the hazard presented to aircraft by birds should be approximately proportional (possibly above a certain threshold) to the density of bird mass in the air. This density is composed of the spatial distribution of bird groups, the number and mean separation of birds in a group, and the weights of the species involved. If radar is to be useful in any warning system, it should be capable of accurately assessing the mass density in a simple automatic way. Space permits only a short account of the relevance of previous work and the present paper to the achievement of this goal.

Previous work has been concerned almost exclusively with the simplest measurement, the density of angels as seen by the PPI and (more rarely) the RHI. The results have been mainly semi-quantitative, because the long-range surveillance radars generally employed have a low resolving power. For a quantitative study of the hazard problem it is essential to fit the radar parameters to the application (Section on p. 55); in particular the pulse volume must be comparable to aircraft and bird flock size. Even if accurate angel densities were obtainable, the PPI presents very little information for assessing bird hazard. For example, the PPI may be saturated with bird angels, but the situation may not be very dangerous to many types of aircraft if the migrants are small birds (under 4 oz say) well separated from each other, which is a common occurrence (Section on p. 78). Again, a few flocks of heavy birds may go unnoticed, and yet be a major risk. In fact, bird hazard may be only weakly correlated with angel number density because of the tendency for heavier birds to flock and to move more frequently than the more numerous small birds.

These considerations indicate that more attention should be given to studying mass density within angels, both visually in the field and by signature analysis, and discovering those radar characteristics of angels, if any, which relate in a simple way to bird hazard. A method of signature analysis has been found for measuring mass density approximately, the latter from the approximate identification of the bird species (Section on p. 78). However, this research is in an early stage, and the method is still too complex for practical use.

Several aspects of bird weight are relevant. (a) Some eighty species of birds are thought to occur regularly on the radar screen in central England. The weight distribution of these "radar species" is plotted in

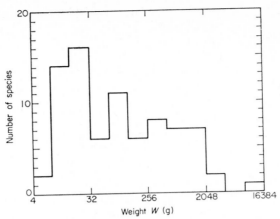

FIG. 13. Weight distribution for eighty "radar species".

Fig. 13. There is a marked reduction in the distribution above 4 lb, in agreement with the distribution of weights reported in strikes (Stables and New, this Symposium). The accumulated weight distribution for these species is shown in Fig. 14. For example, some 40% of species have weights greater than $\frac{1}{4}$ lb. When these two graphs are redrawn for individual bird numbers rather than species, using the arbitrary ratio of individuals to species as abundant: common: regular = 5:3:1, the results are almost identical in form. (b) In general, heavier birds have larger radar cross-sections, as shown in Fig. 3, so that it may be possible to separate high risk angels on the basis of cross-section, particularly

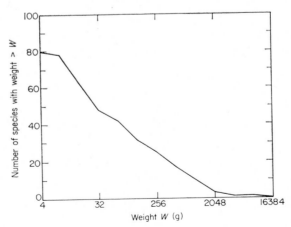

FIG. 14. Accumulative weight distribution for eighty "radar species".

heavy birds in flocks. More important, it may prove possible to automatically distinguish larger birds on a multi-wavelength system, by allowing a variable Rayleigh region to discriminate relative to the optical region. (c) All species heavier than 4 oz fall below the (dashed) curve, $6\nu = V$, in Fig. 6, showing that these higher risk species should be easily separable from other species by WBP and air speed, although this method is too complicated for a monitoring system.

Bird hazard information, once obtainable from radar, may be used in at least two ways: a survey of hazard over a period of a year or two in a given locality, when statistically correlated with season, time of day, immediate weather factors (such as temperature, wind, cloud), etc., may be used to predict future hazard as far ahead as weather predictions are reliable; radar specifically designed for the application may be used to monitor the immediate bird hazard and give warning of danger to air control officers or their computers, in the way that dangerous weather situations are monitored. The former method is being followed widely, and is reported at this Symposium. It is the writer's opinion that, even when the correlation is based on an adequate survey of bird hazard, it is not likely to be more than semi-quantitative, because the stimulus to migration and some other movements is known to depend not only on the listed external factors, but fundamentally on the internal state of the birds, which in turn appears to be influenced by the history of external factors over the previous months, and therefore to vary from place to place and year to year, and no doubt from species to species, in a complex way (see review by Farner, 1955). The statistical forecasting approach will probably continue as a qualitative guide, with least application in areas of complicated weather, such as the Atlantic seaboard of Europe, but it seems to the author that radar will have a more effective role as a monitor of immediate hazard.

Summary

1. A theory of the radar cross-section of a bird is given. The bird is represented as a unit density dielectric 2:1 spheroid. The theory relates cross-section to spheroid size, viewing angle (aspect) and radar polarization. Comparison with available experimental data shows that the theory explains the qualitative features of bird echoes, and may be used for some quantitative calculations.

2. Many angel echoes show modulations which are interpreted as the wing-beat patterns of single birds. These patterns are apparently due to changes in body shape in rhythm with the wing-beat.

3. It is possible to approximately identify the species of bird (in general as one from a group of three or four species, sometimes uniquely) by analysis of the echo signature in terms of flight pattern (wing-beat frequency, duration of flapping and non-flapping periods), air speed, radar cross-section and polarization.

4. The majority of nocturnal migrants over central England fly singly, according to a preliminary study.

5. The similarity of meteorological, insect and bird echoes is greater than is generally recognized. Criteria for separating these types are discussed. More interdisciplinary research is urged.

6. The bird hazard to aircraft is more likely to be related closely to the distribution of bird mass in the air, than to radar angel density. If radar is to be a feasible hazard monitoring device, methods must be perfected for assessing hazard in a simple way from an angel echo. A few suggestions and preliminary results are discussed. Hazard forecasting methods are unlikely to have the required accuracy.

ACKNOWLEDGEMENTS

The author is deeply grateful to Loughborough University of Technology for their generous assistance in making this research possible, and to the Ministry of Technology for their financial support of the project. He wishes to thank Mr L. Larrad, who so ably carried out all radar maintenance and development, and Mr M. Griffiths, for his assistance in procuring, dissecting and measuring specimens, for enumerating the "radar species" and their relative abundance, and for many stimulating discussions about general aspects of migration.

REFERENCES

Aden, A. L. (1951). Electromagnetic scattering from spheres with sizes comparable to the wavelength. *J. appl. Phys.* **22**, 601–605.

Andreasen, M. G. (1966). Correction to "Scattering from Bodies of Revolution". *Inst. elect. electron. Engrs. Trans.* AP-**14**, 659.

Atlas, D. (1964). Advances in radar meteorology. *Adv. Geophys.* **10**, 317–478.

Blacksmith, P. and Mack, R. B. (1965). On measuring the radar cross-sections of ducks and chickens. *Proc. Inst. elect. electron. Engrs.* **53**, 1125.

Cook, H. F. (1951). The dielectric behaviour of some types of human tissues at microwave frequencies. *Brit. J. appl. Phys.* **2**, 295–300.

Cook, H. F. and Roberts, J. E. (1952). Microwaves in medical and biological research. *Brit. J. appl. Phys.* **3**, 33–40.

Coultas, F. W. and Houghton, E. W. (1959). The complex dielectric constant of a feather sample at X- and S-bands. Ministry of Aviation. Unpublished.

Crawford, A. B. (1949). Radar reflections in the lower atmosphere. *Proc. Inst. Radio Engrs.* **37**, 404–405.

Drury, W. H. and Keith, J. A. (1962). Radar studies of songbird migration in coastal New England. *Ibis*. **104**, 449–489.

Eastwood, E. (1967). "Radar Ornithology." Methuen, London.

Eastwood, E. and Rider, G. C. (1966). Grouping of nocturnal migrants, *Nature, Lond.* **211**, 1143–1146.

Edwards, J. and Houghton, E. W. (1959). Radar echoing area polar diagrams of birds. *Nature, Lond.* **184**, 1059.

Farner, D. S. (1955). The annual stimulus for migration: experimental and physiological aspects. *In* "Recent Studies in Avian Biology" (A. Wolfson, ed.), 198–237. Univ. Illinois, Urbana.

Franz, W. and Klante, J. (1959). Diffraction by surfaces of variable curvature. *Inst. Radio Engrs. Trans.* AP-7, S68–70.

Glover, K. M., Hardy, K. R., Konrad, T. G., Sullivan, W. N. and Michaels, A. S. (1966). Radar observations of insects in free flight. *Science, N.Y.* **154**, 967–972.

Goldstein, H. (1951). Origin of the echo. *In* "Propagation of Short Radio Waves" (D. E. Kerr, ed.), chap. 7. McGraw-Hill, New York.

Greenewalt, C. H. (1962). Dimensional relationships for flying animals. *Smithson. misc. Collns.* **144**, No. 2.

Hajovsky, R. G., Deam, A. P. and LaGrone, A. H. (1966). Radar reflections from insects in the lower atmosphere. *Inst. elect. electron. Engrs.* AP-14, 224–227.

Hardy, K. R., Atlas, D. and Glover, K. M. (1966). Multi-wavelength backscatter from the clear atmosphere. *J. geophys. Res.* **71**, 1537–52.

Harper, W. G. (1957). "Angels" on centimetric radars caused by birds. *Nature, Lond.* **180**, 847–9.

Harper, W. G. (1958). Detection of bird migration by centimetric radar—a cause of radar "angels". *Proc. R. Soc.* B, **149**, 484–502.

Houghton, E. W. (1964). Detection, recognition and identification of birds on radar. World Conf. on Radio Met. including 11th Weather Radar Conf. 14–21.

van der Hulst, H. C. (1957). "Light Scattering by Small Particles." Wiley.

Kennaugh, E. M. and Moffat, D. L. (1964). Axial echo area of the prolate spheroid. *Proc. Inst. elect. electron. Engrs.* **52**, 1252–1253.

LaGrone, A. H., Deam, A. P. and Walker, G. B. (1964). Angels, insects and weather. *Radio Sci. J. Res.* **68**, 895–901.

Levy, B. R. and Keller, J. B. (1960). Diffraction by a spheroid. *Can. J. phys.* **38**, 128–144.

Meinertzhagen, R. (1955). The speed and altitude of bird flight. *Ibis.* **97**, 81–117.

Mushiake, Y. (1956). Backscattering for arbitrary angles of incidence of a plane electromagnetic wave on a perfectly conducting spheroid with small eccentricity. *J. appl. Phys.* **27**, 1549–1556.

Ottersten H. (1964). Occurrence and characteristics of radar angels observed with a vertically-pointing pulse radar. World Conf. on Radio Met. including 11th Weather Radar Conf. 22–27.

Roelofs, T. H. (1963). Characteristics of trackable radar angels. Res. Rept. 137, Centre for Radio Physics and Space Research, Cornell University, Ithaca, N.Y.

Schaefer, G. W. (1967). Recent studies of bird flight by radar. *Ibis.* **109**, 476.

Schwan, H. P. and Li, K. (1953). Capacity and conductivity of body tissues at ultrahigh frequencies. *Proc. Inst. Radio Engrs.* **41**, 1735–1740.

Senior, T. B. A. (1964). Scattering by a sphere. *Proc. Inst. elect. Engrs.* **111**, 907–916.

Siegel, K. M., Schultz, F. V., Gere, B. H. and Sleator, F. B. (1956). The theoretical and numerical determination of the radar cross-section of a prolate spheroid. *Inst. Radio Engrs. Trans.* AP-4, 266–275.

Stratton, J. A. (1948). Tables of scattering functions for spherical particles. *Natn. Bur. Stand. Monogr.* A.M.S.4.

Stevenson, A. F. (1953). *J. appl. Phys.* **24**, 1134–1142.

Sutter, E. (1957). Radar als hilfmittel der vogelzugforschung. *Orn. Beob.* **54**, 70–96.

Turcek, F. J. (1958). The proportions of plumage, organic matter and water content in the bodies of some birds. *Acta XIIth Congr. Int. Orn., Helsinki*, 724–729.

A Bird Warning System for Aircraft in Flight

WILLIAM W. H. GUNN and VICTOR E. F. SOLMAN

Canadian Wildlife Service, Ottawa, Canada

The theme of this paper is that radar can readily detect flights of birds that are a hazard to aircraft in flight, and that this information can be used effectively in flight planning and in air traffic control to reduce the number of bird strikes by a significant amount.

It has been argued that since military aircraft must be prepared to carry out training flights and missions at all seasons, and all times of the day or night, losses of aircraft and even crew from bird-strikes must be accepted as a calculated risk involving only one of many operational hazards. It has been argued that the vast complex of national and international air traffic control is a split-second timing operation with no manoeuvring room in terms of either space or time for diversion tactics to by-pass birds and that, in any case, the problems of air traffic control are mounting so rapidly because of other factors that birds are becoming a minor problem scarcely worth consideration. If these viewpoints are valid, then we're wasting our time and yours, but we don't think they *are* valid.

Let's look at the commercial operation first. While the chance of an unforeseeable, random bird-strike in flight will always exist, it is nevertheless possible to define the high-risk conditions within fairly narrow limits. In the first place, we know that most commercial aircraft cruise at altitudes far higher than those used by the vast majority of birds, so that the danger of a strike in the cruise phase is very slight, and comes close to being negligible above, say, twelve thousand feet. Second, the multi-engined aspect of commercial aircraft means that loss of power through damage to one engine may be expensive but not catastrophic. Third, experience has shown that, at present day cruising speeds, wind screens and the rest of the airframe will withstand the impact from one or even a few **small** birds without serious damage. The high-risk conditions are therefore narrowed down to those in which a multiple strike may damage more than one engine and those in which the bird struck is large enough to do serious damage to such sensitive parts of the airframe as the windscreens and stabilizer. Moreover, as the risk at cruising altitude is small, we can concentrate largely on other phases of flight: take-off and climb-out, and approach and landing. The type of risk differs to some extent with the particular flight regime. The duration of the take-off and climb-out phase is relatively brief but it is also the time when most power is required; engine damage is therefore the most critical risk here. In the approach phase, the time period is considerably longer and the speed still quite high, but power is relatively less important, so here we are probably more concerned with structural damage to the airframe. Finally, at landing, the speed is relatively low and the time is also quite short, so the risk of a serious strike is consequently less and probably insignificant unless the birds are of gull-size or larger.

In summary, then, for commercial operators, we are concerned mainly with the take-off, climb-out, approach and landing regimes, and chiefly with small birds in dense flocks, medium-sized birds (e.g. gulls) in relatively dense flocks or large birds (geese, swans, cranes, or vultures, for example) flying individually or in flocks. Moreover, since the risk in the cruise regime is relatively low (above 12 000 feet), we are concerned primarily with airports and their surroundings outward to a radius of 50–75 miles.

Assuming now, for the sake of argument, that we had precise and specific information at hand about bird movements of this type, what would federal regulatory bodies or commercial aircraft operators be prepared to concede in terms of alterations to their normal operational routine in order to reduce the bird strike hazard? The first reaction to this is likely to be "very little or none". But supposing we consider the problem on the basis of what is being done today in terms of another aspect of air safety, for example thunderstorms. Thunderstorms are seasonal in their frequency, local and short-lived in their occurrence, difficult to track with precision, and harder still to predict with accuracy. Yet the high degree of turbulence lurking in their centres may represent a very real hazard to aircraft. Pilots in training are warned to treat them with respect, and not to fly casually through them. Meteorological services go to considerable trouble to provide pre-flight and in-flight advisory information about their occurrence. Air traffic controllers in airport towers and radar centres may change runways, approach routes or altitudes to help aircraft avoid nearby thunderstorms. When there are severe conditions in the immediate vicinity of an airport, pilots may delay their take-off briefly and landings may be delayed or even diverted until conditions become less hazardous. If all this can be done for thunderstorms, it can also be done as readily for flights of birds following patterns known to be hazardous—*provided* that the forecasts are at least as accurate and precise as they are for thunderstorms. This, we think, is a fair enough challenge, and all that need be asked for in terms of elasticity of operational procedure to reduce bird-strike hazards. But is the comparison of hazard between thunderstorms and bird-strikes a valid one? Squadron Leader G. W. Ovans, of the Directorate of Flight Safety, Canadian Forces Headquarters, says: "We have an elaborate warning system that allows us to take appropriate precautionary measures when dealing with thunderstorms. At least in part because of these precautions, we very seldom lose planes or have them seriously damaged by thunderstorms. Yet we do lose planes and have many others extensively damaged by bird-strikes. So far, we have not developed any functional warning system against bird-strikes, but if it can be done successfully for the one, it should be possible and worth while to do it for the other."

Turning to the military side of the bird-strike problem, we can assume first of all that military transport aircraft encounter roughly the same types of hazards as comparable commercial aircraft. In Canada, we do not as yet have large pure jet transports in military service, and this reduces the size of our bird problems. What we do have, however, is the F104 or Starfighter aircraft, used by our squadrons serving with NATO, and in Canada chiefly at the training centre at Cold Lake, Alberta. The F104 is a single-engined jet aircraft which is flown at very low levels and very high speeds. From our point of view, this is a particularly bad combination, since it cruises at altitudes where birds are frequently very numerous (250–500 feet), and at speeds which usually preclude either the pilot or birds from taking avoidance action if collision seems imminent. The windscreens seem able to withstand bird impacts at high speed, and the remainder of the air frame is practically invulnerable to serious damage from bird strikes, but not so the engine. The ingestion of even a small bird can result in serious damage which may lead to loss of power, which in turn means almost inevitably that the aircraft will crash. Fortunately, the Canadian design of ejection seat is extremely efficient, and as a result no pilots have been lost as a result of known bird strikes, but seven F104 aircraft have been lost for certain from bird-strikes and there are two other losses where a bird-strike is one of the more probable causes. At roughly one and a half million dollars per aircraft, we in Canada have felt it worth while to do a considerable amount of research on the problem.

With the Canadian military forces, then, the problem lies largely with engine ingestion of birds in a particular type of aircraft, the F104, where a strike by even a small bird may be catastrophic. A strike is more likely to occur in cruise than during the other phases of the flight regime because most of the flying time is spent in cruise at low altitudes.

By comparison with commercial operations, the problem is more specific with regard to aircraft but considerably less so with regard to the types of bird involved, and distance from the airport.

With the operation of military aircraft, the margin for change in flight plans can be extremely small when, for example, operational exercises are taking place. On the other hand, flexibility may be considerably greater than with commercial operations, particularly as far as training programmes are concerned. In planning training programmes over a two- or three-year period, for example, it may be possible to arrange training schedules in such a way that the peaks in flying periods do not coincide with seasonal peaks in bird migration. Even during seasonal peaks of bird activity, it may still be possible to minimize flying time during hours of the day or night when bird activity is greatest. If there is some leeway in the number of days to be flown per month, an efficient bird forecast and warning system should be able to select, within a given period, days and nights on which the bird hazard is relatively high or low and to offer advice in regard to altitudes and flight routes with the lowest degree of hazard. It would then be up to the operations group to set a threshold for the degree of hazard which would require the altering or postponing of scheduled training flights. The threshold could be adjusted up or down according to the urgency or type of flight programmed.

An effort to operate a bird activity forecasting programme that might be used for operational purposes, was made at the Canadian Forces Base at Cold Lake, Alberta, from May 1 to June 15 and again from August 21 to October 31, 1966. We were at that time already taking time-lapse motion pictures of a Plan Position Indicator (PPI) radar display at Cold Lake, for long-term analysis of the relationship between bird movements and weather conditions. For the above periods, we extended our photographic coverage to include a series of still photographs of a similar PPI display. One photograph was taken each hour around the clock. Each film was exposed for 10 minutes, followed by a two-minute pause, then re-exposed for a final minute. The result was a streak of light representing each substantial bird echo (probably representing a flock of birds). The interruption in exposure caused a break in the track at one end to indicate the direction of movement. Both Polaroid and ordinary negative film were used in about equal quantities. The Polaroid film was quicker and easier to handle but lacked depth. The ordinary negative film, with a two-speed emulsion, provided better contrast and detail, and therefore seemed better for making careful assessments of bird activity, especially in high density situations. The two kinds of film were often used alternate hours.

The hourly series of photographs was delivered to the duty forecaster at about 9 a.m. and 4 p.m. These were rated according to an arbitrary 8-point scale set up from a selection of photographs (see plates 1 & 2) covering the whole range of migratory intensities and provided current evidence of bird movements up to one or two hours before forecast time, which was regularly at 10 a.m. and less regularly at 4 p.m. The forecaster endeavoured to forecast the probable density of bird movement for each hour of the next 24-hour period, basing his decisions on:

(a) the hourly intensity pattern for the previous 24 hours;

(b) the hourly patterns for the past several days, giving an indication of the seasonal trend;

(c) the weather forecast for the next 24-hour period; and

(d) a rudimentary idea of what effect this weather might have on bird movements.

During the spring of 1966, the project was carried out purely on a "dry run" basis, with no influence on operations; in the autumn of 1966, some limited operational use was made of the forecasts.

An over-all assessment of forecast accuracy was made from verification of 2 068 hourly forecasts. Taking errors of plus or minus one in the rating scale as being not significant, it can be said in summary that 77% of the forecasts were accurate, 11% underrated and 12% overrated – on the face of it, a very acceptable rate of forecast for a first attempt. However, further examination showed that much of the accuracy was obtained by forecasting a persistence of the prevailing state. The level of accuracy was much lower if only those hours of greatest bird flight intensity are considered. Of the 119 hours when the intensity was rated at 5, 6, 7, or 8, only 50% of these were correctly forecast in spring and 35% in fall. It is incidentally worth noting that these presumably high-risk situations amount to only 6% of the total number of hours forecast, so that if this relatively small number could be forecast accurately, the practical value of the forecast system would be greatly enhanced.

A review of the results of the project brought forward three main points. First, the arrangement of a 24-hour forecast with a 12-hour updating provided much more lead time than was normally required. A six-hour forecast with a three-hour updating, the standard procedure for meteorological forecasts, would have provided sufficient lead time and allowed greater accuracy in forecasting. Second, there were inherent difficulties in the quality of the radar information. The radar was being operated for other purposes than bird detection and frequent changes in settings of gain, polarization, beam elevation, Moving Target Indicator, and range led to difficulty in standardizing measure-

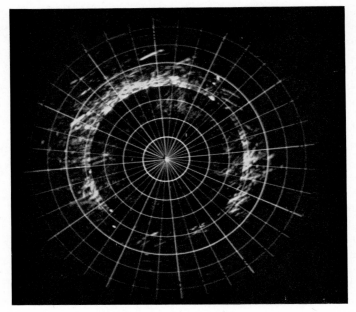

PLATE 1. Density 2 on the arbitrary scale.

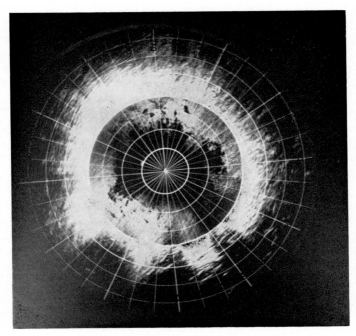

PLATE 2. Density 5 on the arbitrary scale.

ments of intensity of bird movement. Third, and most important, the input of ornithological data was far too inadequate and vague to enable the forecaster to interpret with any confidence the probable intensity of bird activity in relation to the weather forecast. Not only was very little precise information supplied in the way of the relationship between bird movements and the weather, but there was also a great lack of precise information as to the kinds and numbers of birds represented by the echoes on the radar screen. The general working hypothesis for the weather was that headwinds from the presumed direction of migration would be unfavourable for intensive bird migration and that opposing winds would be favourable. It followed that, in autumn, the east side of a high pressure system (following the passage of a cold front) was considered favourable for migration activity and, similarly, in spring, the west side of a high pressure system, or a warm sector following the passage of a warm front, was considered favourable. However, when those factors were considered, it was assumed that the primary direction of migration was northward in spring and was southward in fall. Subsequent study of the time-lapse motion picture films has shown this to be an inaccurate assumption, as the primary direction proved to be northwest in spring and southeast in the fall—a change that would make quite a difference in the assessment of the influence of the forecast weather on bird migration.

The bird intensity forecast project at Cold Lake functioned very well at the mechanical level but showed serious deficiencies in input at the theoretical level. In the past six months, we have begun a programme to make good these deficiencies by studying the influence of weather on bird movements at Cold Lake and by learning more about the relationship between the echoes displayed on radar and the actual numbers and kinds of birds they represent. As this paper is being written, we are about to run a computer programme which will make a multivariate analysis of bird movement data assessed from Cold Lake radar film over a period of 17 months in relation to weather data for the same station and period of time. Since in this operation we will be dealing with bird data and meteorological data from one geographical point only, we do not expect to arrive at any conclusive correlations, but we hope to obtain leads that will help in the next step—an analysis of similar bird and meteorological data for the same period, but this time taken from six locations in Alberta and Saskatchewan instead of just one. This should have illuminating results if we don't become swamped by computer output along the way.

Our second step was to establish an experienced biologist at Cold Lake with instructions to obtain quantitative information about radar echoes by relating them to visually verified numbers and species. He will also attempt to quantify our eight-point scale of density and will investigate local movements of birds that show up repetitively on the radar display.

In the past year a good deal of progress has been made in some parts of Europe towards a workable bird-warning system. In the Netherlands, the R.N.A.F. has set up a bird-warning system based on time-exposure photography of a radar scope at Den Helder. When bird flight intensities rise above a certain level on an eight-point scale, nearby military airports are warned by telephone and a graduated scale of precautions is put into effect. This system is simple, since it is a direct warning based on the latest photograph and avoids the uncertainties of a forecast, but it has the drawback that it has no lead time at all and a serious time-lag may develop if there is any delay in the transmission of information to operations control. In West Germany, special efforts were made to monitor and issue warnings about the spring and fall migrations of cranes across the country, since these are high-risk birds that cross many airport approaches. The programme has worked out well, with enthusiastic support from many field observers. In France, radar films taken at Aix-en-Provence last spring showed dramatically that local movements of birds may be an even greater hazard than migratory flights. Each morning and evening, gulls made flights between a major food source at a garbage dump northwest of Marseilles and a roosting area at the edge of a lake. The flight traverses the northern approach to the main runway at the military base at Istres, at a critical height, some five miles north of the field. This runway, the longest in Europe, is used in the testing of late model jet aircraft and it is not surprising that serious and expensive strikes have been occurring there. It is worth noting that while the motion picture films pinpoint this daily local movement with clarity and precision, still pictures fail to do so because of intermittent coverage and lack of motion. Still pictures are very effective in portraying bird migration taking place on a broad front over a matter of hours, but they are usually ineffective in showing up short-term local movements occurring in only a small portion of the display. The experience at Aix-en-Provence emphasizes the need to give more attention to local bird movements detected by radar, since they may well involve birds in the high-risk category, and quite specific warnings can be made as to when and where they present a danger. In Canada we learned our lesson in this regard one day in October 1966 at Cold Lake, when an F104 aircraft was lost after an encounter with some snow geese (*Anser caerulescens*). The bird movement intensity forecast for that particular hour of that day predicted a low intensity of bird activity. From a quantitative viewpoint this was quite correct. What the forecaster failed to say, and did not know, was that although the number of birds in flight would be low, a fair proportion of them would be geese that had recently arrived from the Arctic Coast a thousand miles to the north, and were moving about during the day to visit local feeding areas.

We should like to close by outlining what might be a workable basis for an effective bird warning system based in large part on radar-derived information. It should work as well, or better, in Europe as in North America because of the closer grouping of airfields and the greater number of weather (and bird) reporting stations.

The bird movement forecast would be prepared every six hours to cover the next six hours. In migration periods it would be updated every three hours, and every hour at times of high risk. It would be issued for a given region covering a number of airfields and would be as specific as possible. Preparation of the forecast would be the responsibility of a roster of biologists, organized in the same manner as duty meteorological forecasters, but covering a much larger area, so that the over-all number of biologists required would not be impossibly large. The duty biologist would be closely dependent on the current meteorological forecast and should be familiar with the synoptic situation on which it is based. It would be his responsibility to interpret the weather forecast in terms of the likely effect on bird movements. He would need to have in support: the experience gained from detailed studies of radar films and comparable weather data; information on known seasonal trends in bird movements in the region; reports of visual observations made in support of the operation; visual verification made of local movements that appear repeatedly on radar; and a backlog of general information drawn from the literature on the migratory behaviour of birds. This last must be weighed carefully since it may be based largely on visual observations that, by themselves, can often give a very misleading idea of what is actually happening.

The forecasts should be handled in the same general manner as local or special weather forecasts. They should be made available with the shortest possible delay to the briefing room for reference and possible action by pilots. On the same basis they should reach airfield controllers and air traffic controllers in radar centres. It might be feasible or desirable to issue bird movement forecasts only when a designated degree of hazard is reached or predicted. Forecasts for military airports should be prepared on a somewhat modified basis, in line with the differing requirements for military flights, as indicated earlier in this paper.

The outlined scheme needs to be strong enough to do the job but not so complex as to become a burdensome operation. Since it would probably take several years to set up such a scheme on a broad scale, it is appropriate to ask whether new generations of aircraft will continue to be vulnerable to bird-strikes, or whether aircraft design can overcome the problem. It seems evident that in the immediate future aircraft are likely to become more, rather than less vulnerable to severe damage from bird-strikes. Larger engine intakes will accommodate larger birds. Larger aircraft carrying many more passengers will make any plane loss all the more catastrophic. Increased speeds, such as are forecast for the take-off and climb-out speeds of the supersonic transports, will greatly intensify the force of impact and give birds even less opportunity to avoid being hit. There is a possibility that an effective guard or bird disposal unit can be designed to protect future jet engines and research on this aspect of air safety has at last begun in the United States. An effective device would greatly reduce the over-all bird hazard but would still give no protection from strikes on the airframe from large birds. It is our belief that the bird-strike problem will not dwindle to an acceptable risk until VTOL (vertical take-off and landing) aircraft are in common use. Meanwhile, in our opinion, any airport that operates without a proper bird-warning system extending approximately 50 miles outwards, just is not trying hard enough in the realm of air safety.

SUMMARY

The bird hazard to aircraft can be reduced by a warning or forecast system based largely on radar-derived information about birds in flight within 50 miles of an airport. Operationally, it could be handled in a manner similar to local weather advisories.

Photography of PPI radar displays now in use at airports would, in most cases, provide an adequate basis for a warning system, although more specific information about the heights of bird flights would be helpful. Multiple-exposure still-pictures give an immediate report on current intensity, location and direction of bird migration flights. Time-lapse motion-pictures give a better opportunity to study local movements and the relationship between weather and bird movements.

A bird-intensity forecast system was tested experimentally at Canadian Forces Base, Cold Lake, Alberta, in 1966. An accuracy of 77% was achieved over 2 068 hours in spring and autumn, but accuracy was much lower when only the hours of greatest bird flight intensity are considered.

A bird-warning system has recently been in effect in parts of Western Europe. A scheme for setting up a warning system is outlined.

Modification of the Habitat as a Means of Bird Control

E. N. WRIGHT

Ministry of Agriculture, Fisheries and Food,
Infestation Control Laboratory, Worplesdon, Surrey, England

Although the birdstrike problem presents many facets, it is clear that the hazard at, or very near to, airports is the major risk to civil aircraft and a substantial part of the risk to military ones. If the numbers of birds frequenting airfields is reduced, the number of birdstrikes will diminish. A variety of methods can be used to tackle the problem and seen in the most simple terms they involve either killing or scaring birds. It is apparent, however, not only from the evidence of the papers contributed to this symposium but from common knowledge derived over centuries, that birds are resilient in their response to adverse conditions. Simply killing large numbers of birds in any healthy population is unlikely to achieve more than a temporary reduction in numbers. Predation, whether natural or artificial, can be a density dependent mortality factor and for a fixed predation pressure (or control effort) more animals will be killed when the population is high than when it is low. Such systems are self-regulating and tend to ensure the survival of both predator and prey species. It may be that the numbers of a nuisance animal can be depressed to an acceptable level, although with birds the legal and practical limitations are severe, but to keep a population below the normal carrying capacity of the environment requires constant effort.

Where one is concerned only to deny animals the use of a limited area it may be sufficient to frighten them away, but birds rapidly become habituated to stimuli that give false warnings of danger and scaring mechanisms must usually be reinforced from time to time by real danger if they are to maintain their effect. Innate social warning systems and associated behaviour patterns are least readily exhausted by over-exposure but, even here a single stimulus cannot be expected to elicit the full response normally released by a series of stimuli. Under natural conditions animals respond to the total situation and to cry wolf too often may eventually result in a conditioned response which does not lead to dispersal. Ultimately the only way to keep animals

E

away from an area is to make the place unattractive to them. It follows that the removal from the habitat of those features that attract birds should be an important objective of every airport manager.

Airports consist essentially of two habitats, the intensely urban reception and servicing areas and the typically rural airfield*. Each of these habitats supports a characteristic community of animals and these will vary depending on the features of the particular airport and the fauna native to the area. Occasionally the airfield may differ radically from the general environment, and in these cases will constitute a micro-habitat to which the indigenous species might be unable readily to adapt themselves. The flight deck of an aircraft carrier represents an extreme example of such a situation. In general, however, airfields closely resemble their surrounding environment and represent a habitat in which the vegetation is either naturally or artificially low in height. They provide wide open spaces with short vegetation and on these physical characteristics alone prove attractive to some species whilst other species avoid them. Most species of gulls and many waders appear to find security in open spaces and roost or rest in exposed places with good all around visibility. Airfields provide these essential conditions with the further advantage that normal access by man is virtually prohibited. They are thus particularly safe places for species that rely on flight rather than concealment to avoid enemies.

It is unfortunate that airfields are in themselves attractive to birds for there must be a limit to the modifications which may be introduced without detracting from the primary function of the area. Two approaches are possible, either the airfield can be made less attractive or more desirable alternatives can be provided. It must be known whether birds frequent a particular airfield because it is the best place or the only available place and separate surveys must be made for each airfield. A very good example of such a study is that being done at Auckland's International Airport, New Zealand, which has been fully reported by Saul (1967). It would seem reasonable that all major international airports be subjected to full ecological investigation to minimize the bird-strike hazard. Equally no new airport should be constructed without due consideration of the hazard which might exist from birds. The desire to build airports on ground which is unsuitable for other forms of development is understandable, but it often means that they are built in places supporting dense bird populations. The initial saving in cost of land might, in the long term, prove a false

---

*The term "airfield" is used throughout this paper to refer to the aircraft movement area as opposed to the terminal buildings and technical site. The entire complex is referred to as "airport" regardless of whether it is a military base or civil air terminal.

economy. Proposals to site London's third airport in the Thames marshes or on the Isle of Sheppey appeared to ignore the fact that large numbers of waterfowl over-winter in these areas, which also support many gulls and waders throughout the year.

One significant way of modifying an airfield is to alter the vegetation. In Britain the areas between runways and hardstandings are traditionally grass-covered and are regularly mown to a height of a few inches. Simply to allow the grass to grow to a greater height might be sufficient to deter the smaller gulls, by limiting their vision and thus affecting their sense of security. The inability to spread their wings freely might be an additional deterrent. The grass mixtures commonly used on airfields may prove unsuitable for this treatment and it may be necessary to sow species with greater strength in the stem if matting is to be avoided. A consequence of the longer grass might be an increase in the number of small mammals and where birds of prey are numerous this could be quite unacceptable. For instance at Vancouver airport over 500 owls, mostly short-eared owls (*Asio flammeus*), were trapped and released elsewhere during a three-year period (Lewis, 1967); under these circumstances allowing the grass to grow long could create a bigger problem than it set out to solve. This is not the case everywhere and in New Zealand the method has been very successful (Saul, 1967). Currently in Britain long grass is being grown experimentally on a number of airfields and an attempt made to assess the effect on the bird populations. It is too early to evaluate these experiments, but the initial findings have been satisfactory in that the larger birds have mostly avoided the long grass areas. At one airfield starlings (*Sturnus vulgaris*) have been found to prefer the longer grass and the situation will have to be carefully watched.

Standing water is another physical characteristic which can attract birds though this is rarely found on airfields in Britain. Where airports have been built on low-lying land and it has been necessary to elevate the runway above the general level, the additional earth required is often excavated on the site, leaving shallow trenches which become permanent ponds. These are attractive to waterfowl, especially during the shooting season when the airfield affords refuge from hunters. If the depression has been scooped out, leaving shelving edges, reed beds can develop and provide roosting places for starlings.

Accepting that the physical characters of airfields favour their use by some species rather than others, many variables remain which may influence the number of birds present at any time. In some places the ebb and flow of migrants may be responsible for the main fluctuations in numbers, and Bridgman (1965) has shown that on three airfields in south-western England there were pronounced seasonal changes both in species and numbers. Normally these fluctuations are not independent of the attractions offered by the airfield and few would dispute that the availability of food must exert a controlling influence. Lack (1954) points out that within the favoured habitat, dispersion outside the breeding season can be adequately explained by supposing that individuals or flocks avoid areas where food is scarce and tend to settle where it is abundant. It must, therefore, be an advantage to ensure that an airport does not provide birds with an attractive and abundant source of food, either natural or man-made.

The "permanent pasture" vegetation of most British airfields ensures a fairly stable soil fauna within the limits set by soil type, pH and water table. Food in the form of earthworms, leatherjackets (*Tipula* sp.) and wireworms (*Agriotes* spp.) which is eaten by many species of birds is thus available. Much research may be necessary to establish what food organisms are present and for which species they represent a major source of food. This point is important because reduction of the soil fauna will not affect the numbers of those birds which are not dependent on it. For instance, it seems doubtful whether total elimination of the soil fauna would influence the number of herring gulls (*Larus argentatus*) visiting an airfield, but common gulls (*Larus canus*) might find the area less attractive. The literature on the food of different species of birds is sadly incomplete and owing to the existence of local feeding preferences a separate investigation at each site would be necessary. The invertebrate soil fauna of an airfield can be eliminated by chemical means, but treatment of large areas is expensive and toxic residues may persist. Van Tets (personal communication) has reported an improvement in the bird problem at airports in Australia following treatment with Telodrin, but a small-scale trial with chlordane on a British airfield was inconclusive. The chlordane was applied at the rate of 12 lb per acre, and during the following 4 months regular counts were made of the numbers of birds on treated and control areas. Throughout this period corvids showed a preference for the treated plot while starlings preferred the control area. Gulls, mostly common gulls, showed a preference for the control area at first but finally favoured the treated plot. Observations were discontinued when the flocks began to show normal seasonal dispersal, it being obvious that the number of birds visiting the treated plot was similar to the number on control areas. No adverse effects of the treatment were noted but earthworms collected up to $3\frac{1}{2}$ months later were found to contain residues of β-chlordane ranging from 0 to 35 p.p.m. Chlordane residues on grass averaged 64 p.p.m. 14 weeks after treatment but fell rapidly as growth and cutting began. A year after application small residues of β-chlordane could still be detected in some earthworms and on grass. In view of the persistence of these residues and the lack of positive evidence that much could be achieved by this means no further experiments have been done. It might be that the use of a less persistent organo-phosphorus or carbamate compound would be more acceptable, and where a closer relationship can be shown to exist between birds and the soil fauna of the airfield this technique ought to be further explored.

Birds also feed on the vegetation of airfields, and in this respect the choice of grass is fortunate for only waterfowl are likely to graze it to any extent. Solman (1966) cites the example of ducks visiting a Canadian airport to graze and in consequence being involved in several collisions with aircraft. Geese not infrequently visit certain airfields in Scotland and these large birds could be a very real danger, although there is no record of any accident on their account. Fortunately the waterfowl problem is not acute in Britain and alternative grazing is available everywhere. A more serious problem arises where the airfield turf contains clovers (*Trifolium* spp.) which are attractive to wood pigeons (*Columba palumbus*) at certain times of year (Murton *et al.*, 1966). There is every reason to believe that eradication of the clover would discourage pigeons from visiting airfields and in the eastern half of England the expense of applying suitable selective herbicides might well be justified. The standard grass mixture used on airfields incorporates 1% English white clover seed and a useful first step might be to omit this potential wood-pigeon attractant.

Lucerne is an alternative to grass that has been proposed by the Dutch authorities, and Van der Heyde (1965) reported that it was being grown on Schiphol airport because it is less attractive to birds than grain. In England the growing of lucerne is not looked on favourably, both because it presents a number of cultural problems and because it is feared that it would be attractive to wood-pigeons. Heather (*Erica* sp.), ling (*Calluna* sp.) and bracken (*Pteridium* sp.) are plants that occur naturally on some airfields and each fulfils the requirement of being unattractive to birds, yet they might encourage small rodents and certainly present a fire hazard at certain times of year. Potatoes have been proposed as a profitable alternative and during part of the year this crop would provide excellent ground cover. Difficulties would arise at harvest and planting time, however, when the cultivations would attract large numbers of birds. In principle it seems wrong to permit the growing of crops within airfield boundaries but where land is scarce it is understandable that people wish to make full use of their limited resources. If it is undesirable to grow crops that will attract birds it is equally undesirable to allow natural vegetation that bears fruit or seeds and the airfield periphery should be inspected with a view to the elimination of such species.

Ironically it is not the airfield but the urban part of the airport which is the main source of food for birds. Large quantities of food waste from aircraft galleys, restaurants and public enclosures has to be disposed of, and if this is not done efficiently it can attract scavenging birds. Garbage tips where edible waste is readily available frequently have attendant flocks of gulls, corvids, and starlings that contain hundreds of individuals. Whilst the birds are actually feeding they present no hazard but their flights to and from the food source may cross the airfield. With gulls the association of airfield and garbage tip represents a more positive hazard because together they fulfil the two basic needs of food and a safe resting place. Having fed at the tip gulls fly to the airfield to rest and this pattern of behaviour has created a bird problem at airports throughout the world. Some countries have threatened legislation forbidding garbage tips within a certain distance of airports and there is abundant evidence to justify such measures. At airports where local tips have been closed down an improvement, sometimes a complete cure, of the gull problem has been reported. Where total closure is not possible a change to a different tipping schedule or method can help, but once birds have become accustomed to feed at a particular tip it is very difficult to get rid of them. This is purely a man-made problem and, since the equipment necessary for efficient garbage disposal is available, is easily soluble if money can be provided.

Sewage farms are another source of attraction to birds, primarily starlings and black-headed gulls (*Larus ridibundus*) and, like rubbish dumps, they often occur near airports. Generally very little can be done about existing installations although screening of filter beds and settlement tanks is possible. New plant should be designed to eliminate the attraction to birds and recent installations seen by us have been satisfactory in this respect.

It is not practicable to extend habitat management far beyond the airport perimeter. For one thing it would be an enormous task to attempt to change the environment so that the whole district became unattractive to birds and, for another, one would not have the authority to do so. What can be done with comparatively little trouble is to identify local centres of bird activity and either take some specific action in negotiation with the owners of the property, or take account of the bird concentrations when planning aircraft movements. Communal roosts and breeding colonies are both likely to give rise to problems and it should be considered whether anything can be done to disperse them. Starling roosts are intolerable in the vicinity of busy airfields because of the strike hazard during the periods of the birds' arrival and departure each evening and morning. By eliminating the favoured roosting habitat, for example reed beds and scrub, the risk that a roost will become established can be minimized. Corvid roosts give rise to similar hazards but the answer is less readily found in cultural methods for such roosts are usually located in mature woodland which the owners are reluctant to fell. The same applies to rookeries, and wherever possible they should not be allowed to remain in close proximity to airfields for young rooks are particularly prone to collide with aircraft. Species that roost or breed on the ground might be discouraged by cultivating the land and those that like water be driven away by the drainage of wet areas.

Although bird infestations of terminal buildings, workshops, car parks, etc. may be considered somewhat remote from the aircraft movement area, concentrations of birds in and around these buildings are nevertheless undesirable. Feral pigeons (*Columba livia*) present the greatest hazard because they take occasional flights in compact flocks and with each bird weighing about 1 lb a multiple strike could have serious consequences. Starlings, house sparrows (*Passer domesticus*) and jackdaws (*Corvus monedula*) are other species that frequently colonize airport buildings in Britain, and although the immediate removal of all these birds might be the task of pest control operators their exclusion by good design and proofing should be the objective.

Airport authorities are not usually enthusiastic about the environmental approach to bird control; it is a costly business and the benefits may not be immediately apparent, yet it holds greater promise of success than alternative methods. In Canada, the National Research Council, acting through a specialized Committee has pursued a vigorous investigation into the bird problem at all the important airports. As a result an extensive programme of habitat modification including improved drainage, filling of low areas, clearance of scrub and nesting cover has been established. The growing of crops on airfields has been banned unless it can be shown that they are unattractive to birds. As a result of the measures taken, which include selected bird dispersal techniques, it is claimed that Air Canada experienced a 25% reduction in bird strikes during 1965 compared with 1964 (Solman, 1966).

Perhaps the most thoroughly studied airfield in the world from the birdstrike point of view is the American base at Midway atoll in the Pacific. At this Naval Station aircraft collide with albatrosses (*Diomedea* spp.) at the rate of between 300 and 400 per year, and one aircraft out of every five that hits an albatross on take-off either abandons the take-off or jettisons fuel and returns for an inspection of the damage. About 70 000 Laysan albatrosses (*D. immutabilis*) and 7 000 black-footed albatrosses (*D. nigripes*) nest at Midway each year, and almost every conceivable control method has been tried including disturbance, noise, gunfire, radar, smoke and olfactory repellents. Adult birds, nests, eggs and chicks have been destroyed and moved, obstructions to flight have been erected and bulldozers have levelled the dunes. Of all the measures taken the habitat management has been the most successful; levelling of dunes reduced the amount of soaring, and hard surfacing of the area up to 250 yd on either side of the main runway made it impossible for the birds to build nests. It was found, however, that birds dispossessed by these operations were not readily accepted into the rest of the colony and actually posed an increased strike hazard. It was therefore recommended that before treatment of an area the birds in it be caught and humanely killed thus preserving the rest of the colony undisturbed.

Direct control was tried in the area enclosed by the runways where the population was estimated at over 6 000 albatrosses. During the spring of 1957 6 266 adult and young birds were removed and the following year a further 4 739 were taken. Two years later, in 1960, 196 chicks were counted in this area and by 1962 there were again 1 126 breeding pairs of albatrosses in the area (Robbins, 1966). This illustrates how futile destruction programmes can be unless the pressure is maintained or the killing is backed up by environmental changes.

In spite of the measures taken the latest reports indicate that the birdstrike problem at Midway is far from being solved. There is even a suggestion that the base might be abandoned because the risks are no longer acceptable. If this can happen at Midway it can happen elsewhere too; it is to be hoped the example will not pass unheeded and man will not over-rate his ability to fly in direct competition with birds.

SUMMARY

A large proportion of all collisions between birds and aircraft occur at, or very near to, airfields and in the interest of flight safety the numbers of birds in the vicinity of airfields should be reduced wherever possible. Killing of birds will provide only temporary relief and habituation limits the usefulness of most scaring methods. The ultimate answer is to make airfields and their immediate surroundings unattractive to birds, or at least to those species that constitute the major hazard.

The open nature of the airfield habitat attracts some species, such as gulls, and deters others. Within limits one can alter this habitat by draining wet areas or allowing grass to grow long where normally it is kept short. Such measures can be helpful in discouraging birds but a more important consideration is the availability of food. The presence of clover can attract wood-pigeons and many species feed on soil invertebrates. Selective herbicides and insecticides can be used to reduce this natural food supply but it is costly and toxic residues may persist for long periods. A more important source of food, in terms of numbers of birds attracted, is the edible waste from aircraft galleys, restaurants and public enclosures. Where airfields have refuse tips nearby, and the majority do, flocks of gulls commute between the tips and the airfield, one site providing food and the other a "safe" resting place. This pattern of gull behaviour has created a problem at airports throughout the world.

Environmental control is costly but it offers the best hope for a long-term solution to bird problems. At Midway atoll, where almost everything has been tried to reduce the hazard due to albatrosses, habitat management was the only method to show any success. Even so the bird problem at Midway is far from being solved and it is to be hoped the example will not pass unheeded.

ACKNOWLEDGEMENTS

I should like to thank Mr. C. J. Bridgman, who made all the field observations and collections during the chlordane experiment, and Mr. A. Taylor who carried out the chemical analyses. I also wish to acknowledge the financial support received from the Ministry of Technology and the co-operation of numerous individuals and departments, especially the Royal Air Force, in facilitating studies of the problem.

REFERENCES

Bridgman, C. J. (1965). Seasonal variations in bird numbers on airfields. *In* "Le problème des oiseaux sur les aerodromes." Institut National de la Recherche Agronomique, Paris.

Lack, D. (1954). "The Natural Regulation of Animal Numbers." Clarendon Press, Oxford.

Lewis, M. F. (1967). Associate Committee on Bird Hazards to Aircraft. Bulletin No. 5. National Research Council, Ottawa, Canada.

Murton, R. K., Isaacson, A. J. and Westwood, N. J. (1966). The relationships between wood-pigeons and their clover food supply and the mechanism of population control. *J. appl. Ecol.* **3** (1), 55–96.

Robbins, C. S. (1966). Birds and Aircraft on Midway Islands 1959–63 Investigations. U.S. Fish and Wildlife Service Special Scientific Report – Wildlife No. 85.

Saul, E. K. (1967). Birds and Aircraft: A Problem at Auckland's New International Airport. *J. R. Aeronaut. Soc.* **71**, 366–376.

Solman, V. E. F. (1966). The ecological control of bird hazards to aircraft. Third Bird Control Seminar. Bowling Green State University, Bowling Green, Ohio, U.S.A.

Van der Heyde, J. J. M. (1965). Moyens utilisés pour eloigner les mouettes et autres oiseaux de l'aeroport de Schiphol. *In* "Le problème des oiseaux sur les aerodromes." Institut National de la Recherche Agronomique, Paris.

E*

Discussion

Sir Peter Wykeham opened the discussion by relating an incident that occurred at the beginning of the last war.

At dawn on 6th September, 1939, radar plots were seen in the Thames estuary area. These were later thought to be the first noted instance of bird detection on radar. At the time they were plotted as enemy, being correlated with the reputed sightings of German aircraft by searchlight crews. AA guns opened fire against unseen targets, and fighters were ordered into the air. Their sound and movement added false confirmation to the first suspicions of enemy activity, and more and more fighters were scrambled, whose controllers strove to bring them into contact with the growing "enemy". The formations certainly came into contact, but as they were all friendly, and no Germans whatever were present, the position became confused, and the final arrival of most of the fighters in southern England did nothing to elucidate it. At last, when all friendly aircraft ran out of fuel and had to land, it was apparent that when they left the air no one remained behind. This engagement, known to history as "The Battle of Barking Creek", emphasized the importance of the new radar "filter" organization, which eventually proved so potent a weapon in the complex structure of air defence.

SEUBERT: One of our contractors, Mr. Frank C. Bellrose, is a waterfowl authority in the Mississippi Valley. He has been flying at night in a small aircraft equipped with auxiliary lights, and has made observations of migratory birds. He recently has been doing this in conjunction with the WSR-57 Weather Bureau radar station located at St. Louis, Missouri; and he reported to me that at times there are so many bird targets that the radar is useless. He plans to work in conjunction with the radar station to determine just how well the radar operators can differentiate between the plane and nearby flocks of waterfowl. I am sure that Mr. Bellrose does not find the individuality that Dr. Schaefer reports. This implies many isolated birds. Certainly with waterfowl we usually would find groups of birds. Are you speaking primarily about small birds, Dr. Schaefer?

SCHAEFER: The majority of long range migrants fly singly.

BOURNE: After speaking up at length this morning for one pressure group, the R.A.F. birdwatchers at risk, I now speak up for a second as the first of David Lack's radarwatchers. The R.A.F. have come to ornithologists at two separate periods for advice on bird interference problems with their radar, the first time during the last war, when the radar was still comparatively crude but already able to track a flock of geese across the country; and again when the interference problem became more severe in the late 1950s, when I was incidentally consulted myself over some false alarms during the Suez affair

(Lack, 1958, 1959). On the latter occasion they afforded us facilities to study birds with radar until, perhaps, what with the "Vassal" security leak and the introduction of new apparatus, they felt that the ornithologist problem was becoming worse than the bird one and the band of British radarwatchers (among whom I feel inclined to include Dr. I. Nisbet in New England even if we must allow Canada credit for Dr. Schaefer) was scattered. By this time, after nearly five years with people contemplating birds with the main distant early warning radar systems on both sides of the Atlantic we were inclined to consider that we led the world in the study of bird migration with radar, though as far as I know nobody consulted us seriously about bird-strikes; in the succeeding five years all this experience has been allowed to go to waste (though I dare say we could still teach our Canadian friends a thing or two).

Now, with the team including what I would have thought were several of our best younger ornithologists with a score or more of years of radar experience between them scattered to the four winds and generally fed up with the subject, we hear that the R.A.F. aircraft damage bill is about a million pounds a year, though we still have to go to the Canadians to learn the nature of the damage and see a demonstration of how it can be reduced. We should have done this; if we had been asked, we could have done it; instead, with all the brains and technical resources available in this country, as usual somehow the initiative got lost between competing departments under a stale and unimaginative management with liaison restricted by the Official Secrets Act so that somehow the connection was never made. Now on the ornithological side at least some of us contemplate the Canadian reports with a wild surmise, rather like Stout Cortez and his gang looking at the Pacific, and wonder why it couldn't happen here too. This is the sort of reason why progressive graduates leave the country.

In general, one would have thought that our radar was ideally designed to assess bird-strike risks. This should have been obvious with the first widely-shown films made by Ernst Sutter at Zurich airport with British ground-controlled approach radar, seen by most of the international ornithological establishment at the XIIth International Ornithological Congress at Helsinki in 1958, where they created a sensation. These showed not only the general level of bird activity overhead, but also among other things evolutions of a flock of gulls before going to roost beside the nearby lake. The distant early warning radar with which we worked in England showed a much larger area on a small scale with less detail of local events, but again it should have been possible to see sufficient of all types of bird activity in the upper air to permit an assessment of the hazard that it presented to aircraft. One knew that most display-controllers did not recognize the significance of what they were seeing, but still one assumed that someone in the hierarchy, somewhere, knew it and was considering its usefulness, while we got on with our allotted tasks of studying bird migration with their apparatus.

The position with British radar five years ago was that it had a shorter wavelength and produced if anything a rather better picture of bird movements than American radars such as the one whose results were shown briefly in the Canadian film. This was not necessarily an advantage, because at times the picture was largely obscured by traces due to small birds which were shown less well by the American sets, which in consequence gave a better view of the large birds and flocks which present a really serious hazard to aircraft. On the other hand, it is not really a disadvantage, since when small birds are moving, large ones usually are too. Using radar, it was normally possible to assess all the bird activity above two or three hundred feet except where the screen was obscured by ground or cloud returns, that is, in the upper air where birds cease to be readily visible to ground observers but become an increasing hazard to aircraft. The best view was of course obtained of migrants, but with attention it was also possible to distinguish other types of high-flying bird activity as well, including the assembly, evolutions, and dispersal of roosting birds, and soaring birds over the countryside at large, whenever they ascended high enough to register on the sets, which is, of course, when they become a hazard to aircraft. One would expect a G.C.A. set to show up individual hazards threatening its airfield. With a good range-height indicator (though I seldom had one) one would expect to be able to assess the heights to which birds were ascending.

One would expect that this sort of information would have obvious applications for assessing bird-strike risks. Over the course of time we made fair estimations of the seasons and weather conditions under which various types of migrants move, and this would now be fairly predictable, and their presence in the air could be confirmed at once with suitable radar as they ascended. We also know that most migrants move in the first half of the night, from about 45 minutes after dusk, though soaring species move when updraughts are best developed in the middle of the day, when local birds also start soaring; so that the risk from soaring birds (which seem likely to present the worst hazard on cross-country flights) can also be assessed as well. Daily movements to and from roosts are less easy to see, because they get lost among ground returns, but can also be distinguished with care, and there should be no difficulty in distinguishing the height at which flocks do evolutions above their roosts in the evening as well, thus assessing the risk from this worst of all hazards. Finally, the birds weighing over four lb which present particular hazards because they exceed the weight allowed for in armouring aircraft are few in number and usually individually recognizable on radar, so that their passage might be plotted individually (especially in such cases as flocks of geese) and aircraft warned away from them. With proper training, display controllers should be able to recognize bird hazards on their radar themselves and be able to warn aircraft of them directly.

My own research in Scotland was far removed from the main regions where birds and aircraft come into collision, but provides a few illustrations of what could be done. The most numerous migrants at Fair Isle Bird Observatory between Orkney and Shetland are shown in the following table, with the time of their maximum abundance. It seems likely that they include the main species

TABLE I

*The abundance, weight, and season of passage of bird migrants at Fair Isle**

(Redwing: the commonest migrant (*Turdus musicus*)	30 329	80 g	Most late Sept.–Nov., intermittently to May)
Common gull (*Larus canus*)	19 345	400 g	Most April–May, Aug.–Oct.
Fieldfare (*Turdus pilaris*)	17 082	150 g	Most Oct.–Nov., then intermittently till May
Blackbird (*Turdus merula*)	13 559	100 g	Most Oct.–Nov., late March
Turnstone (*Arenaria interpres*)	7 963	150 g	All year
Redshank (*Tringa totanus*)	6 573	120 g	All year
Lapwing (*Vanellus vanellus*)	6 499	150 g	All year
Woodcock (*Scolopax rusticola*)	3 848	200 g	Maxima early Nov., early April
Curlew (*Numinius arquata*)	3 184	400 g	Maximum late June–Aug.
Golden plover (*Charadrius apricarius*)	2 606	150 g	Most May–June
Purple sandpiper (*Calidris maritima*)	2 253	100 g	Most Sept.–Dec., March–May
Ring plover (*Charadrius hiaticula*)	1 970	100 g	Most late Aug.–Sept.
Black-headed gull (*Larus ridibundus*)	1 941	400 g	Mainly late March–Oct.
Snipe (*Capella gallinago*)	1 929	100 g	All year
Cormorant (*Phalacrocorax carbo*)	1 723	4 000 g	Most Sept.
Grey geese (*Anser spp.*)	1 288	3 000– 8 000 g	Most Oct.–Nov.
Heron (*Ardea cinerea*)	1 230	1 500 g	Most Sept.
Mallard (*Anas platyrhynchos*)	1 216	1 000 g	Most Nov.
Whimbrel (*Numenius phaeopus*)	1 155	300 g	Most May–June
Lesser black-backed gull (*Larus fuscus*)	943 +	1 500 g	Mid-March–mid-Sept.

* This includes birds weighing over 100 g recorded over 1 000 times in the period 1948–60.

causing threats to aircraft and, in fact, the second commonest species, the Common gull *Larus canus*, belongs to the group that causes most damage in Britain, the gulls. As it happens, while on autumn migration and in winter gulls soar around in a casual sort of way. The Common gull proved to have a very compact and spectacular spring migration associated with the onset of particular weather conditions, namely, the passage of a ridge (Fig. 1). During a short period in late March and April large numbers crossed the country towards Scandinavia at a considerable altitude in the middle of the day, some following the coast when they came to it to leave in a relatively concentrated stream from headlands (Fig. 2). This movement, and especially the hazard off headlands where the concentrated stream went out to sea, clearly presented a considerable temporary hazard to aircraft only recognizable with radar, though very obvious on that. A number of other phenomena visible with radar present similar hazards of a less well-defined character,

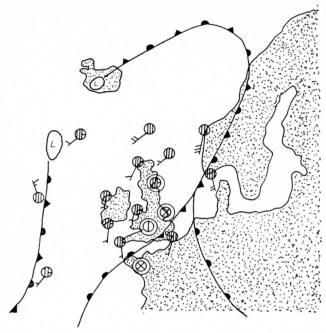

FIG. 1. The conditions under which the largest emigration of Common gulls occurred in 1960: the weather map for 0600 hrs on 7 April. The birds started to leave Scotland when the first front passed east, and could be seen with radar departing NNE in high-flying flocks as the ridge followed on east during the day. Nothing could be seen from the ground.

and it would surely be useful to be able to warn aircraft away from the relevant areas and altitudes where the hazards are seen. I am still puzzled why so little attempt has been made to investigate such possibilities.

The Chairman referred to the degree of control already exercised over aircraft movements which had to take account of such factors as the presence of other aircraft, weather conditions and prohibited flying areas. To include the avoidance of birds would greatly add to the complexity of the flight plan and even though computers might be used to analyse the information there was a danger of over-burdening the pilot. He went on to describe an unusual animal hazard on airfields.

CHAIRMAN: The problem posed by birds on airfields becomes serious only when aircraft movements are fairly frequent. Juba airfield in southern Sudan used to be a favourite lounging-ground for elephants, but while aircraft movements were only one a week this gave little trouble to the drowsy staff or the equally placid elephants. When the movements rose to one a day the elephants had to be herded by specially-hired teams of men, and by the time

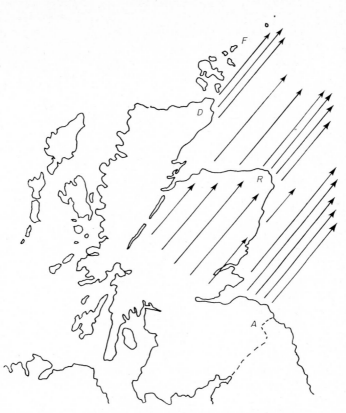

FIG. 2. The general pattern of departure of Common gulls leaving Scotland by day in spring. *A, R, D* are St. Abb's, Rattray and Duncansby Heads, *F* is Fair Isle, where migrants are recorded when they meet bad weather in the form of a front associated with SE winds at sea.

it reached six a day there was no alternative but to fence the airfield in, at great expense to the local government, and to the obvious disapproval of the elephants.

Air Commodore Wright, Director of Flight Safety (R.A.F.) asked Dr. Solman if he thought the Canadian approach to the use of radar was equally applicable in Britain as in North America. This led to a general discussion on the capabilities of radar and what the observer would actually see on the screen. Dr. Schaefer asked if any collisions between birds and aircraft had actually been recorded on radar.

SOLMAN: In the course of review of several hundred thousand feet of 16 mm movies of PPI displays we have noted on several occasions when an echo of an aircraft appeared to collide with an echo caused by birds. In at least one case the aircraft immediately altered course because of damage. Incident reports have confirmed the occurrence of the strikes shown on the PPI display. Perhaps it would be more correct to say that after incident reports on bird strikes had been received it was often possible (from time and location) to isolate the film frames which showed the echoes of the birds and aircraft before, during and after impact.

BROWN: If migrating birds could be forecast or identified flying on, or across an airways corridor at a specific flight level there is no reason whatever under normal air traffic control procedures why that flight level could not be considered as being occupied and traffic routed along flight levels above and below. Little or no inconvenience to the airline operator would occur.

SOLMAN: We have had only limited use of height finding radar and so have not much data from that source on altitudes at which birds fly. From ground observation and pilot reports we know that Blue and Lesser Snow geese *Anser c. caerulescens* migrate at heights up to 10 000 to 12 000 feet while a bird impact on an aircraft at night at 10 000 feet in late August was identified as a thrush *Hylocichla* sp. from feathers which caught under the windscreen wiper on the aircraft. Ground observation and pilot reports have confirmed that Broadwinged hawks *Buteo* sp. ride thermals up to at least 10 000 feet during their migration south around the west end of Lake Ontario.

HARTLEY: Speaking non-professionally as the inhabitant of a property a few miles from the proposed new Stansted airport I would like to know whether the high population of gulls in the Thames Estuary was a major factor in the decision not to place London's third airport on the Isle of Sheppey.

WRIGHT: At the time of the public enquiry about Stansted airport I wrote to the Board of Trade pointing out the probability of a considerable bird hazard in the vicinity of the alternative sites at Sheppey and Cliffe which were being strongly advocated in some quarters. Whilst I should like to think that my advice was heeded I have no evidence that it was and I really do not know the answer to your question.

BRIDGMAN: At Stansted airport gulls usually only appear in comparatively small numbers during wet weather and they can normally be persuaded to go elsewhere with little difficulty. Rooks *Corvus frugilegus* pose the greatest problem at Stansted because the rookery is nearby. As a result it is difficult to scare them away for any length of time. If the airport is extended the problem may be greatly reduced by the clearance of trees carrying the rookery.

SOLMAN: Do birds pose problems by nesting or roosting inside aircraft hangars where feathers, droppings and nesting material may cause a nuisance in aircraft engine maintenance? We have the problem at some installations and have found that poisoning, trapping, shooting or other means are not always successful in stopping the problem.

WRIGHT: We experience this in Britain too but, at least in theory, it does not pose a flight hazard because adequate inspection can detect any damage before the aircraft leaves the ground. In practice there is an element of risk especially to military aircraft parked on dispersal and subject to emergency call. The human factor plays an important part because maintenance staff often encourage birds by tossing them scraps from their lunch packets. I recall an incident in a commercial airline workshop where house-sparrows were nesting on top of the lights in the hangar roof, eventually a nest caught fire and fell to the ground in flames. The management immediately called in pest control operators who began catching the sparrows with stupefying baits whereupon the maintenance men came out on strike in protest. Unfortunately this is fairly typical of the irrational attitude one often meets where birds are concerned. Wherever practicable it is recommended that the points where birds usually gain access to buildings, such as eaves, skylights, ventilators, be proofed against entry. In the long-term it is encouraging that plans for new buildings and landscaping at airports have sometimes been submitted for comment in respect of possible bird problems.

SPARKS: You said in your talk that airfields ought not to be placed where the dangers of bird strike are more great. Now in view of the plans to build a military airfield on the island of Aldabra in the Indian Ocean, where there are great numbers of frigate birds, do I take it that you think that the bird strike problem there is not insuperable?

WRIGHT: I am sure that the Ministry of Defence is ready to acknowledge that the frigate birds at Aldabra are likely to present a considerable hazard. But a potential bird hazard exists at every airfield; we have had an example today of an emergency landing caused by a single sparrow so we can only recognize more or less risk at different airfields and at different times. The American base at Midway must have the worst bird problem of any existing airfield, and there are many strikes there, yet, to my knowledge, there has never been a fatal accident at Midway. There can be little doubt that an airfield on Aldabra would be in the high risk category, comparable to Midway rather than any established R.A.F. bases, but one cannot describe the problem as either soluble or insoluble. Ultimately only the people who fly the aeroplanes can decide what risks are acceptable and what are not, and this must be related to the operational requirement and type of aircraft to be used. The capital cost, availability of alternative sites and conflicting claims for other development or conservation must also be weighed in the final decision. Someone must do all the sums and make the final choice: it is an unenviable task.

WYNNE-EDWARDS: Frequent reference has been made to gulls, lapwings and starlings being involved in air-strikes, especially on or near airfields. Would it be true to conclude that the great majority of air-strikes in this country are caused by a handful of species, or is a wider spectrum of birds involved?

WRIGHT: On a world basis gulls are by far the most troublesome birds but a broad spectrum of species have been involved in strikes. In Britain about a dozen species constitute the major hazard and of these the black-headed, common and herring gulls, lapwing, wood-pigeon and rook are most frequently encountered. Jackdaws, oystercatchers, golden plover and starlings may be especially troublesome at particular airfields. We have a standing request for any bird remains recovered following strikes to be sent to our laboratory for identification but the number of returns to date is too few to provide a proper basis for assessing relative frequency of collisions with different species. In particular we feel that many strikes involving small birds are never reported at all simply because they have not caused damage.

SOLMAN: The following list of 30 species of birds have been involved in bird strikes in Canada:

Common loon	*Gavia immer*
Great blue heron	*Ardea herodias*
Mallard	*Anas platyrhynchos*
Pintail	*Anas acuta*
Green-winged teal	*Anas carolinensis*
Red-shouldered hawk	*Buteo lineatus*
Ring-necked pheasant	*Phasianus colchicus*
Gray partridge	*Perdix perdix*
Killdeer	*Charadrius vociferus*
American golden plover	*Pluvialis dominica*
Black-bellied plover	*Squatarola squatarola*
Upland plover	*Bartramia longicauda*
Baird's sandpiper	*Erolia bairdii*
Dunlin	*Erolia alpina*
Glaucous-winged gull	*Larus glaucescens*
Great black-backed gull	*Larus marinus*
Herring gull	*Larus argentatus*
Ring-billed gull	*Larus delawarensis*
Rock dove	*Columba livia*
Great horned owl	*Bubo virginianus*
Snowy owl	*Nyctea scandiaca*
Short-eared owl	*Asio flammeus*
Common nighthawk	*Chordeiles minor*
Black swift	*Cypseloides niger*
Barn swallow	*Hirundo rustica*
Thrush	*Hylocichla* sp.
Brown-headed cowbird	*Molothrus ater*
Swamp sparrow	*Melospiza georgiana*
Lapland longspur	*Clacarius lapponicus*
Snow bunting	*Plectrophenax nivalis*

At this point the discussion returned to the application of radar with Dr. BOURNE again stressing that in his view there had been a conspicuous lack of consultation between official departments and outside bodies.

THOMPSON: I should like to make only one point, and that is to lay the canard that the Ministry of Aviation (now Ministry of Technology) has consulted no ornithologists other than those in government service. Over ten years ago the Ministry of Aviation sought the help of Oxford University, in the person of Dr. Niko Tinbergen; his graduate students were given grants by the Ministry of Aviation for work on airfields and birds over a period of several years.

[It would also have been relevant to point out that Dr. Schaefer received help from the Ministry of Technology in the form of equipment on loan and that his current programme of research is substantially financed by that department. Ed.]

Dr. Solman pointed out that in Canada all liaison on bird-strikes was dealt with through a National Committee.

SOLMAN: The Associate Committee on Bird Hazards to Aircraft appointed by the National Research Council of Canada has members representing the following Departments or agencies:

	Number
Air Canada	1
Canadian Air Line Pilots Association	1
Canadian Pacific Airlines	1
Department of National Defense	1
Canadian Wildlife Service	4
Department of Transport	2
National Research Council	3
Rolls Royce of Canada	1

The Chairman and Secretary are included in the members representing the National Research Council. Two of the Canadian Wildlife Service members are employed on contract.

The success of the committee in reducing bird hazards to aircraft is due to the dynamic nature of the chairman, Mr. M. S. Kuhring, his ability to coordinate the activities of the members and to cut red tape, and the willingness of the agencies represented on the committee to pool their resources of manpower, equipment, transport and funds to do the job without formality. To augment the staffs of the agencies contracts are made with qualified persons to assist in the work for periods from a few months to as much as three years. As many as 13 contractors have been employed at one time on different jobs at different locations in Canada and Europe.

SEUBERT: I would point out that in our studies of bird hazards at both military and civil airports in the U.S., we have made use of local non-government ornithologists and ecologists.

Following up this point Dr. Solman drew attention to the discrepancy between visual and radar observations of migration.

SOLMAN: Before radar studies on bird migration were extended over large areas most data on bird migration was gathered by visual observation and was concentrated where observers were located. At one point in our study we employed 18 radar units simultaneously to cover Canada almost from east to west coasts. Viewed in that manner, migration was seen to take place simultaneously across areas hundreds of miles wide. Much of the heaviest migration showed up on radar at night when visual observation would be very difficult. We are being forced to the opinion that the bulk of migration is not seen by visual observers and that it often occurs over much larger areas at one time than was believed earlier. Reverse migration, in relation to inclement weather, appears to be frequent rather than exceptional.

WRIGHT: I should like to pay tribute to the Canadian effort in tackling this problem. Their Committee has set a standard of co-operation and achievement to be admired. Largely through the enthusiasm and persuasion of their Chairman, Mr. Kuhring, Britain, France, Germany and Holland now have similar groups. Our first speaker, Mr. Stables, is Chairman of the British Group known as the Bird Impact Research and Development Committee.

MARTIN JONES: The official British Bird Strike Committee might have got further in this field if outside ornithologists had been more freely consulted.

JARDINE: Can someone tell us what proportion of strikes occur at airports as opposed to "en route"?

SOLMAN: With civil aircraft about 70% occur near airports and only 30% further away, with military aircraft it is the other way round. Modification of the airport habitat has reduced the number of strikes by around 25%.

The session concluded with the showing of a short film, made in Canada, to illustrate the work of the Associate Committee on Bird Hazards to Aircraft.

REFERENCES

Lack, D. (1958). Recent Swiss and British work on watching migration by radar. *Ibis* **100**, 286–287.
Lack, D. (1959). Watching migration by radar. *Br. Birds* **52**, 258–267.

Birds and Agriculture

Chairman's Introduction

R. K. CORNWALLIS

Most people probably regard farming as a highly traditional affair that changes but slowly, if at all. It is, therefore, important that they should realize that we are in the midst of an immense technical revolution. There have been greater changes on our farms in the last twenty years (and more especially in the last decade) than in the previous two thousand.

Mechanization; the substitution of chemical for traditional rotational practices; the increase of arable crops, especially cereals, at the expense of grassland; the accompanying removal of hedges and the drainage of wet land; all these mean great changes in farms as habitats for wild life.

Farmers look upon the majority of birds with indifference. Others they value either as providing sport or as allies against weeds (an example is finches that eat wild oat seeds) or insect pests. A few species with which their interests directly conflict—and these are the subject of today's two sessions—they regard as pests. This attitude *is*, of course, traditional. Hence the medieval adage about sowing corn: "One for the pigeon; one for the crow; one to rot; and one to grow".

The changes that are taking place in the pattern of agriculture are undoubtedly increasing the area of conflict between birds and men. On permanent grassland, for example, birds do little damage; but this has fallen from comprising 62% of all farm land to 42%. New crops such as peas and brussels sprouts grown for the freezing trade are much damaged by pigeons and corvids, and cereals (now occupying 31% of farm land as compared with 18%) are open to attack by these species and by sparrows.

Farmers are hard-headed, practical men who like to do something forceful to combat their problems. To them the only good pest is a dead pest. It is hard to convince them that the one-upmanship and the moral support from Government of subsidized cartridges were, in truth, only a device for killing one pest-bird so as to make it easier for another one to survive.

The Rook Problem in North-East Scotland

G. M. DUNNET and I. J. PATTERSON

Culterty Field Station, University of Aberdeen, Scotland

The rook *Corvus frugilegus* is generally regarded at least as a nuisance and frequently as a serious pest by arable farmers. No clear assessment of its economic status has been made, and clearly this will vary from place to place according to regional patterns of agricultural practice and regional variation in rook populations. This paper is intended as a brief report of a long-term study of the rook in Aberdeenshire, generously supported by the Agricultural Research Council. It is not possible here to provide the detailed results of the work, but we will first present a description of the agricultural background of the area and the way in which it is utilized by rooks so that any feeding habits of potential harm to agriculture can be seen in relation to the total feeding activities of the birds. This will be followed by an account of the seasonal changes in the distribution and abundance of rooks in the study area and consideration of the factors bringing these about, so that problems of controlling rooks may be more clearly appreciated.

THE AVAILABILITY OF FIELD CROPS AND THEIR UTILIZATION BY ROOKS

The general study area comprises the drainage area of the Ythan Valley (*ca.* 270 sq. miles) in eastern Aberdeenshire, and the intensive study area of about 10 sq. miles lies within it, at Auchmacoy, near Newburgh. The entire area is intensively cultivated, with a gradual change in progress from relatively small (up to 200 acres) mixed farms with their rotation of cereals, root crops and grass, to larger farms tending to specialize in the production of grain, milk, potatoes or pigs.

Each fortnight we follow a set transect (or circuit) through the area and record the numbers of fields with different crops. Similar transects are carried out weekly to record the numbers and distribution of rooks among these crops. Data are given in Table I, from which we have calculated an "index of utilization" of each crop by rooks. When this index is unity it indicates no selection of the crop; when greater than

TABLE I

The proportions of fields of different types, and the distribution of rooks among these fields in the intensive study area, September 1965 to July 1966

		Jan.	Feb.	Mar.	Apr.	May	June	July	Aug.	Sept.	Oct.	Nov.	Dec.
Grass	%F	52·3	51·4	48·6	48·6	55·1	55·4	51·5	51·5	64·5	63·5	63·6	55·1
	%R	33·1	21·8	8·9	8·7	45·2	71·4	63·5	87·5	58·0	24·2	22·4	69·4
	Index	0·63	0·42	0·18	0·18	0·82	1·29	1·23	1·70	0·90	0·38	0·35	1·26
Braird	%F	5·6	5·6	5·6	5·6	25·2	0	0	—	0	0	0	4·7
	%R	0·75	0·63	2·2	0	16·9	0·49	0	0	0	0	0	0
	Index	0·13	0·11	0·39	0	0·67	—	—	—	—	—	—	0
Plough Cultiv.	%F	27·1	29·0	33·6	15·9	9·5	0·93	0	—	0	5·6	9·3	23·4
	%R	19·5	9·0	32·7	30·0	7·0	2·2	0	0	9·3	12·5	25·2	3·6
	Index	0·72	0·31	0·97	1·89	0·74	2·44	0	—	—	2·23	2·71	0·15
Sown	%F	0	0	0	18·7	3·8	0	0	—	0	0	0	0
	%R	0	0	4·3	50·5	19·2	0	10·8	2·1	0	0	0	0
	Index	—	—	—	2·70	5·05	0	—	—	—	—	—	—
Stubble	%F	11·2	10·3	8·4	8·4	0	0	0	—	5·6	21·5	20·5	13·1
	%R	25·0	47·6	10·8	0·87	0	0	—	5·7	28·1	60·6	45·7	17·6
	Index	2·23	4·62	1·29	0·10	—	—	—	—	5·02	2·85	2·23	1·34
Roots	%F	3·7	3·7	3·7	2·8	0·93	8·4	8·4	—	6·5	5·6	3·7	3·7
	%R	0·51	0·67	2·4	0·39	3·9	1·9	0·08	0	0·27	0	0	0
	Index	0·14	0·18	0·65	0·14	4·19	0·23	0·01	—	0·04	0	0	0
Stock food	%F	—	—	—	—	—	—	—	—	—	—	—	—
	%R	21·1	20·2	38·7	9·5	7·9	24·2	25·6	4·7	4·3	2·7	6·7	9·4
Total fields		107	107	107	107	107	107	107	—	107	107	107	107
Total rooks		2 513	2 659	1 415	1 252	2 726	2 447	2 421	1 700	2 948	1 476	2 386	1 070

The index of utilization is the % rooks (R) divided by the % fields (F). %F, % of fields on crop circuit. %R, % of total rooks on intensive circuit.

unity, a positive selection of the crop by rooks, and when less than unity, an avoidance. While this index is probably a valid measure of the relative amount of time rooks spend on different crops, it is not necessarily an indication of the proportional amount of their food that rooks take from these crops. The availability of crops and their index of utilization are illustrated in Fig. 1. This shows that whenever grain was available, either as a sowing or on stubbles, it was preferred. Grassland was selected in summer (except for a small peak of preference for grass in December), while cultivated land was preferred in both spring and autumn and root crops only in May. There was no preference shown for braird (i.e. sprouted) grain at any season. Rooks feeding in grass fields and stubbles can hardly have any adverse economic effects for the farmer, but on sown fields and on root crops they may cause damage by removing grain and by breaking down drills and damaging the crop. It is important, from the point of view of controlling rook damage, to note that the peak index of 4·19 on root crops in May involved only 3·9% of the rooks, whereas the high indices on sown grain in April and May involved 20–50% of the rooks.

THE ROOK POPULATION

DISPERSION

The rook is a social species with a clumped dispersion pattern, usually feeding and flying in flocks, roosting communally in large gatherings, and nesting together in rookeries. A complete description of the local density and dispersion pattern of the rook entails three main problems: (1) the dispersion of the "focal points" of the population, namely the rookeries and the communal roosts; (2) the dispersion of the birds around rookeries, and (3) movement beyond the local area.

Dispersion of rookeries
All rookeries in the study area have been mapped (Fig. 2) and the nests counted annually from 1963 to 1967. The rookeries were found to be fairly evenly scattered over the whole area, though bigger ones seem to be farther from their neighbours than smaller ones.

Dispersion of communal roosts
Outside the breeding season (during which they roost in their rookeries) rooks from different nesting colonies roost communally. In the Ythan Valley many small roosts are used in summer and autumn, but in midwinter the birds are concentrated in five large roosts (Fig. 3). It is

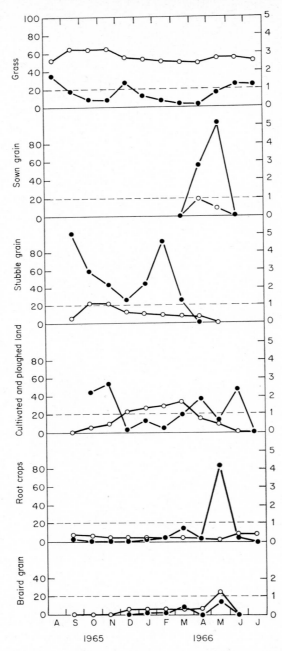

Fig. 1. Seasonal changes in the occurrence of crop types and their utilization by rooks in the Intensive Study Area. See Table I and text for explanation. ○, Per cent of field types; ●, index of utilization.

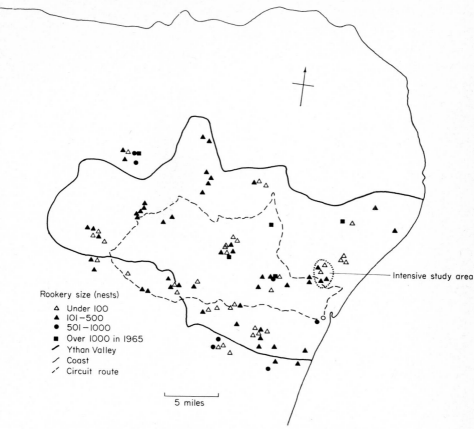

FIG. 2. Dispersion of rookeries in the Ythan Valley, Aberdeenshire.

difficult to assess the effect of this concentration on day-time rook density throughout the area. In the morning, most birds fly quickly to the rookeries and disperse to feed from there so that the rookery remains the centre of dispersion. However, the evening return is often more gradual so that in the late afternoon there may be large concentrations of rooks near the roosts.

Dispersion of rooks around the rookeries

Since the rookery forms the centre of activity more or less throughout the year, it is important to describe the areas which are occupied for feeding by the rooks from particular rookeries, the dispersion pattern of the birds within these feeding areas, and the relation between the

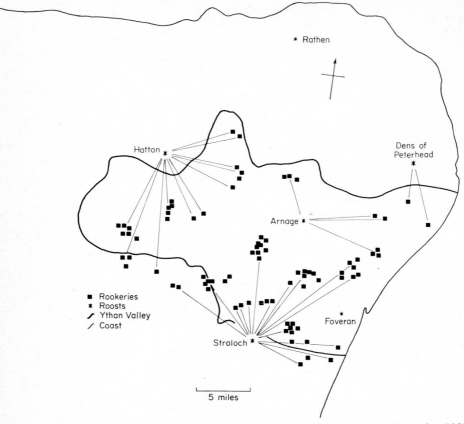

FIG. 3. Winter roosts used by rooks in the Ythan Valley, Aberdeenshire, December 1965.

feeding areas of neighbouring rookeries. Work on this question is concentrated on two rookeries, South Artrochie and Macharmuir, at Auchmacoy. The boundaries of the Auchmacoy study area were based on preliminary observations on the feeding range of birds from these rookeries. Two main methods are used.

(1) *The description of the dispersion pattern of rooks during the day* by traversing the whole area at weekly intervals (the "Intensive Area Circuit") and noting the position and size of all rook flocks seen.

(2) *The collection of sight records of marked rooks whose nesting place is known* by identifying as many tagged birds as possible on a specially designed weekly traverse of the area, and at the same time regularly identifying marked birds at nests in each of the rookeries.

In addition, flight-lines between rookeries and feeding areas are plotted, mainly in the breeding season.

The results for 1965 and 1966 are similar, and the dispersion of rooks in the area showed consistent seasonal changes. The 1966 results are given in Figs. 4–8, and may be summarized as follows.

Autumn and winter (early September to late February). During this period, a variable, often large proportion of the birds are present in the rookeries during the day (Fig. 11), and the birds feed close to the rookeries, often in relatively large flocks (Fig. 4). The feeding areas of the two study rookeries overlap, but are separated from those of the surrounding rookeries by a clear gap.

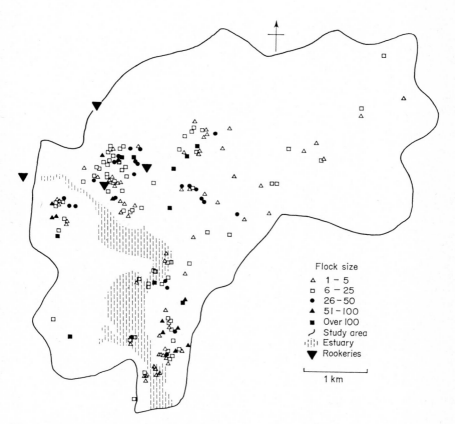

Flock size

△ 1 – 5
□ 6 – 25
• 26 – 50
▲ 51 – 100
■ Over 100
⌡ Study area
⦙⦙⦙ Estuary
▼ Rookeries

1 km

FIG. 4. Dispersion pattern of rook flocks in the Intensive Study Area. Data from weekly circuits in September, October and November, 1966, superimposed.

The breeding season (early March to early June). Observations from a hide showed that the females rarely if ever left the nest from a few days before the first egg was laid until the young were almost able to fly (at about 28 days). Most of the birds in the fields at this time must, therefore, be males and non-breeding birds. Figure 5 shows that the birds feed farther from the rookeries than in the autumn and winter, with an extension of range particularly to the east, but the joint feeding area of the two study rookeries remains distinct from those of their neighbours. This extension to the east is into an area where there are no established rookeries, and away from the area used by neighbouring rookeries. Sight records of marked birds known to be nesting in one of the rookeries confirm that they feed only within this area (Fig. 6).

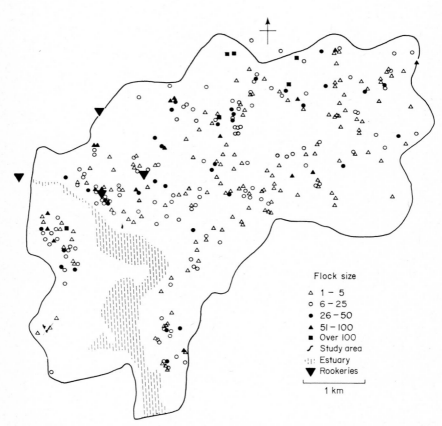

FIG. 5. Dispersion pattern of rook flocks in the Intensive Study Area. Data from weekly circuits in March, April and May, 1966, superimposed.

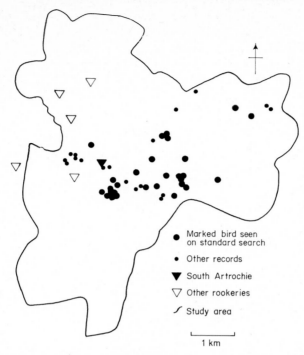

Fig. 6. Breeding-season sight records of birds which bred in South Artrochie rookery in 1966.

Summer (mid-June to early September). This period begins when the young are able to fly strongly and start to accompany the adults to the feeding grounds, leaving the rookeries deserted by day; it lasts until the autumn resurgence of nesting activity. There is now a wider scattering of much smaller flocks, right out to the limits of the area searched (Fig. 7) and close to the neighbouring rookeries. This suggests that many birds may feed beyond the boundaries of the study area in summer.

The seasonal changes in feeding range are summarized in Fig. 8, which shows a progressive increase in the range of marked birds from the main study rookery from autumn to summer. Some of these patterns are similar to those described by Pinowski (1959) in Poland.

In 1965 three rookeries to the north of the main area were also studied and were also found to have a joint feeding area, distinct from the areas of neighbouring rookeries. The rooks from them showed similar seasonal changes in feeding range.

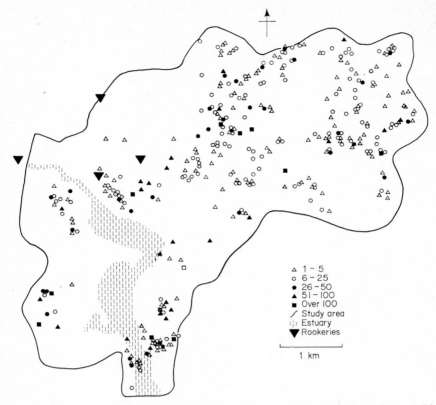

FIG. 7. Dispersion pattern of rook flocks in the Intensive Study Area. Data from weekly circuits in June, July and August, 1966, superimposed.

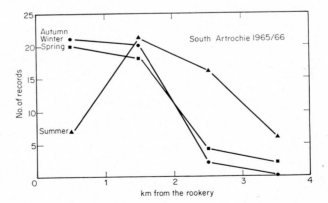

FIG. 8. Distances of marked birds from the rookery in which they bred in 1966.

POPULATION SIZE AND DENSITY

In the Ythan Valley

Annual counts of nests in each rookery in the Ythan Valley are totalled in Table II. They show a marked increase from 1963 to 1966, with a levelling off in 1967. We cannot account for the low population counts in 1963, but it may be that rooks were severely reduced in the bad winter of 1962/63 and have since recovered to their "normal" level. The "rook density" of 70·8 nests per sq. mile within the Ythan Valley contrasts with figures of 11·8 and 25·3 for Hertfordshire as a whole in 1945 and 1960–61, respectively (Sage and Nau, 1963), and a maximum of 45 (for Berwickshire) in a list of nineteen British localities (Coombes, 1961).

TABLE II

Numbers of rook nests in the Ythan Valley (270 sq. miles), 1963–67

	1963	1964	1965	1966	1967
Total	14 157	16 764	18 261	19 211	18 930
% Change		+13·5	+9	+5·2	−1·5
Nests per sq. mile	52·4	62·1	67·6	71·2	70·8*

* Two long established rookeries with 196 nests were found for the first time in 1967. This figure is based on the actual total 19 126, not 18 930 which is given above for comparative purposes.

In the intensive study area

It was shown that two rookeries in the intensive study area— Macharmuir and South Artrochie—shared a common feeding ground. In addition, there is a good deal of interchange of birds between these rookeries and we have chosen them as a population unit for study.

This population has been counted using three independent methods. (1) *Nest counts* are made regularly during March and April and the *maximum* count is taken as an index of the population. The pattern of change in the number of nests in a rookery is not always sigmoid (cf. Busse, 1965), but in South Artrochie it usually has a sharp peak (Fig. 9). For this reason, our nest counts throughout the Ythan Valley are restricted to the second half of April. (2) *Roost counts* are made weekly or fortnightly throughout the year by one of two procedures depending on the roosting behaviour. When they roost in their rookeries (March–

F

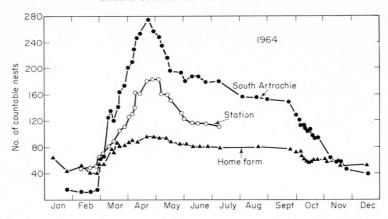

FIG. 9. Seasonal changes in the number of countable nests in three rookeries in the Auchmacoy area.

July), the rooks are flushed late in the evening, either by broadcast distress calls (Plate 1) or by a shot, and photographed in a flock, using very high speed polaroid film. They are then counted on the print. Checks are made at almost every census to make sure there is no emigration, to ensure that feeding activity has stopped, and to count the number of jackdaws present. When rooks leave the area to roost, they are counted out of the area on their flight-lines in the afternoon or evening. (3) *The intensive area circuit*, mentioned under Dispersion (p. 124), enables us to examine about 95% of the area and so obtain an estimate of the number of birds using the area. There are problems of detecting all the birds and of missing or double counting as the circuit takes about 2 h. to complete. Results from this method are influenced by dispersion patterns of the rooks by day, while those from the roost count are not.

Data from these censuses have revealed a repeatable annual pattern of variation in population size and density (Figs. 10 and 11). Part of this pattern is influenced by the presence of rooks in the rookeries by day during spring and autumn. From the points of view of the "natural" regulation of rook populations, and of the impact of rooks on the agriculture of an area, the following aspects of this pattern can be considered, with a view to correlating them with available resources and amount of damage caused.

(1) *The size of the roosting population in winter.* So far, we are unable to account for the difference between winter numbers and the breeding population. We cannot exclude the possibility of migrant overwintering rooks in the area.

Plate 1

(2) *The size of the breeding population.* This has not varied in the two years shown, and maximum nest numbers are similar for the five years of the study.

(3) *The maximum size of the post-breeding population in late May—early June.* Although the lower peak in 1967 is associated with poorer breeding than in 1966, the difference between the April population and the peak cannot be accounted for in terms of breeding output from these rookeries.

(4) *The minimum roosting population in August.* This level may well vary according to the "severity" of the summer feeding conditions and the timing of the onset of harvest.

(5) *The minimum rook density in the intensive area in late summer.* This is related to (4).

Variations in population size can be brought about by three processes acting separately or in combination. These are breeding, mortality and movement. We must consider next to what extent each contributes to the annual pattern.

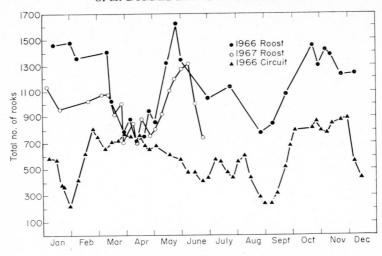

Fig. 10. Seasonal changes in the number of rooks in the intensive study area. Roost counts are of birds roosting in the study rookeries or flying out of the study area to roost. Circuit counts are the total numbers of rooks detected on transects of the study area in mid-morning.

BREEDING

Each year a sample number of trees in the rookeries has been selected at the beginning of the breeding season and the history of each nest built in them was followed, from visits made at intervals of 3–4 days. Details of laying-dates, clutch-size, hatching and survival of nestlings are available, but we have summarized the information by calculating from the sample, after making allowance for temporary and incomplete nests, the total production of young rooks for each rookery in 1966 and 1967 (Table III). These data refer to young surviving to the age of 21 days, after which they cannot be approached in the nest without risk of causing premature departure.

The influence of breeding output should be seen most clearly in the size of the post-breeding population. In 1966 the increase between April and late May amounted to about 750 birds, although only 466 young survived to the age of 21 days. In 1967 the respective figures were about 500 and 304. Although the poorer production in 1967 was associated with smaller post-breeding numbers, it is clear that additional factors were involved. We have evidence from observations in the rookery that many pre-breeders (1-year- and possibly 2-year-old rooks) come to roost in the rookeries in May, but we do not know where they come from. In view of the considerable fluctuations which occur later

TABLE III

Estimated production of young in South Artrochie and Macharmuir rookeries, 1966 and 1967

| | South Artrochie | | Macharmuir* | | Total young produced | Young produced per countable nest |
	Maximum no. of nests	No. of young produced	Maximum no. of nests	No. of young produced		
1966	263	316	117	150	466	1·2
1967	225	187	124	117	304	0·87

* Estimated from maximum number of nests × young production per study nest in South Artrochie.

in the year, it seems unlikely that variations in local breeding success are important in regulating rook numbers. Other evidence given below shows that when local breeding output is virtually eliminated by shooting, the breeding population does not usually appear to be adversely affected.

MORTALITY

It is difficult without following individually marked birds over a series of years to give precise estimates of mortality for different components of the population. Few useful data on rook mortality are available. Sage and Nau (1963) give the mortality of young birds in the

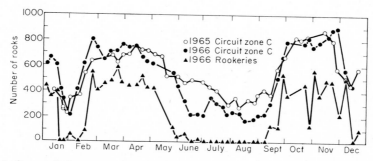

FIG. 11. Seasonal changes in the number of rooks counted in the central part of the intensive study area, in two seasons. The counts of birds in the rookeries were made at the end of the transect, usually just before noon.

first year of life as 70 ± 10%, but this is derived from Coombes' statement (1960) of 60–80% in the absence of shooting. Coombes also suggests that the average adult mortality is of the order of 16% per annum. Other values given by Sage and Nau are calculated from incomplete data. We have some data on survival of adults established in South Artrochie rookery, indicating an annual mortality of about 7·5–11% (Table IV). It is clear, even from this small sample, that mortality is concentrated in the summer months (contrasting with Lockie's (1956) conclusion that winter is the critical season for rooks near Oxford), and it seems likely that young birds will be even more vulnerable than adults. High mortality in summer is consistent with the seasonal pattern of food availability.

Grain crops are available for most of the year except in June, July and August (Fig. 1), and also in March if sowings are late. In March newly cultivated land is usually also available, but in the summer months grass is the only choice. In grass fields rooks feed largely on leatherjackets and earthworms. In midsummer the former emerge, and in warm dry weather the latter may go deeper in the soil and not be available (Fig. 12). This suggests that midsummer, especially in dry years, is the most critical time of the year for rook food, and other evidence from trapping, weights and mortality supports this.

Work is now in progress to measure the amount of food present in the important crop types, and the kind and amount obtained by the rooks.

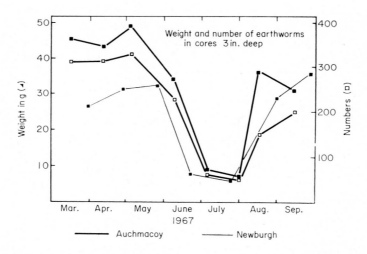

Fig. 12. Seasonal variation in the number and weight of earthworms, from 40 cores (4 in. diameter, 3 in. deep) from grass fields, 1967.

TABLE IV

Survival rates for tagged regular attenders in South Artrochie rookery*

	Autumn 1965	Spring 1966	Autumn 1966	Spring 1967
1. No. alive	40	40	37	36
Mortality (%)		0	7·5	2·7
2. No. alive		8	7	7
Mortality (%)			12·5	0

Estimated annual mortality rates:

    Autumn 1965 – Autumn 1966, 3/40 = 7.5%
    Spring   1966 – Spring   1967, 5/48 = 11.0%

*Disappearance from the records in spring or autumn when rooks use the rookeries extensively by day (Fig. 11) is taken as death.

So far, we have few data on survival of pre-breeders, but we have some observations on the mortality rate of young at fledging time. At South Artrochie, 101 and 89 young were ringed in the nest in 1966 and 1967, and of these, 13 and 26 were recovered dead in the rookery during May. No shooting occurred in this rookery so that this value approaches the natural mortality rate. However, in many rookeries in the area, particularly large rookeries in estate grounds, heavy shooting of young takes place, and the severity of this shooting and its effect on subsequent population size is given in Table V. Heavily shot rookeries have shown a greater increase in numbers than lightly shot ones. The number of young reaching 21 days (pre-fledging) produced per nest in the study rookeries has varied between 0·87 and 1·2 (Table III), and these values can be used to get some assessment of the proportion of young shot.

In the field, young rooks can be distinguished from adults by their feathered faces for about a year. The proportion of young can be obtained by ageing samples of rooks in the study area and in rookeries. There are considerable biases involved in this sampling owing to differences in the dispersion patterns of young and old birds and interpretation is difficult. However, the decrease in the proportion of young during the summer (Fig. 13) will certainly involve both movement and mortality, and the maximum and minimum values each year are important parameters.

TABLE V

Changes in rookery size in relation to the number of fledglings shot

Estate		1963	1964	1965	1966	1967
Haddo House	No. of nests and % change between years*	1 824	+20　2 186	+12　2 443	0　2 440	+4　2 546
	No. of young shot*	8 476	4 033	4 493	2 962	2 667
Esslemont	No. of nests and % change between years	1 453	+48　2 142	+20　2 567	0　2 565	+9　2 797
	No. of young shot		3 000	2 500	2 951	1 594
Selection of heavily shot rookeries		6 683	+20　7 999	+23　9 848	+11　10 949	+1　11 037
Selection of lightly shot rookeries		2 270	+0　2 273	+16　2 648	−9　2 412	+2　2 468

* From estate records.

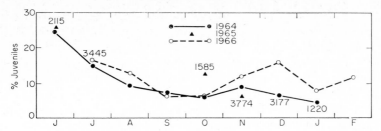

FIG. 13. Seasonal changes in the proportion of juvenile rooks in the Ythan Valley. The figures against the points show representative sample sizes.

MOVEMENT

It has become clear to us that movement is probably the most important of the three processes in determining the size of local rook populations. The decrease in the populations in summer is due at least in part to dispersal, and the increase in autumn is clearly a result of a change in dispersal. Ringing of juveniles has shown that considerable movement may occur within a few months of leaving the nest. Young rooks marked at Auchmacoy have been reported from as far afield as Inverness, Keith, Fraserburgh, Inverurie and Ballater, distances of up to 100 miles, indicating a strong dispersal, probably occurring mainly during their first summer. It may be important to note here that our intensive study area being near the sea contains peripheral rookeries so that effects of movement may be over-emphasized. However, it is abundantly clear from the data given in Table V that increases in rookery size cannot possibly be accounted for in terms of local young production. As an additional example, the annual counts of nests in Arnage Castle rookery, from 1963 to 1967, were 340, 1 059, 1 339, 1 761 and 2 129—an increase of 300% in the first year. Stewart (1930) describes a similar situation.

There is now increasing evidence that winter flocks of pre-breeding rooks occur with distinct dispersion patterns and daily routines (cf. Coombes, 1960, p. 415), and that the rook population can be thought of as "two-tiered", consisting of adult breeders established in rookeries, and unestablished birds. Understanding of how the pre-breeders eventually become established in breeding units is of fundamental importance to the problem of control of rook numbers, and we are now studying this aspect of the work in detail. There are about 500 individually identifiable tagged rooks in the study area, representing all categories of the population, and detailed observations on these over a period of years, in relation to social behaviour of rooks in rookeries and feeding areas, should reveal the processes involved.

F*

In this study, we have now established the annual patterns of agriculture and of rook numbers, dispersion and the utilization of resources. Biological processes affecting rook numbers have been examined and it should soon be possible to construct testable hypotheses concerning the "natural" limitation of rook numbers. Similarly, the descriptive phase of rook diet and feeding distribution is almost complete, and experiments can be designed to measure the amount of damage caused by rooks and to assess the effectiveness of control measures.

SUMMARY

This is a preliminary report of a long-term study of a local rook population in an intensively cultivated part of Aberdeenshire. The food and feeding of the rooks is related to the agricultural environment, and potentially damaging activities of the rooks are indicated. An attempt to quantify these in terms of loss of profit to the farmers is now being considered.

Annual counts of nests indicate that the rook population of the Ythan Valley (270 square miles) has increased by about 35% between 1963 and 1966 to a density of about 71 nests per square mile, the highest recorded for Britain. Seasonal changes in the size and dispersion of a local population are described, and estimates of breeding output and adult survival are given. It is concluded that movement of pre-breeding birds is most important in the determination of the population level.

We suggest that summer is likely to be the critical period of the year for rooks, owing to the difficulty of obtaining food then, and that survival during summer may determine the number of potential recruits in the area. The standard practice of shooting young rooks in May is shown not to be effective in controlling the numbers in local populations.

ACKNOWLEDGEMENTS

We would like to acknowledge our appreciation of the facilities for this study made available to us by the proprietors and factors of the Auchmacoy and Slains Estates and also to Mr. C. D. Scott and Mr. J. S. Leith on whose farms much of our work is carried out. Professor V. C. Wynne-Edwards has given us stimulation and encouragement at all times, and Dr. R. A. Fordham, Mr. J. W. H. Conroy and Mr. D. Y. Evans have taken part in some aspects of the work.

REFERENCES

Busse, P. (1965). Nest building dynamics of a breeding colony of rook (*Corvus frugilegus* L.). *Ekol. pol.* A, **13**, 491–514.

Coombes, C. J. F. (1960). Observations on the rook, *Corvus frugilegus*, in south-west Cornwall. *Ibis* **102**, 394–419.

Coombes, C. J. F. (1961). Rookeries and roosts of the rook and jackdaws in south-west Cornwall. *Bird Study* **8**, 32–37.

Lockie, J. D. (1956). Winter fighting in feeding flocks of rooks, jackdaws and carrion crows. *Bird Study* **3**, 180–190.

Pinowski, J. (1959). Factors influencing the number of feeding rooks (*Corvus frugilegus frugilegus* L.) in various field environments. *Ekol. pol.* A, **8**, 435–482.

Sage, B. L. and Nau, B. S. (1963). The population ecology of the rook in Hertfordshire. *Trans. Herts. nat. Hist. Soc. Fld. Club* **25**, 226–244.

Stewart, W. (1930). The rook in Lanarkshire, 1922–29. *Scott. Nat.* 1929–30, 15–21.

The Oystercatcher – A Pest of Shellfisheries

P. E. DAVIDSON

Ministry of Agriculture, Fisheries and Food,
Fisheries Experiment Station, Conway, Caernarvonshire, Wales

INTRODUCTION

In few of the cases where birds have been accused of being pests of fisheries have there been any very detailed studies. The few which have been published deal mainly with oceanic fisheries like the South African pilchard or the South American anchovy, or they concern estuarine and freshwater problems such as predation by the red-breasted merganser *Mergus serrator*, or goosander *M. merganser*, on salmon and trout (White, 1957; Mills, 1962). Littoral bird predators in the British Isles include the eider duck *Somateria mollissima*, preying on mussels (Milne and Marriott, in preparation), and the subject of our study, the oystercatcher *Haematopus ostralegus*, feeding on the commercial stocks of cockles and mussels (Davidson, 1967).

Oystercatchers feed on a great variety of lamellibranch and gasteropod shellfish, as well as on crustaceans and worms. However, it is the habit these birds have of concentrating in large flocks in areas rich in commercially exploited cockles and mussels which brings them into conflict with man. The cockle fishery has, since the mid-1950s, been the more important of the two economically, and it is the one which has suffered most from the depredations of the oystercatchers (Plate 1). This has led the Ministry to concentrate a good deal of effort into the study of this fishery and its problems. The annual value of the cockle industry, according to the official statistics, is £100 000–£200 000, although this may be an underestimate of its true value, as will be explained later in this paper. Imports of cockles, almost solely from Dutch sources, certainly exceed £100 000 per annum.

These figures may not seem high when viewed on a national scale, but when it is realized that the fishery is often concentrated in very small communities, the impact within such a community can be very large indeed. There is also an expanding export market for processed shellfish, and cockles figure largely in this.

PLATE 1. Shells of cockles opened by oystercatchers and left on feeding piles in the Burry Inlet.

THE GENERAL BIOLOGY OF THE COCKLE AND ITS FISHERIES

The cockle occurs at mid-tide level on the beach and most of the large beds are in sheltered waters of large bays and estuaries, where the flat expanses of muddy sand which provide ideal conditions for it are found. The eggs of the cockle are shed into the water, where fertilization takes place during the summer months and the larvae spend several weeks in the free-floating planktonic stage before settling to the bottom and metamorphosing into the adult form. All its life the cockle is at the mercy of the weather. As a larva it can be blown out of sheltered areas and never find a suitable place to settle, and as an adult it is vulnerable to being killed by overheating in summer (Orton, 1933), by freezing in winter (Crisp, 1964), or by being washed out of the sand during storms. Cockles may settle in extremely high numbers in some years (Hancock recorded densities of 17 500 per m² in the Burry Inlet in 1963), whereas in other years there is practically no settlement at all. The sheltered areas of the Burry Inlet and the Thames Estuary have more stable fisheries than the more exposed areas such as Morecambe Bay.

There are few other natural predators of cockles. Fish will take quantities of small spat, but once these have grown to 15 mm or more the only major predators are birds and man (Hancock and Urquhart,

1965). Natural mortality rates are high; Hancock records 48% per annum as normal.

There are five main traditional cockle-fishing areas in the British Isles, and each of these exhibits a different relationship with the oyster-catcher. Both the Thames Estuary and the Wash are areas of large-scale cockle production which have very little trouble from oystercatchers. The flocks in the Thames area are small, but there is some evidence of a tendency to increase (Dare, 1966) which may lead to problems in the future. The Wash flocks total 10 000–15 000, but these are so dispersed at low water, and the effect of other factors, such as movement of banks, is so great that the damage attributable to oystercatchers is masked.

Morecambe Bay and the Dee Estuary are areas where cockle fishing was once a major industry, but due to the interaction of bird predation, the cold winter of 1962–63, and a natural low point in these variable fisheries, the cockle stocks have been annihilated. The cockles which remained in the fishery in the autumn of 1962 were rendered moribund by the cold and, unable to close quickly or tightly, they became an easy prey to the birds. Some factor, possibly the low level of the surviving adult stock, has prevented a good spat settlement since that date, and the migrant oystercatchers, pausing for a while on passage through the area, remove what few spat have managed to settle and grow during the summer months. The virtual total removal of the cockles is aided by the presence of moderate supplies of a secondary prey species, *Macoma balthica*. This provides the staple diet of a small resident winter population of birds, which can then remove the last few cockles as they are found. The fifth cockle industry is in the Burry Inlet in South Wales and is dealt with below.

The Burry Inlet Cockle Fishery

This fishery has normally ranked third to Morecambe Bay and the Dee Estuary in the catch statistics, with landings of around 25 000–30 000 cwt per annum. Between 1955 and 1962 the fishery ran on a year-to-year basis: cockles settling in one year would reach legal commercial size in the following autumn (14–18 months later), when they would form the basis for both the fishery and the food for the birds. They would be practically fished out in the 12-month period to the next autumn, when the succeeding year's spat would enter the fishery. In order to conserve the stocks the fishermen imposed a voluntary limit on their catches of two bags per person per day. This helped to prolong the fishery for the 12-month period but, of course, did nothing to lessen the predation of the oystercatchers during the winter months. Under these circumstances the birds were regularly taking 30–40% of the stocks each year, which was substantially more than was taken by the fishermen.

Following the drastic reduction in the cockle stocks after the cold weather of January 1963, there was a remarkable spat settlement on the nearly empty beds in the summer of 1963. Densities of young spat in excess of 17 000 per m² were recorded (Hancock, personal communication), and when these matured to a fishable size in 1964 they gave rise to the present abundance of cockles. At first the market outlets for cockles were insufficient to take full advantage of this huge stock, but the manpower and fishing effort has increased as the market has expanded. In the summer of 1966 Severnside Seafoods reopened their processing plant at Penclawdd, and early in 1967 both Severnside and Milford Coldstorage Co. started deep-freezing cockles from the area. These activities provided an outlet for a further 6 000 cwt per month.

Any policy aimed at controlling predation by birds must be economically worthwhile, and, to judge this, the value of the fishery must be calculated in some detail. This is not an easy calculation to make, because there are many different outlets for cockles, each of which commands its own price. The Ministry's official statistics are based on the total landings and the value per cwt at first sale; this gives a minimum estimate of the value of the fishery. Prior to 1966 only about 10% of the cockles were sold in the shell; the remaining 90% were sold as cooked meats at a price which has risen from 2s. per pint in 1956 to 2s. 6d. in 1963, and more recently to 3s. This results in the gross value of the fishery to the local community being much higher than is indicated by figures based on the value of cockles sold in the shell. Before using these figures to calculate a true value for the fishery the variable meat yield from the cockles throughout the year must be taken into consideration. Table I gives the estimated gross value of the landings in 1965, assuming that only 10% of the cockles were sold in the shell. This value of the fishery, therefore, would appear to be between one and a half and two times the official figure.

Until very recently almost the whole of the income from the fishery was shared amongst the local community. The boiling plants are manned by fishermen or their families, and most of the hawking and market sale of cockles is undertaken by the fishermen's families. However, some of the secondary profits are now lost to the immediate area, as the bottling and freezing are done in Bristol and Milford Haven.

The considerable expansion of the market for fresh cockles and the substantial quantities now taken for bottling show that the demand is far from fully satisfied. Severnside alone could expand with present

TABLE I

Calculated value of the Burry Inlet cockle fishery for 1965, showing estimates of the effect of allowing for the sale of the cockles by the fishermen as cooked meats and not as shell cockles

Month	Landings (cwt)	Value of 10% sold in shell at £1 per cwt	Meat yield (pints per cwt)	Value per cwt @ 2s. 6d. per pt	Value of 90% sold as cooked meats
January	3 388	339	10	25s.	3 809
February	3 198	320	10	25s.	3 598
March	3 949	395	10	25s.	4 440
April	3 654	365	10	25s.	4 109
May	4 177	418	12	30s.	5 637
June	4 266	426	14	35s.	6 717
July	4 330	433	20	50s.	9 741
August	3 386	338	20	50s.	7 439
September	4 269	427	20	50s.	9 203
October	3 650	365	18	45s.	7 390
November	3 774	377	16	40s.	6 793
December	3 077	308	12	30s.	4 260
	45 118	4 511			£73 136
				Plus 10% shell cockles	4 511
				Total value landings	£77 647*

*cf. value of £45 118 shown in "Sea Fisheries Statistical Tables", which is the value as "shell cockles" ≡ £1 per cwt.

facilities to two and a half times their present output from the Inlet, and this would allow them to cut down the quantity imported. First, however, there must be better prospects for maintaining the fishery at an adequate level.

STUDIES OF THE BIRDS

An assessment of the level of predation attributable to oystercatchers has been one of the major aims of this study. This followed the pattern of the early work done by Drinnan (1957). Monthly counts of birds in the Inlet were made, and observations taken of the feeding rates of individual birds. From these data the total offtake of cockles can be calculated.

The monthly counts of birds in the Burry Inlet showed substantial seasonal variations (Fig. 2), and the pattern of these variations was different from that found in some other parts of the country. Full counts have only been possible in a limited number of places, and these show that in Morecambe Bay, the Dee Estuary (Fig. 3) and Conway Bay (Fig. 1) the peak numbers of birds are to be found during periods of maximum migration. In Morecambe Bay this is associated with the birds feeding on the few cockles present, and the fall-off in numbers of birds comes when these food reserves have been exhausted. The Burry

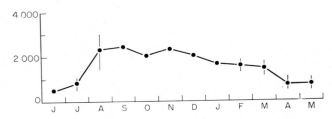

FIG. 1. Counts of oystercatchers in Conway Bay, 1965–67.

Inlet seems to be unique in the British Isles in that here the highest oystercatcher numbers occur in midwinter. The migratory movement in this area is represented by the September peak which characteristically falls, or at least levels out, before the main peak in November–December. Whether the peak count represents the total number of birds visiting the Inlet each year, or whether this is only part of a larger population of birds passing through the area was not clear until a marking programme was carried out. The results of this programme

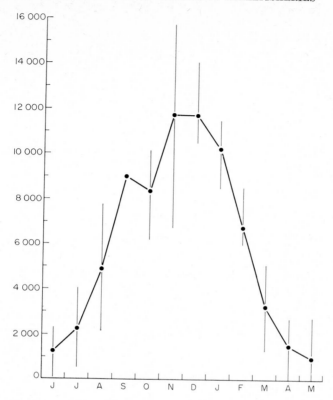

FIG. 2. Counts of oystercatchers in the Burry Inlet, 1961–67, showing deviation from mean. N.B. The counts for the abnormal winter 1963–64 have been omitted from the average.

tend to support the former hypothesis and will be discussed more fully later.

In Table II the figures are given for cockle stocks in the Burry Inlet for four winters and the average bird counts for the winter months. It will be seen that the winter of 1963–64 was exceptional both in respect of the very low numbers of mature cockles present (columns 3 and 4) and the low number of birds. In this case there are good grounds for the view that the shortage of available food caused many of the birds to winter elsewhere. The bird numbers in each of the other three winters were remarkably constant, with a maximum variation of about 10% from the mean value of 8 490. The preferred food of the oystercatcher is second-year cockles. The numbers of these in the Burry Inlet show very great fluctuations, 3 192 million in 1964–65, down to 33 million in 1965–66. The effect of these fluctuations may, however, be masked by

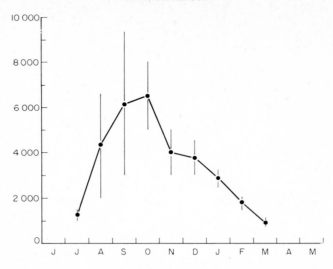

Fig. 3. Counts of oystercatchers in the Dee Estuary, 1963–65.

the fact that, in years when second-winter cockles were scarce, the birds were able to take advantage of at least part of the abundant stocks of third-winter cockles. However, when total stocks of cockles of two year and upwards were low, even enormous stocks of spat failed to provide the birds with sufficient food. It seems that in normal winters the number of birds may not be controlled by the availability of the preferred food.

Table II

Cockle stocks in the Burry Inlet, and the associated average bird counts, for four winters

		Numbers of cockles $\times 10^6$				Bird numbers
	Spat	Second winter (preferred oystercatcher food)	Estimated third winter	Total older than second winter	Total	
1962–63	2 648	1 071	200	282	4 001	8 250
1963–64	10 615	10	80	104	10 729	3 150
1964–65	194	3 192	2	40	3 426	7 850
1965–66	5 717	33	1 745	1 775	7 525	9 380

FOOD INTAKE OF THE BIRDS AND COMPARISON WITH STOCK AND FISHING LEVELS

Both direct observation of the birds feeding on the cockle beds in the Burry Inlet and the analysis of gut contents of birds shot while feeding show that their diet consists entirely of cockles. The quantity of food taken was investigated by the same methods used by Drinnan (1957), namely by observing feeding rates and calculating the percentage of the tidal exposure time during which the feeding rates were maintained.

In the Burry Inlet the feeding rates varied over a wider range than Drinnan reported for the Morecambe Bay area, but this was largely associated with a greater range in modal size of cockles from different areas within the Inlet, and with variation of meat content at different observation periods during the winter. An average of all the feeding rate observations gave a mean of 1·2 cockles per min when the birds were feeding on second-winter cockles. This rate was maintained for 55% of the $8\frac{1}{2}$ h for which, on average, the cockle beds were exposed each tide. These figures give an average intake of 336 cockles per daylight tide per bird.

It is known that the activities of the birds are linked to a tidal cycle, not a diurnal one (Drinnan, 1957); they feed at low water, irrespective of daylight or darkness. To calculate total daily intake the night feeding rate needs to be known; the only attempt to estimate this was made by Drinnan (1958), but for this work he used captive birds in small cages and presented them with food during a full 24-h period. His results indicated that at night the birds feed at half the daylight rate. In February 1967 an attempt was made by the author to make direct observations of feeding birds in the field at night. A small boat was moored in an area known to be used by feeding oystercatchers. The observers boarded the boat at dusk as the tide flooded, and remained in the boat during the high-tide period. The birds followed the ebbing tide and as soon as the beds dried out they started feeding in the vicinity of the boat. Using ×10 binoculars and an infra red telescope the birds could be seen feeding. On the particular area chosen for these observations, birds had been observed feeding during the daylight tide at a rate of one cockle per min. At night, rates close to these were again observed, viz. six cockles in 7 min and five cockles in 6 min. The conditions prevailing at the time of these night observations were fairly bright with a full moon, but heavily overcast. The lights from Llanelli also added to the illumination and it may be that these feeding rates were higher than would be the case in periods of dark moon or heavy mist. These feeding rates agree well with results obtained by Dr. J. B.

Hulscher (personal communication), who found that when captive oystercatchers were fed on mussels, with which they were presented for limited periods both during the day and night, they consumed slightly more during the dark periods than the daylight ones.

All the observations and experiments so far to determine night feeding rates have been rather inadequate, so when total consumption and feeding rates have been calculated the more conservative estimates obtained by Drinnan have been used. Thus, the figure of 336 cockles – calculated above as the tidal consumption of one oystercatcher – becomes 504 cockles per day. The average meat content of a second-winter cockle is 0·65 g, and this gives the food intake of an oyster-catcher as 327 g per day (wet weight).

In any predator-prey relationship many independent variables can operate to influence the degree of predation. Any attempt to build an overall picture of the damage done to cockle fisheries by oystercatchers must either become so comprehensive and involved as to be almost impossible to undertake, or it must be very broadly based, endeavouring to allow for some of the variables in an attempt to produce a reasonable estimate of the level of predation. By averaging feeding rates taken at different times and in different months some of the inherent variation due to cockle size and condition should have been allowed for. Likewise the percentage feeding time is a compound of several sets of observations.

Bearing these provisos in mind, and knowing the daily food requirements of the birds, calculations of the equivalent number of second-winter cockles required by the bird population in any given winter can be made. For the Burry Inlet this has ranged between 240 and 860 million from 1961 to 1965 (Table III). Comparisons can be made directly with stocks of cockles as assessed by the Ministry's surveys carried out each May and November, and with the fishery landings. It can be clearly seen that in years of moderate stocks the birds can account for up to 70% of the total of second-winter cockles, whereas in years of high stock levels they may account for no more than 20%.

Anomalies occur in the calculations when in 1963–64 and 1965–66 the stocks of second-winter cockles appeared insufficient to provide the minimum food requirements for the birds. In the former winter large quantities of spat cockles were available and were indeed consumed by the birds, and in the latter winter when the second-winter cockles were again scarce, the birds were forced into taking third-winter cockles. In times of shortage the birds will also feed on the subcommercially stocked areas higher on the shore, where growth of the cockles is poor and meat content low. These cockles are not included in the stock surveys, as they are outside both the commercial fishing grounds and the birds' normal feeding grounds.

The foregoing calculations indicate that the oystercatcher is a major predator on the cockle beds. Even if allowance is made for *ca.* 50% annual natural mortality of the cockles (Hancock and Urquhart, 1965), substantial reduction in the birds' predation would be expected to lead to a marked increase in the number of cockles available to the fishery.

Physical protection of the cockles is impracticable on an open beach, and over the area of several square miles involved techniques of scaring the birds would be ineffective. Control of the birds must be by their removal from the area.

Movement Studies

Before control methods can be adopted for any predator there should be a full study of the factors affecting its population. In the case of the oystercatcher much of this information has been obtained by ringing and colour-banding: the former was carried out within the British Trust for Ornithology scheme.

Ring recoveries from these birds indicate that the major wintering flocks comprise elements received from all the principal breeding

Table III

Stocks of second-winter cockles in the Burry Inlet, with the associated total mortality, fishing landings and estimates of the requirements of the birds expressed as second-winter cockles

| | Numbers of cockles $\times 10^6$ | | | | |
	Stock of second-winter cockles (millions)	Total mortality (millions)	Fishing mortality (millions)	No. of birds	No. of cockles required by birds (millions)
1962–63	1 071	801	27	8 250	757
1963–64	10	46	20*	3 150	240*
1964–65	3 192	1 132	141	7 850	743
1965–66	33	14	N.A.	9 380	860

N.A. Not available at time of writing.

* Anomalies in the table are due to the expression of fishing landings and bird requirements in terms of second-winter cockles only. The bulk of the actual cockles concerned under these headings in 1963–64 were cockles older than second-winter for fishing mortalities and spat cockles for oystercatcher food.

grounds of northern Britain, the Faroes, Iceland and Norway (Dare, 1966). The breeding birds are widely dispersed along most of the northern coasts and river valleys, with typical concentrations of only one or two pairs per mile. Even where colonization has spread inland only one pair will usually be found in any one field. These facts obviously preclude any effective control, aimed at one particular fishery, from being carried out on the breeding grounds, even if sufficient nests could be found. Control on the wintering grounds depends upon the possibility of being able to bring effective action to bear against flocks resident in a specific area, and thereby giving direct relief to that area.

Knowledge of the local movements of the oystercatchers month by month and from area to area during the winter has come in the main from the use of colour-bands. Birds caught in the winter months were marked, using coloured plastic leg bands with unique colour codes to denote each time and place of capture. Subsequent recapture and field observation of these marked birds has enabled a fairly detailed analysis to be made of the return to wintering grounds over a period of several years, and of the midwinter movements of the birds (Dare, in press).

Observations have shown that there is a high tendency for oyster-catchers ringed in one wintering area to return to or revisit that area in subsequent winters. A similar picture holds for the Conway Bay area of North Wales. In the Dee and Morecambe Bay areas the percentage of local colour-banded birds present is higher than of birds ringed in other areas, but due to the failure of the food supply the total number of birds has fallen, and with it the general return rates of colour-banded birds. The mussel-feeding birds of Morecambe Bay do, however, show a high return rate to the original area of ringing. Directly complementary to this high return rate is the significantly lower proportion of colour-banded birds originating from surrounding areas which is found in any given flock, even when the differences in numbers originally marked are allowed for. Few birds from Morecambe Bay are seen in North Wales, and hardly any in the Burry Inlet. Likewise, very few midwinter sightings of Burry birds have been made anywhere but in the Burry Inlet and its immediate vicinity.

Dealing specifically with the Burry Inlet, which has been well studied for five years, no obvious dispersion from the area has been recorded once the birds have arrived in the autumn, although the colour-banding and ringing has been carried out, in the main, at the period of maximum migratory movements. No colour-banded birds have been seen south of the area, despite careful searches in the south-west of England, where there are regular wintering flocks. There is a little interchange between the Burry Inlet and the neighbouring Three Rivers area, whose birds must be reckoned as a secondary part of the same wintering population. Even in this closely associated area few colour-banded birds are normally seen, as compared with the Burry Inlet itself.

It is clear then that there is a marked tendency for oystercatchers to return in successive winters to one particular wintering ground and that, once there, there is little dispersion into neighbouring areas. These facts support the contention that the removal of birds from an area would be of lasting benefit to the fishery of that area. Whether these birds would be replaced by adults normally resident in other areas, or by young birds which would otherwise pass by on their migration route (Buxton, 1957), is a question which can only be solved by studying the results of a control programme. Such a programme would be closely monitored, and observation of the movements of colour-banded birds and of the flock age composition would soon reveal any large-scale influx.

CONTROL METHODS

On their wintering grounds oystercatchers occur either in dispersed feeding flocks or in dense flocks of up to several thousand birds roosting along the high-tide mark. Roosts may be formed on rocky outcrops, sand and shingle spits, open beaches or saltmarshes. The birds flight from the feeding grounds as the tide floods and usually approach the roost along well-defined flight-lines. This behaviour pattern suggests three methods of control, two during the flighting stage and one at the roost. The most obvious method would be by shooting. This is highly selective, but firing a 12-bore shotgun into a closely packed flock of flying birds inevitably results in a high risk of non-fatal wounding. Although this is undesirable, control by shooting cannot be dismissed in the face of opposition to the use of other more humane control methods.

The second method available against flighting birds is the flight net. This traditional wader-catching method uses a 6-ft high, large-meshed net, rigged on poles across the open sands. Birds approaching or leaving the roost after dark fly into and become tangled in the net. This method is entirely indiscriminate in its catch, although some control over the species caught can be exercised by the careful siting of the net and the use of the appropriate mesh size. There is also an unavoidable mortality factor involved in flight-netting which is not desirable when protected species are caught. However, like shooting, this method of control cannot be dismissed while the use of other more suitable methods is denied.

The method of control preferred by M.A.F.F. is cannon-netting at the roost. Large missile-propelled nets are set at the birds' high-water

roost and fired over them when they come to roost. The use of several
separate nets enables the operator to fire only those which will cover
oystercatchers and thus avoid unnecessary capture of protected species.
All the birds are captured alive and any marked birds or protected
species which have been caught while roosting on the edge of the flocks
can be released. Injury rates are very low with cannon-netting (less
than 0·5%), and are due mainly to birds being struck by the projectiles.
Disturbance in the netting area is minimal, as the net is set during low
water when the roost areas are deserted. Only the actual firing disturbs
the birds and this effect does not last for long. The nets fired over
roosting birds at one high water have often become the roost site for
birds on the succeeding high water.

Particularly in the Burry Inlet, the need for control of oystercatchers
is pressing. The basic investigations have been very thorough, and now
only by a trial period of control can they be extended further.

Summary

1. Oystercatchers winter in the British Isles and gather in large flocks
in areas of commercial fisheries, particularly cockle fisheries.

2. A consideration of the five main cockle fisheries shows that some
are more affected by oystercatchers than others; the Burry Inlet is a
particularly serious case.

3. A detailed analysis of the economic importance of the Burry Inlet
fishery shows that its real value to the local community is nearly twice
that to be expected from calculations based on the sale of cockles in the
shell at wholesale rates.

4. In Morecambe Bay, the Dee Estuary and Conway Bay the peak
numbers of birds occur in the autumn at times of maximum migration.
The Burry Inlet seems to be unique in this country in having its peak
population during the winter months. This peak is not dependent on
the size of the stock of second-year cockles, their preferred food.

5. On an average one bird consumes over 500 cockles per day, which
is equivalent to about 325 g of flesh (wet weight).

6. The food requirements of the birds during the winter months are
expressed as numbers of second-year cockles, and these figures are
compared with the total stocks and fishing landings.

7. It is shown that, if the fishery is to maintain a steady high level
of production, control of the oystercatcher is necessary.

8. Ringing and colour-banding studies indicate that the Burry Inlet
winter population is stable and largely discrete.

9. Control methods are discussed and reasons given for a strong
preference for cannon-netting.

REFERENCES

Buxton, E. J. M. (1957). Migrations of the oystercatcher in the area of Britain: results of ringing. *Br. Birds* **50**, 519–524.

Crisp, D. J. (1964). The effects of the severe winter of 1962/63 on marine life in Britain. *J. Anim. Ecol.* **33** (1).

Dare, P. J. (1966). The breeding and wintering populations of the oystercatcher (*Haematopus ostralegus* Linnaeus) in the British Isles. *Fishery Invest., Lond.* Ser. II, **25**, No. 5.

Davidson, P. E. (1967). A study of the oystercatcher (*Haemotopus ostralegus* L.) in relation to the fishery for cockles (*Cardium edule* L.) in the Burry Inlet, South Wales. *Fishery Invest., Lond.* Ser. II, **25**, No. 7.

Drinnan, R. E. (1957). The winter feeding of the oystercatcher (*Haematopus ostralegus*) on the edible cockle (*Cardium edule*). *J. Anim. Ecol.* **26**, 441–469.

Drinnan, R. E. (1958). Observations on the feeding of the oystercatcher in captivity. *Br. Birds* **51**, 139–149.

Hancock, D. A. and Urquhart, A. E. (1965). The determination of natural mortality and its causes in an exploited population of cockles (*Cardium edule* L.). *Fishery Invest., Lond.* Ser. II, **24**, No. 2.

Mills, D. H. (1962). The goosander and red-breasted merganser as predators of salmon in Scottish waters. *Freshwat. Salm. Fish. Res.* No. 29.

Orton, J. H. (1933). Summer mortality of cockles on some Lancashire and Cheshire Dee Beds, 1932. *Nature, Lond.* **132**, 314.

White, H. C. (1957). Food and natural history of mergansers on salmon waters in the maritime provinces of Canada. *Bull. Fish. Res. Bd. Can.* No. 116.

Some Predator–Prey Relationships in Bird Damage and Population Control

R. K. MURTON

*Ministry of Agriculture, Fisheries and Food,
Infestation Control Laboratory, Worplesdon, Surrey, England*

If the feeding habits of an animal seriously deprive the farmer of his crops, two basic remedies for reducing the damage exist. First, means may be sought to give physical protection to the crop at risk by using a convenient form of netting, caging, possibly a repellent chemical, or some form of scaring device—these can range from the crude scarecrow to a sophisticated recording of a distress call. Second, damage may be mitigated by attempting through some method to reduce the number of animals causing the damage, and this alternative might involve shooting, trapping or poisoning and even the use of reproductive inhibitors. In the past the tacit assumption has been made that killing techniques have cumulative benefits. Nowadays it is much more generally appreciated that animal populations comprise dynamic systems, and that killing may remove an expendable surplus without affecting total population size. Artificial predation may even alter the age structure of an animal population without reducing the total number of individuals which optimally can be supported by the environmental resources. Before embarking on any control programme aimed at artificial population reduction it is essential to study the factors governing the normal reproductive and mortality rates of the species, and to define the level of kill that must be achieved to outweigh natural losses. At the same time it is most helpful to understand the animal's general biology in case there are weak links which can be exploited. Indeed, this is essential because in most situations man behaves like any other predator and is subject to the same biological principles which govern other predator–prey interactions. Having emphasized this point it is necessary to examine the nature of these interactions in more detail in order to debunk certain generalizations which are current. In particular, it is often claimed that many of our pest birds would not have reached this status had man not systematically killed off their natural predators. The assumption is made that these predators once controlled the numbers of their prey. Yet when evidence is available it often shows that

157

predators take only a doomed surplus of their prey, turning to other foods when catching becomes difficult. Thus golden eagles *Aquila chrysaëtos*, hen harriers *Circus cyaneus* and foxes *Vulpes vulpes* mostly catch surplus dispersing grouse *Lagopus lagopus scoticus* without controlling population size (Jenkins, Watson and Miller, 1964). The goshawk *Accipiter gentilis* chiefly feeds on wood pigeons *Columba palumbus* when numbers of the latter reach a peak after the breeding season and many inexperienced juveniles are flying (Murton, in preparation). But much of this population surplus is later lost through food shortage (see below), and it becomes evident that predation by goshawks lacks the characteristics that could make it an effective regulatory agent.

A simple predator–prey relationship as studied by Gause (1934) in laboratory cultures of *Paramecium* is characterized by an initial increase in prey density, when predator numbers are low, followed by a rise in predator density in turn causing a fall in prey numbers. This results in fairly regular oscillations. In nature such interactions are relatively rare, and are likely to become unstable through chance fluctuations which result in pest proportion outbreaks of the prey or chance extinction of the predator. The nearest examples are to be found in certain Arctic game bird populations such as the black grouse *Tetrao tetrix* and capercaillie *T. urogallus* which in winter are specialized herbivores each adapted to feed on only one major plant food (Siivonen, 1957), or those birds of prey like the kestrel *Falco tinnunculus* or barn owl *Tyto alba* which feed on small rodents and which appear to show fairly regular oscillations in numbers (Parslow, 1967). More often, and because most bird species take a relatively wide range of foods, their predation is such as to damp oscillations in their prey numbers (Tinbergen and Klomp, 1960). Such predation may be economically important in the case of forest-living insectivorous birds, which may reduce the frequency of insect pest infestations (see, for example, Morris, 1963). The ability of birds to damp oscillations in their prey numbers follows from the typical feeding response depicted in the inset to Fig. 1 which is discussed later.

When man becomes the predator his numbers do not casually vary with prey density, although the same effect can be achieved because economic or social considerations usually cause a relaxation of hunting effort when returns become unprofitable. Nevertheless, in theory a sufficiently high and maintained hunting effort could hold a pest population below an otherwise optimum level and could even result in extinction. In practice, the difficulty is to achieve and maintain a sufficiently high rate of kill. The problem becomes even more intractable when man behaves like so many natural predators and has numerous prey, so that he tends to switch from one to the other depending on the ease of attack. This might not matter if sufficient individuals were killed but in the two best studied cases, the red grouse and wood pigeon, a very intensive shooting pressure is shown to do no more than remove individuals which would in any case be lost. Grouse numbers are ultimately determined by the availability of suitable heather supplies operating via a territorial system which spaces the birds and governs their breeding success (Jenkins *et al.*, 1963). After breeding, territories are established in the autumn and there are always surplus birds, especially juveniles, which are unsuccessful and which move to less productive parts of the moor where they die—either of starvation or because, as mentioned, they fall easy prey to predators. The important point is that there are always surplus birds left over, after the shooting season, which will never obtain territories. In other words, in every year more grouse could be profitably shot, and Jenkins (1962) considers that where grouse are driven it is probably impracticable, if not impossible, to shoot them too hard. A sensible policy for improving grouse shooting prospects involves improving the habitat and not trying to increase grouse numbers by hand-rearing or by killing predators.

A peak in wood pigeon numbers is found following breeding in August and September, but natural losses caused by food shortage are heavy though variable, depending on grain and tree-fruit availability in late autumn—at this time juveniles suffer most—and numbers are finally reduced and adjusted to the amount of clover available in midwinter (Murton, Westwood and Isaacson, 1964). Again winter shooting has been shown to do no more than remove a surplus of birds already doomed to starvation, without reducing crop damage. While no form of shooting limits population size (age structure and mortality rates are unaffected by shooting; Murton, 1966) it is debatable to what extent lone-wolf gunners operating in the period March–July bring about substantial savings in crop damage. Until this point is resolved, decoy shooting, and for that matter any shooting over a vulnerable crop for direct crop protection, is supported by a Government subsidy administered via the Rabbit Clearance Society movement. The subsidy is, however, paid for crop protection not for population control.

An interesting facet of the old-style winter battue shoots was an inverse density-dependent relationship between numbers shot and number of birds at risk (Murton *et al.*, 1964). It arose because the number of interested participants was limited and roughly constant from week to week and year to year. These people surrounded the woods to shoot the birds returning at dusk. As they used double-barrel 12-bore guns each man could potentially shoot two birds per flock. But this limit stayed when pigeon numbers were high and flock size increased, so that this kind of predation was least efficient when pigeon numbers were highest and control was most needed. Of course, not many people killed two birds each time; there are many records of people using over twelve cartridges per pigeon (cartridges cost about 7*d*. each). It is extremely difficult to make the layman or sportsman appreciate such kinds of interaction and it is not surprising that the findings of the grouse workers and ourselves, which are essentially the same, have not been readily acceptable to the people directly affected.

In 1962–63 a particularly hard winter reduced the pigeon population throughout Britain by up to two-thirds; many birds were shot as they flopped about brassica fields in an emaciated state and it can be questioned how much crop damage was prevented by bringing forward the time of death by a day or two. It took only two breeding seasons for the wood pigeon population to regain its previous level and in many areas only one season. Yet, judged by the amount of money paid in cartridge subsidies, the number of birds shot each year before or since has stayed roughly constant, or at least the subsidy has. If the argument is made that this level of shooting controls pigeon numbers (as say the advocates of shooting for population control) there should have been little or no recovery after only two years. If it is argued that the shooting effort was relinquished when prey density fell, this would support the constant fear and cry of pest control officials. The truth of the matter must be that the shooting level serves only to crop a constant number but varying proportion of the population surplus. Thus it is revealing that the subsidy has varied from year to year only slightly and to a much smaller extent than the actual pigeon population. Furthermore, in spite of the fact that the winter battue shoots, which previously accounted for about half the subsidy, were withdrawn from support in 1965 and a saving of half might have been expected, this has not been realized. It cannot be accepted that because birds are not shot in February they cause damage and have to be accounted for later in the year, because we already know that by this time they will be dead. The only conclusion is that the amount of money claimed for pigeon shooting has achieved an arbitrary level, acceptable to all concerned, but that it cannot possibly be related to pigeon numbers. At this stage it is not possible to say whether the money is usefully spent in damage prevention as distinct from population control.

Another popular belief ascribes a beneficial role to those predators which eat the eggs or young of harmful species. The percentage of wood pigeon eggs taken by jays *Garrulus glandarius* and magpies *Pica pica* increases directly with breeding density, effectively causing parallel variations in the reproductive rate (number of offspring produced per pair). But because the post-breeding mortality rate vastly exceeds these variations they have no effect on total population size even one month after the end of the breeding season (Murton and Isaacson, 1964). Population size is not regulated by the reproductive rate, and of course, the mortality rate balances the reproductive rate not vice versa. It is possible to define the approximate level to which fecundity would need to be reduced to cause a decrease in wood pigeon numbers. For example, supposing that a safe reproductive inhibitor could be found, it would have to be applied on a scale that would depress the natural total reproductive output by at least 70% under present circumstances. In the case of the feral pigeon *Columba livia* the efficiency would need to be even more, because this species enjoys a higher reproductive output and a consequent higher compensating juvenile mortality rate. The adult mortality rate of wild living rock doves is similar to that of the wood pigeon (about 30% compared with 36% per annum (Murton and Clark, 1968). Thus an enormous effort and a highly effective and safe agent would be needed if the population is to be directly affected. The high mobility of birds and the speed with which vacant areas are filled makes it impossible to visualize this kind of control on a purely local basis.

It is of interest that for several ubiquitous species such as the blackbird *Turdus merula* and song thrush *T. philomelos* it is known that nesting success and total reproductive output are respectively higher on farmland and in suburban gardens than in the species' natural woodland habitat (Snow and Mayer-Gross, 1967).

The differences result from the absence of natural predators in the more artificial habitats. Now it happens that much of the damage to ripening fruit, particularly soft-fruits and cherries, which is done by blackbirds and starlings *Sturnus vulgaris* occurs in June and July in drought conditions when the birds are unable to find soil litter invertebrates. The cultivated fruits provide a stop-gap food for many juveniles which afterwards soon die. In this situation it would be advantageous to encourage natural nest predators. Conversely, the shooting of juvenile rooks as they leave their nests is futile because they suffer their heaviest mortality in June and July, again when summer droughts cause earthworms to move beyond probing reach and before cereals ripen, and population size is naturally controlled at a season when the birds do no damage at all. Again this illustrates the need to consider each species on its own merits and not to assume that a particular control technique has universal applicability.

While man seems unable to achieve the scale of kill necessary to reduce the numbers of abundant species like the wood pigeon, rook and red grouse, the same arguments do not necessarily apply to less common species such as the raptors and owls where the predator (man) may outnumber the prey (hawks). Even so, Jenkins *et al.* (1964) have shown that in spite of intensive persecution—most predatory birds and mammals were killed at every opportunity by gamekeepers in Glen Esk—a similar number reappeared each year. At most the keepers may have depressed the early summer breeding stock but were unable to prevent all breeding and the consequent adequate replacement by those young which were reared locally on nearby estates. The question thus arises as to whether the marked decrease of buzzards *Buteo buteo* in eastern England during the nineteenth century was mainly due to persecution with the coincident rise in game-preservation as Moore (1957) has suggested. This decrease also applied to the carrion crow *Corvus corone* and raven *C. corax* and most authorities (for example, Stevenson, 1866; Ticehurst, 1932) blame the perniciousness of game-keepers, while even today East Anglia has a paucity of crows which Prestt (1965) attributes to keepering. It would be useful to know for certain whether these are genuine examples of a sufficiently high shooting pressure controlling a bird, because there would then be grounds for hoping that sufficient effort could realistically be applied in other areas of northern Britain and Scotland where carrion/hoodie crows are troublesome. But the big decrease of these partly scavenging species in East Anglia can also be correlated with a large and coincident decrease of sheep farming and a marked loss of carrion, and it is conceivable that keepering may have tipped the balance only when assisted by a radical environmental change.

Predator–prey interactions are also displayed by the individual as distinct from the population. Figure 1 shows the amount of cereal seed wood pigeons find and eat on stubbles or grain sowings per minute depending on grain density. In these circumstances, where no alternative food choice exists, the response is typical of the simplest kind of predator–prey interaction, normally most often shown by invertebrates. Vertebrates have a marked ability to learn and in most natural situations they encounter many different foods when hunting and are perforce required to exercise a choice. The result is shown inset in Fig. 1 where it is seen that the early functional response of the predator is now represented by a sigmoid curve (for examples, see Holling, 1965). This kind of response curve is also shown by pigeons when a new food like tic beans or maple peas (which in our experiments are often treated with α-chloralose to make a stupefying bait) are spread on a cereal stubble or sowing. At the lower densities the birds find the bait by chance; at slightly higher bait densities they learn that a good food

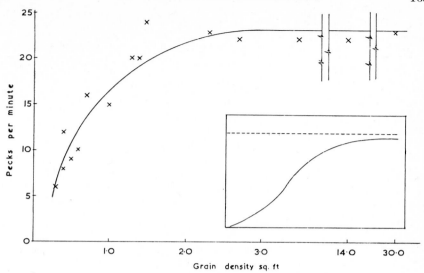

FIG. 1. Number of cereal grains eaten (pecks per minute) by wood pigeons according to food density. Modified from Murton *et al.* (1963). Inset to show proportion of a preferred food eaten per unit time against food density (solid line) when alternative prey is available. The dotted line represents the total food consumption (100%). (From Holling, 1965.)

source exists which is worth hunting for and a deliberate searching element is introduced into their behaviour. In Professor L. Tinbergen's (1960) words they develop a "specific search image". This results in food items being found more often than could be expected on the basis of chance encounters alone and causes the characteristic sigma stage in the functional-response curve. At still higher bait densities the birds take a constant proportion and feed at a constant rate irrespective of bait density, and the response curve now levels off. The density and feeding-rate at which this happens depends on how attractive the bait is relative to the alternative; with tic beans spread on a clover field the level is high, with tic beans on a cereal sowing it is low because the cereal grains are preferred. If we wish to catch birds with a stupefying bait it is apparent that the density of bait necessary to achieve an optimal feeding response without undue bait wastage can be defined precisely and will vary with field conditions. There is no advantage in increasing bait density beyond an optimum point.

  The characteristic curve in Fig. 1 depends on the time it takes the birds to locate each grain, which in turn depends on their effective visual range and also on their speed of searching and the time needed to pick up and swallow each grain after it has been found. The last function imposes the element of constancy found above a threshold food density. In practice the birds increase their searching rate as food density falls until a point is reached when further compensation becomes impossible. A similar response is found when pigeons are feeding on clover instead of grain and, because the birds feed in flocks, the mechanism whereby natural population control in relation to food stocks is achieved depends on this fundamental curve (Fig. 2).

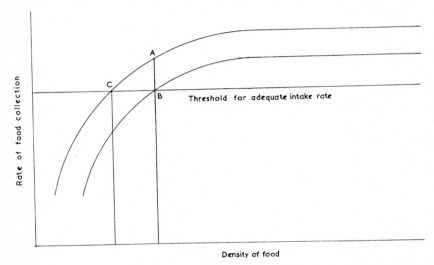

Fig. 2. Derived from Fig. 1 plus other observations to show the amount of food (clover) eaten per unit time by a dominant (top curve) and by a subordinate wood pigeon (lower curve), according to food density. The food density below which an adequate intake rate cannot be maintained is given by the vertical line from A–B for a subordinate individual and from C for a dominant flock member.

Within the feeding flocks a social hierarchy exists. This is possible because the flocks stay relatively constant in composition and each bird tends to keep to the same position relative to other individuals, this stability persisting over many weeks in some instances. Feeding flocks are by no means a haphazard collection of individuals subject to constant change. We have demonstrated this in the field by plotting the distribution of birds marked individually with plastic wing tags which can be identified up to 300 yd away. Depending on food density, dominant birds determine the rate of food searching to ensure an optimal intake rate relative to food density in accordance with the predictions of Fig. 2. Birds low in the social hierarchy, if they are to remain in the flock, must adopt the same searching rate. However, these individuals must also devote much time to avoiding conflict with dominant birds and they do this by moving to the front and sides of the flock, where they only have birds on one side of them. Hence, in addition to looking for food low-rank flock members must constantly look up to avoid getting too close to the other birds, and in consequence their food intake rate becomes depressed (Table I). The technique of measuring feeding rates under field conditions has already been described and discussed (Murton *et al.*, 1963).

Why do subordinate birds stay in the flocks when by moving to another part of the same field they could seemingly feed at a normal rate? The answer is that this is not the case as Table I shows. The feeding rates of birds eating alone, with no flock nearby, were measured on the same fields as flocks were watched feeding, although this was often on a different day. It is unusual for a pigeon to feed alone but whenever we saw such a bird we noted its feeding rate. Often a flock would be recorded on the same field, and representative feeding rates be taken, either a day or two before or after the single observation; if not, the record was discarded. Thus in all cases we could prove that the food density for observations on single or flock-feeding birds was constant. The reason for the flock habit appears to be that it serves as an important anti-predator device, increasing the awareness of potential danger above that achievable by a single individual. In fact, individuals feeding in isolation show considerable nervousness and constantly look up so that their feeding rate suffers. It therefore seems that a subordinate bird will always do better in a flock, even though its feeding rate is lower than its flock-mates. Although, as will be shown, population control is mediated via the flock structure, this process is a consequence of and not the *cause* of flocking. There is no need to think that the social hierarchy has evolved as a mechanism for population control.

Given that for any density of food a small proportion of the flock will have a lower than normal feeding rate, two response curves are plotted in Fig. 2, although in practice there would be individuals in intermediate categories. Now for a wide range of food densities the fact that some birds have lower than normal feeding rates may not matter, because their intake rate will still be higher than the threshold for adequate nutrition (this can be defined). For this range of food densities flock size may bear little or no relationship to food density, in other words population size is not demonstrably determined by food stocks. A corollary is that the amount of damage caused to a crop will also not be a direct function of population size nor of crop density (Murton *et al.*, 1966). While this situation holds it is impossible to predict areas of

TABLE I

Feeding rate of wood pigeons feeding alone or in a flock

Field reference	Date of observation	Feeding rates of flock members						Feeding rates of single individuals		
		Average flock members			Subordinate birds					
		Pecks/min (± S.E.)	Paces/min (± S.E.)	No. indiv. exam.	Pecks/min (± S.E.)	Paces/min (± S.E.)	No. indiv. exam.	Pecks/min (± S.E.)	Paces/min (± S.E.)	No. indiv. exam.
221	10.ii.66	119 ± 6·3	11 ± 3·8	7	82 ± 17·4	20 ± 10·7	7	58 ± 6·7	28 ± 9·2	6
218	21–24.ii.66	111 ± 8·1	15 ± 5·0	7	88 ± 20·5	11 ± 4·9	4	58 ± 6·3	21 ± 8·1	5
219	24–28.ii.66	113 ± 10·6	16 ± 5·6	15	No records			57 ± 7·3	31 ± 18·9	5
4C	2–10.iii.66	112 ± 18·2	22 ± 5·2	11	69 ± 4·7	25 ± 12·9	4	46 ± 13·5	24 ± 12·4	10

Clover density was high on all fields so that the normal feeding rate would be expected to be constant for average individuals in the flock, i.e. the feeding rates would lie on the flat part of the curve in Fig. 2. The figures for pecks/min for average flock members indicate that a constant intake rate was achieved while the same appears true for those birds feeding in isolation, that is, their intake rate was depressed by a constant amount.

potential crop damage, and a policy based on scaring may be inadequate simply because the birds have a wide choice of other places to feed. This situation occurs when wood pigeons feed on growing and ripening peas in early summer. The choice of feeding field may depend on a host of chance factors; for example, proximity to the breeding woods, amount of disturbance, previous habits. One grower may suffer extensive and costly damage, while averaged over the area damage may be too slight to justify expensive remedial action involving wide-scale killing.

With decreasing food density a point is reached when the feeding rate of subordinate birds falls below the optimum (point B in Fig. 2). Birds experiencing such conditions may move from one flock to another so that by this means flock size becomes adjusted to and related to food stocks, and, furthermore, the amount of crop damage is now related to population size and density. Eventually the individuals which are forced from flock to flock die of starvation and such birds, apart from being grossly underweight, have enlarged adrenal glands and a general stress syndrome. Sometimes birds forced out of those flocks occupying the better feeding grounds accumulate on fields where feeding conditions are poor, and such flocks may experience most of the mortality occurring in the district. Because of the above mechanism, which effectively ensures early intraspecific competition, the proportion of starving birds to be found at any one time is very low, precisely because the process is dynamic and adjustment is continuous. When the feeding rate for all the flock members reaches point C in Fig. 2 the feeding ground is no longer adequate. On clover-leys and pastures this point occurs at clover densities around and below 50 leaves per sq. ft. Although much food still appears to be available this is not the case because an adequate collection rate cannot be maintained. On grain stubbles point C occurs at lower grain densities for wood pigeons than it does for finches because the wood pigeon is better adapted to this feeding niche. This is the meaning of the interspecific competition envisaged by Darwin.

It is sometimes possible for birds forced out of a feeding flock to chance upon new and previously unexploited food sources, as, for example, when pigeons move on to the first spring grain sowings. There are many parallel situations in which birds forced to leave a flock, or unable to maintain a territory in a fully inhabited area, may cause damage. A good example is provided by ravens and crows in parts of highland Britain. Dominant birds hold territories in preferred hill districts, while those individuals (often the younger animals) unable to obtain such a territory form non-breeding flocks outside the optimal habitats. In the marginal habitats these birds may concentrate on other food sources and in some cases form the bulk of birds that congregate round lambing flocks of sheep. Clearly, in such circumstances, the prevention of attacks on newborn lambs by corvids is not best achieved by the indiscriminate and wasteful slaughter of all individuals, irrespective of whether or not they hold territories. It is because interactions of this kind are so legion in nature that it is always safest, in the absence of detailed knowledge, to concentrate remedial action only at the actual place where damage occurs.

This paper may appear, therefore, in many ways to depict a negative approach to "bird-pest control", but knowing what not to do can save a lot of unnecessary expenditure of time and money. This is especially true in a subject where numerous and often conflicting interests, for example shooting for food or sport, wild-life conservation and bird protection, crop protection, anti-cruelty concern, must all be reconciled and where it is frequently the case that a bird can be designated a pest in only the most parochial terms. When for many desirable reasons the most effective agents for population control are denied usage it behoves us to recognize and define the limitations of the remainder.

Summary

1. Most predators, including man, which prey on birds can be shown to take a doomed surplus of their prey without affecting the total changes in numbers occurring between years or even between seasons; hence, such predators cannot be considered as regulatory agents of the population. In effect this means that most game birds are under-exploited while conversely the cropping level of pest birds is insufficient to reduce numbers below the level of natural fluctuations.

2. The feeding rate of the wood-pigeon varies with changes in the density of its food; grain on stubbles and sowings or clover on pastures and leys being considered. The feeding curve represents a simple predator-prey response and increases to a point at which further increases in food density are not accompanied by changes in the feeding rate.

3. Wood-pigeons feed in flocks within which there is a social hierarchy and this causes subordinate birds to move to the flock edge and to have lower food intake rates. The shape of the functional response curve and the flock habit means that a subordinate bird will encounter food shortage before the food supply considered in isolation is limiting. A mechanism exists, therefore, which enables flock size to be related to food density only within a restricted range and which accounts for the observation that only small numbers of starving birds can be found at any one time.

REFERENCES

Gause, G. F. (1934). "The Struggle for Existence." Baltimore.

Holling, C. S. (1965). The functional response of predators to prey density and its role in mimicry and population regulation. *Mem. ent. Soc. Can.* **45**, 1–60.

Jenkins, D. (1962). Research into grouse management. *Shooting Times*, August 1962, 874–875.

Jenkins, D., Watson, A. and Miller, G. R. (1963). Population studies on red grouse, *Lagopus lagopus scoticus* (Lath.) in north-east Scotland. *J. anim. Ecol.* **32**, 317–376.

Jenkins, D., Watson, A. and Miller, G. R. (1964). Predation and red grouse populations. *J. appl. Ecol.* **1**, 183–195.

Moore, N. W. (1957). The past and present status of the buzzard in the British Isles. *Br. Birds* **50**, 173–197.

Morris, R. F. (1963). The dynamics of epidemic spruce budworm populations. *Mem. ent. Soc. Can.* **31**, 1–333.

Murton, R. K. (1966). A statistical evaluation of the effect of wood-pigeon shooting as evidenced by the recoveries of ringed birds. *The Statistician* **16**, 183–202.

Murton, R. K. and Isaacson, A. J. (1964). Productivity and egg predation in the woodpigeon. *Ardea* **52**, 30–47.

Murton, R. K. and Clark, S. P. (1968). Breeding biology of the rock dove at Flamborough, Yorkshire. *Br. Birds.* (In press.)

Murton, R. K., Isaacson, A. J. and Westwood, N. J. (1963). The feeding ecology of the woodpigeon. *Brit. Birds* **56**, 345–375.

Murton, R. K., Westwood, N. J. and Isaacson, A. J. (1964). A preliminary investigation of the factors regulating population size in the wood-pigeon. *Ibis* **106**, 482–507.

Murton, R. K., Isaacson, A. J. and Westwood, N. J. (1966). The relationships between wood-pigeons and their clover food supply and the mechanism of population control. *J. appl. Ecol.* **3**, 55–96.

Parslow, J. L. F. (1967). Changes in status among breeding birds in Britain and Ireland. *Br. Birds* **60**, 2–47.

Prestt, I. (1965). An enquiry into the recent breeding status of some of the smaller birds of prey and crows in Britain. *Bird Study* **12**, 196–221.

Siivonen, L. (1957). The problems of the short-term fluctuations in numbers of tetraonids in Europe. *Pap. Game Res.* (*Finnish Game Foundation*), *Riistat. Julk* **19**, 1–44.

Snow, D. W. and Mayer-Gross, H. (1967). Farmland as a nesting habitat. *Bird Study* **14**, 43–52.

Stevenson, H. (1866). "The Birds of Norfolk," Vol. 1. J. van Voorst, London.

Ticehurst, C. B. (1932). "A history of the birds of Suffolk." Gurney & Jackson, London.

Tinbergen, L. (1960). The natural control of insects in pinewoods. I. Factors influencing the intensity of predation by songbirds. *Arch. neerl. Zool.* **13**, 265–343.

Tinbergen, L. and Klomp, H. (1960). The natural control of insects in pinewoods. II. Conditions for damping of Nicholson oscillations in parasite-host systems. *Arch. neerl. Zool.* **13**, 344–379.

Discussion

CAMPBELL: Table V (Dunnet and Patterson) shows that the number of young rooks shot in 1966 and 1967 agrees fairly closely with your own "production per countable nest" figures given in Table III. But the figure for young shot in 1963 suggests a very much higher production, as much as four young per nest, assuming that all the young were shot, which is, of course, most unlikely.

DUNNET: We do not believe the keeper's figures.

LOCKIE: Administratively it is convenient to have National schemes of control and destruction but biologically there is not always much justification for them since the habits and behaviour of many animals vary from place to place. The rook is a case in point. Dr. Dunnet gave good evidence that rooks were most short of food in July and not at all in winter. I found in a dry year in Oxfordshire that rooks were short of food in July when they broke down standing grain to eat the green seed. Winter was also a time of scarcity— birds were found dead emaciated and food-fighting was at its most intense. I have two questions: what do rooks eat in N.E. Scotland in winter particularly when the ground is frozen? What is the position in Aberdeenshire with regard to the social hierarchy and food-fighting of rooks?

DUNNET: In the coastal regions of the north-east of Scotland, winters are not as severe from the weather point of view as one might think. When ground is not frozen, which is normally the great majority of the time, earthworms and leatherjackets are abundant and readily obtained from the surface layers of the soil. Even under frozen conditions there is normally an abundance of spilt grain on the stubble fields. In the years for which we have measurements, the density of this grain and the number of stubble fields remain adequate right through until the early spring when cultivation begins again. Also, in winter, rooks spend a considerable amount of time in the rookeries, and cannot readily be caught in baited traps except during severe snowstorms. By contrast, in summer rooks are thinly dispersed over the ground, there is no feeding situation other than grassland available, and in grassland the number of leatherjackets is drastically reduced owing to their emergence, and earthworms have gone deeper into the soil and are not available. Rooks are low in body weight, are readily caught in baited traps during summer, and spend no time in the rookeries. A great deal of their time is spent in searching for food, and at this season the rooks are moulting. All these observations suggest to us that summer is a much more critical period for the rook in north-east Scotland than is winter.

PATTERSON: I have measured the rate of fighting over food in rook flocks over the last two years and find that this rate in almost all situations is very low and reduced each bird's food intake by less than one per cent. In addition, rooks in our area in winter seem to spend less than half of their time in feeding, so it is difficult to see how food-fighting could produce a significant mortality. It must be emphasized, however, that there has been no severe winter weather during the period of study.

BOURNE: In the late 1940's I carried out a breeding census of several hundred square miles of the country around the South Downs behind Brighton in Sussex. The centre of this area was then a waste, after years of neglect followed by use as a battle training area during the war, and covered with young scrub and long grass. While there were large rookeries around the periphery, there were very few rooks' nests in the centre, though large flocks, apparently largely young birds, fed there later in the summer. Within the next few years the whole area was ploughed up and put under grass and arable farming, and many rookeries of hundreds of nests were founded within a year or two, transforming the whole picture. The rooks were clearly extremely sensitive to land usage. The presence of birds in the derelict land in summer, when the Aberdeenshire ones met a food shortage and fed on grassland, also suggests that the birds must spread out into marginal land of this type where there is a low breeding density. In particular, in Scotland during summer one might expect that they would take to marginal hill grazings unsuited to them in winter and spring, which might explain the summer fall in numbers?

DUNNET: This is an interesting example of the relationship between rook numbers and agriculture, and it is useful to have these details. We have made enquiries about the occurrence of rooks in upland situations in summer and several observers have reported the presence of feeding flocks in mid-summer on heather moors in north, and north-east Scotland, and in the Pennines.

DR. MELLANBY emphasized the difficulties and drawbacks of measuring the soil fauna including earthworms using soil-core samples and asked what steps were taken to overcome these problems and to what extent they mattered for the present purposes.

DUNNET: I take Dr. Mellanby's points. Our measurements of abundance of worms were made from soil cores three inches deep which is probably as deep as rooks normally probe. It will be difficult to relate any such measure of food abundance to its actual availability to rooks, since availability will also be affected by the behaviour of both the worms and the rooks. For example, aestivating worms, which are quite inactive, occur within these cores, and may be inaccessible to rooks and so would further reduce availability in summer. On the other hand, large *Lumbricus terrestris*, by their mobility, may be vulnerable to rooks but not to our sampling technique, and this presumably large proportion of the earthworm biomass may need to be studied.

DR. MELLANBY asked about the effects of destroying wood-pigeon nests because judging from the population dynamics of the species June would seem the best time of year to attempt population control, that is, after natural mortality factors had already taken their toll.

MURTON: Reducing the population in June, even if feasible, would have no value if breeding productivity between July and September countered these reductions and it was the damage liable to occur in, say, December that we wished to reduce. For all practical purposes it is not realistic to expect sufficient control effort to be applied in June to have a lasting effect and as most wood-pigeon damage occurs before this time or after the following breeding season it could not be mitigated by this approach. If lasting population reductions could be achieved in June that would be a different matter. Nest destruction was instituted to reduce the number of juveniles surviving to cause brassica damage with the first snow falls of December and January. The technique depended on fairly widescale co-operative effort and this was not forthcoming—if one farmer participated but his neighbour did not, this nullified his own efforts. The method has, therefore, passed out of favour. I should add that the reproductive rate of animals within the range of values normally experienced does not control total population size. Of course if no progeny are produced populations must decay but the point is that a very high reduction in fecundity must be achieved to be effective. In general, such a high degree of efficiency does not appear to lie within the realms of practical possibility using existing legal procedures.

KEAR: I have been asked to say a few words about a group of birds not sufficiently pestiferous to warrant a formal paper at this symposium. Since 1961 the Wildfowl Trust has been carrying out investigations into the impact of waterfowl on agriculture; in particular, we have tried to establish the food of geese, swans and duck through the winter and to assess the effect they have on any crops they take (Kear, 1963a). Special studies have been made of such aspects as the fertilizing value of the manure geese and swans leave behind on land they graze (Kear, 1963c), and variations in traditional feeding patterns with changes in agricultural practice (Kear, 1963b, Kear 1965a). As a large part of the British wintering flocks breeds in Iceland, the interaction of the greylag goose *Anser anser* with Icelandic agriculture has been examined also (Kear, 1967).

We find that the bulk of autumn and early winter food taken by wild geese, mainly greylags and pink-footed geese *A. brachyrhynchus*, is harvest waste from stubbles and old potato fields. Here their activities are of benefit in keeping down weeds and in preventing the carry-over of diseases such as mildew and eelworm. For instance, *Agropyron* (couch grass) runners, *Equisetum* roots, and numerous weed seeds occur in their stomachs, as well as the unharvested grain and potatoes which are a nuisance in the following crop. There is no evidence that the grass the birds take during autumn and winter is damaged by their attentions; in a rigorous climate much of what the geese remove from pastures would be frosted and lost anyway. Indeed, nutrient chemicals return to the soil faster from the goose droppings than from the more slowly decaying grass that dies naturally. Experiments in Scotland have shown no loss in silage yield when grass was clipped in February and March (Kear and Rodger, 1964). Three years grazing trials in England using captive geese similarly showed no reduction in harvest yields after autumn grazing of young grass (Kear, 1965b) and after winter and spring grazing of cereals—even when crops were grazed on wet and frosty days and at very high pressures (Kear, 1965c, and unpublished). A single season's work in Scotland is still producing harvesting results. It looks as if there is a slight, but very slight, reduction in winter-wheat grain yields and no difference in spring barley yields at a pressure of 11 000 goose hours per acre, which is about 2 000 goose-hours per acre more than the field ever actually suffers.

There is evidence that damage or loss is caused in the following cases: (a) by the removal of "spring bite" grass needed for stock, particularly ewes and lambs, in March, April and sometimes May; (b) possibly to winter- and spring-sown cereals in Scotland if grazed in late April or May, this is the possibility at present under investigation; (c) very rarely to germinating beans in May; (d) to any water-logged field of young grass or winter-wheat if the geese remain for long periods, that is, if they roost on it and pack the soil badly—mere grazing does no harm; (e) at any time of winter to turnips in a few restricted parts of west Scotland (Kear, 1962).

We know that effective ways of removing damaging geese from fields exist if farmers are allowed to combine shooting (under Section 4, subsection 2(a) of the 1954 Act) with non-lethal scaring methods. A report, setting out ways in which farmers can protect their crops, has been published (Kear, 1963d). We have since then contacted a manufacturer and are encouraging the development of a scaring device which, from experience over a number of years, we think may be particularly frightening and efficient at removing birds. It produces not only a shot and alarm calls but a visual simulation of a dying bird. A feathery object is projected up at irregular intervals and falls in a direction determined by the wind. It is then slowly drawn back to the firing mechanism in such a manner that it appears to struggle.

To summarize, geese usually arrive in Britain too late to damage un-harvested crops, and at first confine their attention to harvested fields where they do more good than harm. During the mid-winter period they tend to concentrate on grass or winter-wheat and there is no evidence that they do much harm at this time. Before the birds leave in April and May they may graze young cereals, but apparently again with little effect on yield. However, in the spring, when they with other wild animals are often eating grass in direct competition with hungry stock, their depredations are unwelcome. If it seems necessary to remove the flocks from spring grass, a very wet winter-wheat field or from turnips, scaring methods are available.

In Iceland the picture is different. Many geese breed away from areas of agricultural importance but one species, the greylag, is present on farmland at a time when crops are growing, and damage is certainly apparent. Here methods of cultivation, such as the siting and fencing of crops, as well as efficient scaring, would ease the problem considerably.

THORPE: Dr. Kear has just described a fearsome device that she is developing to scare wild geese from farmland. She has pointed out that the greylag goose can only really be regarded as a pest when it competes with farm stock by grazing the "spring bite", so important to the farmer for his milking ewes. If this device is to be used in such a situation, are we not in danger of defeating our own ends, by scaring the wits out of the sheep? It seems likely that the solution to the problem presented by the greylag as a competitor for spring grass lies in preventing the build-up of the very large concentrations of these birds, but this in turn is bound up with the problem, as yet unresolved, of the detailed distribution of this goose in the late winter.

KEAR: The usual system of preparing a field to provide "spring bite" is to top-dress it with fertilizer early in the year and then to rest it from stock for at least two weeks until plant growth is adequate. Top-dressing in itself usually discourages geese for a while; I am suggesting that a farmer uses this device for some five days before he wants to graze a damage-prone field, then leaves only the imitation dead goose (suitably protected from the sheep). If the device is effective at all, the geese will associate the body with the alarming sounds and "death struggles" witnessed earlier and avoid the field; experience indicates that this is likely.

A really efficient scaring device, to which birds will not habituate quickly, may be useful also in breaking up potentially damaging concentrations of geese earlier in the autumn. With our advice the Department of Agriculture for Scotland is running field trials this winter using various bird scarers. The pattern of goose distribution in relation to food supply throughout the season continues to be investigated.

DR. HAMBURY delivered a short communication on the subject of oyster-catchers, emphasizing that the slaughter of these birds in the Burry Inlet was not consistent with the conservation aims of an adjacent nature reserve. He claimed that any control campaign would be likely to disturb the reserve. Furthermore, the detrimental effects of the oystercatcher on the cockle fishery must be set against the aesthetic needs of people who enjoy watching wild-life. He made the valid point, applicable to wild-life conservation in general, that a monetary estimate could not be placed on the value of wild-life but that this inability should not negate its importance. In an age when human stress syndromes are becoming more and more widespread who could deny the benefits to society of the means to relax in an undisturbed environment. He made the further point that there had been no control operations against the oystercatcher in the Burry Inlet district for fourteen years yet there was now a cockle glut.

A heated discussion followed, many speakers making the point that the slaughter of oystercatchers could not be reconciled with our present understanding of bird population dynamics nor with our present enlightened attitudes towards wild-life conservation. The chairman suggested that the research workers concerned refrain from dealing with individual comments as they arose but rather answer all at the end of the discussion and in the main this was done.

THOMPSON: In the absence of Dr. H. A. Cole, Director of Fisheries Research, I should like to make the point that, leaving the question of the control of oystercatchers on one side, the work on oystercatchers and cockles carried out over the past ten years or so is among the most thorough population studies published in Britain. I also have a question.

Mr. Davidson has shown that oystercatchers in the Burry Inlet are highly dependent on cockles; since the cockle stock is expected to dwindle, what does he think the birds will feed on in future? He has also indicated that the cockles in Morecambe Bay have been virtually eliminated by oystercatcher predation. I should like to know what the oystercatchers are feeding on in Morecambe Bay.

DAVIDSON: A decline from the present stock level of cockles would in the first instance have no effect on the numbers of birds as the food does not under normal circumstances appear to be a limiting factor. Below a certain minimum stock, however, shortages of cockles would depress the bird population numbers (see below). The oystercatchers now remaining in Morecambe Bay are predominantly those which fed on mussels. There is no indication of any decline in their numbers. The big drop involved the birds feeding on the cockle beds.

DARE: The origins and subsequent fate of the immense numbers wintering on the Morecambe Bay cockle beds in the 1950s are, unfortunately, not known. (Virtually no ringing was done at that time.) There is no evidence of a massive mortality, nor of sudden large influxes into other British wintering haunts. It seems likely, therefore, that most of the Morecambe Bay cockle eaters were displaced to major wintering grounds on the Continent, possibly to the Dutch Waddenzee (350 miles E.S.E.) or to western France (350–600 miles south of this bay).

GIBBS: Mr. Davidson has told us that many of the oystercatchers wintering in Britain breed in the Faroes and other parts of Northern Europe. I should like to put what I consider to be the Faroese point of view. The "tjaldur" is the Faroese national bird, and gives its name, for example, to the islands' own liner, plying between Torshavn and Denmark. The species breeds commonly all over the Faroes, at a density greater than that found almost anywhere in Britain (Dare, personal communication), and is very much a part of the Faroese scene. It is certainly not a pest in the Faroes, and indeed may be beneficial since it feeds largely on invertebrates in hayfields and sheep pasture. No Faroe man would dream of harming an oystercatcher; perhaps we ought to think twice before starting to kill their breeding birds.

[Dr. Gibb's contribution caused considerable amusement as it was purposely delivered in light-hearted and facetious tones and he concluded with the suggestion that if the British Government persisted in its plans to persecute Faroese oystercatchers, then the Faroese Government would retaliate by sinking a British trawler.]

CONDER: Can Mr. Davidson reconcile the Ministry of Agriculture's withdrawal of a subsidy on cartridges to shoot wood-pigeons on the grounds that this winter shooting was ineffective in controlling wood-pigeons, Mr. Wright's statement in the first paragraph of his paper "Simply killing large numbers of birds in any healthy population is unlikely to achieve more than a temporary reduction in numbers", with his own statement "it is shown that, if the fishery is to maintain a steady high level of production, control of the oyster-catcher is necessary"?

GREENWOOD: Mr. Davidson's work, while showing that oystercatchers eat many second-year cockles in the Burry Inlet, does not show that more cockles would be available for the fishermen if the oystercatchers were not present and he is careful to stress that the control measures he advocates are experi-mental—for "a trial period". It would be less destructive and less likely to do lasting damage to the ecology of the area to perform exclusion experiments. Unfenced areas, areas from which fishermen are excluded, areas from which fishermen and oystercatchers are excluded, and areas from which fishermen, oystercatchers and fishes are excluded should be compared.

DAVIDSON: If Mr. Greenwood consults the paper by D. A. Hancock and A. E. Urquhart (1965), he will find that such experiments have already been performed.

GREENWOOD: If these experiments were conclusive, there would be no need for experimental control measures, the results of the "experiment" being known beforehand. If not conclusive, they should be repeated.

OLNEY: What number of oystercatchers would need to be removed from the Burry Inlet to have an effect?

DAVIDSON: I emphasize that we only visualize undertaking an experiment at this stage but estimate that we would need to remove a significant number, say 5 000 or 50% of the average winter population.

MURTON: I have three points. First, although you claim that oystercatcher numbers do not appear to be related to cockle stocks your figures suggest that the proportional change between the maximum November or December population and February numbers is positively correlated with overall cockle stocks. In other words, in those years when there is a big percentage drop in oystercatcher numbers (this may involve emigration more than direct mortality) cockle stocks are low and vice versa. Second, both birds and men are competing for the second-year cockles but the recruitment rate of cockles into the third year age category may not be greatly altered by either form of predation. The important question is not what proportion of second-year cockle stocks are depleted by oystercatchers, but whether or not the fishermen suffer by being in direct competition with the birds during the winter. Birds or no birds the fishermen will have fewer cockles to fish at the end of the winter than at the beginning. Third, from a purely economic point of view the best form of cockle exploitation would involve taking as big a cull as possible at the beginning of the winter, before oystercatchers, or other mortality factors, take their toll. Although this implies the use of seasonal labour and mechanization I cannot believe the difficulties to be insurmount-able because the frozen pea industry faces the same fundamental problem.

BOURNE: The proposal to start killing oystercatchers in the Burry Inlet surely presents conservation interests with an example of the type of case in which they must make a stand. Most of us do not like to see any birds killed, though occasionally when they start killing other birds even the most ardent conserver is placed in an awkward predicament. When widely dispersed species such as rooks or gulls or even bullfinches become a nuisance, most of us would regretfully agree that there was a case for thinning them out. Eventually we come to the point where we must stick; where there is a threat to the last remnants of an important population or habitat so that it becomes necessary to try to ensure that it is not eliminated entirely; or where local action becomes a threat to local concentrations of widely dispersed species so that its influence will be felt over a much larger area, as when bird populations from a wide area gather to breed or moult or winter at a limited number of special resorts. This seems an example of the latter case; in order to suit the convenience of an extremely small local industry in South Wales oystercatchers from a vast area extending north to Iceland and Scandinavia are to be sacrificed. Even if adult oystercatchers are faithful to established winter quarters, it seems likely that any noticeable reduction in the local flocks will soon be filled by wandering young birds, until the slaughter involves half the increase of western Europe. The birds do not even seem to be adversely affecting the productivity of cockles; they are merely harvesting them rather more efficiently than the fishermen, and it is not entirely clear that the fishermen would do much better if the birds were removed. Scientists are going mad if they think that such a debatable collection of arguments will be accepted as a basis for a noticeable reduction in the number of oystercatchers on a continental scale.

DAVIDSON: In the light of recent studies of other species of birds, especially pests like the wood-pigeon (Murton, 1965) and the African quelea (Ward, 1964), serious doubts have been expressed as to the feasibility of controlling any avian pest by methods involving slaughter. Indeed, in the case of the wood-pigeon, the Ministry subsidy on cartridges for shooting has been withdrawn. Further explanation of the intention to proceed on an experimental basis with the control of oystercatchers is therefore necessary.

The basic factors which negate any economic control project with such species as the wood-pigeon, stem from the inherent over-production of any thriving, stable animal population. A surplus of young individuals is produced which must be lost, either by emigration or death, in order to avoid a population explosion. This is effected by the population being, at some stage in its annual cycle, limited by its food supply, a recurring seasonal shortage which implements the natural control mechanisms.

This situation does not appear to apply to the oystercatchers wintering in the Burry Inlet. There the population is typically composed of approximately 70% of adult birds, 25% second- and third-winter immatures, and only 5% of first-winter birds. This suggests that there is no colossal over-production and that killing would affect mainly adult birds, unlike wood-pigeons and bullfinches, where it is mainly the inexperienced first-winter birds which are shot or trapped. In such classic studies as those of the Northern bobwhite (*Colinus virginianus*) in North America (Errington, 1945) culling of the adults has been shown to result in a reduction in the pressure from predators and food supply on the survivors with a resultant increase in the breeding success. There is no connection between the wintering flocks of oystercatchers and any particular area of their breeding range. Culling of the winter population in the Burry Inlet would involve birds drawn from all parts of the breeding areas, where they would comprise only some 2–3% of the resident summer population. Removal of such a small percentage of birds from a breeding population is unlikely to have any marked effect on its reproductive success and hence on the recruitment to the ranks of the adults.

Nothing is known of the manner of recruitment of young oystercatchers to the wintering flocks, but this may be influenced by competition with the adults. Many British oystercatchers appear to spend their first winter on the continent (Dare, 1968), but this does not appear to be true of the young Faroese and Icelandic birds, which more than replace those British first-winter birds which have emigrated. Recruitment is one aspect of the study which will be given special attention following any experimental removal of birds.

Unlike the agricultural pests studied in detail, the oystercatcher is a carnivore and inherent differences may be expected in the relationship of the bird to its food supply. Typically with herbivores, the food present at the end of the summer has to suffice the population throughout the winter (with a very limited addition in the case of the wood-pigeon, resulting from winter growth of clover). Frequently the food supply is insufficient to maintain the total postbreeding population of birds, and their numbers decline in order to accord with the food supply. With the oystercatcher this situation does not normally appear to arise. Except during the very unusual winter of 1963–64 when the stocks of "available" cockles in the Burry Inlet were at a very low ebb, the average number of birds for the six winter months has been steady from year to year ($\pm 10\%$) whereas the cockle stocks have fluctuated enormously.

As explained earlier, the oystercatcher prefers cockles of about 18–20 mm, that is chiefly those in their second winter. These form the main bulk of what may be termed the "available" food supply. Cockles smaller than this are taken by the birds but their meat content is so low that the birds cannot entirely satisfy their food requirements by eating them. Cockles larger than the 18–20 mm group are also taken by the birds, but the effort required to open them is such that feeding on them on the exposed beds is uneconomic. These small and large cockles may, together, be termed "non-available" food as regards the main bulk of the birds' diet.

In the absence of available food supplies many birds will leave the area, as happened in the winter of 1963–64 when stocks of all age groups of cockles, other than spat, were very low. Again, in the current year (1967–68) the younger age groups (1–4 yrs) are scarce and the dominant year-class of cockles is now in its fifth winter. These are non-available to the birds and, at the time of writing (November 1967) the numbers of oystercatchers in the Burry Inlet are declining rapidly after reaching their normal early autumn level in September. In the remaining years since 1961 the available stocks of cockles have ranged from 1 000 million to 3 200 million, whereas the average bird numbers have ranged only between 7 900 and 9 400, or about a 7–8% variation from the mean.

It has been suggested that the annual fall in bird numbers from the November–December peak to the March level represents mortality due to food shortage. Certainly over this period the condition of the cockles becomes poorer and the meat content may fall by up to 50%. However, even in the coldest weather in January or February, when also the condition of the cockles is at its poorest, the birds do not spend all the available time feeding, as would be expected if the food supply were becoming critical.

That the birds' numbers in the Burry Inlet are not closely linked to the food supply is also suggested by the situation which existed in 1965. Bird numbers fell off rapidly in January and February from 10 500 to 4 500 in early March. There was a very limited recruitment to the cockle stocks available to the birds in the summer of 1965, due to the poor settlement of 1964, and after fishing and natural mortality, the available stocks in the autumn of 1965 were very much lower than those of the earlier part of the year (Table II). Even so, the average number of birds in the Inlet for the six winter months 1965–66 was 9 380, the highest recorded during the six study years, and the December peak of nearly 16 000 was also the highest recorded. This would not have been expected had food shortage been a major cause of the decline in numbers in the previous January and February.

A more likely explanation for the late winter fall in numbers, and one which is supported by the pattern of ring recoveries and colour-band sightings is in terms of an early movement of adults back to the breeding grounds, as it is known that some birds appear on their breeding territories before the end of January. Dead birds are very seldom found in the Burry Inlet which is very well patrolled by bird-watchers and wild-fowlers and where any unusual mortality is soon seen, as evidenced by the very rapid reports received by the Ministry when birds have been shot by irresponsible gunners and left lying out on the sands.

To summarize, there does not seem to be any noticeable natural mortality of oystercatchers taking place on the wintering grounds due to food shortage. The population consists mainly of adult birds. Of possible factors regulating the level of the wintering population, food is not thought to be a major one. A density-dependent spacing or traditional wintering behaviour pattern established in the adult birds appears to be more likely. The mechanism of recruitment of young birds to the wintering flocks is not known, but may be controlled by competition with the adults. It is therefore concluded that any control by man would be additional to natural mortality and not an alternative to it, as in the other species studied. If the conclusions from colour-banding studies are correct, and the Burry Inlet population is discrete and not subject to rapid influxes from birds in the surrounding areas, control should be beneficial both in the short term and in the longer term from winter to winter. Only a trial period of control can answer the outstanding questions and give an opportunity to study the vital aspect of factors affecting subsequent recruitment of birds to the area.

REFERENCES

Dare, P. J. (1968). The movements of oystercatchers (*Haematopus ostralegus* L.) visiting or breeding in the British Isles. *Fishery Invest., Lond.* Ser. 2, **25**(9). (In press.)

Errington, P. L. (1945). Some contributions of a fifteen year study of the Northern bobwhite to a knowledge of population phenomena. *Ecol. Monogr.* **15**, 1–34.

Kear, J. (1962). Feeding habits of the Greylag Goose *Anser anser* on the island of Bute. *Scott. Birds* **2**, 233–239.

Kear, J. (1963a). Wildfowl and agriculture. *Nature Conserv. Mon.* **3**, 315–328.

Kear, J. (1963b). The history of potato-eating by wildfowl in Britain. *Wildfowl Tr. Ann. Rep.* **14**, 54–65.

Kear, J. (1963c). The agricultural importance of wild goose droppings. *Wildfowl Tr. Ann. Rep.* **14**, 72–77.

Kear, J. (1963d). The protection of crops from damage by wildfowl. *Wildfowl Tr. Ann. Rep.* **14**, 66–71.

Kear, J. (1965a). Recent changes in Scottish barley acreages and the possible effect on wild geese. *Scott. Birds* **3**, 288–292.

Kear, J. (1965b). The assessment by grazing trial of goose damage to grass. *Wildfowl Tr. Ann. Rep.* **16**, 46–47.

Kear, J. (1965c). The assessment of goose damage to cereals by grazing trials. *Intern. Union Game Biol. Congr. Trans.* **6**, 333–339.

Kear, J. (1967). Feeding habits of the Greylag Goose *Anser anser* in Iceland, with reference to its interaction with agriculture. *Intern. Union Game Biol. Congr. Trans.* **7**, 615–622.

Kear, J. and Rodger, J. B. A. (1964). Wild geese in east Scotland. *Scott. Agric.* **43**, 123–126.

Hancock, D. A. and Urquhart, A. E. (1965). The determination of natural mortality and its causes in an exploited population of cockles (*Cardium edule* L.) *Fishery Invest., Lond.* Ser. 2, **23**(2).

Murton, R. K. (1965). Natural and artificial population control in the woodpigeon. *Ann. appl. Biol.* **55**, 177–192.

Ward, P. (1964). The war against the Quelea bird. *New Scient.* **22**, 736–738.

Urban Bird Problems

R. J. P. THEARLE

Ministry of Agriculture, Fisheries and Food,
Infestation Control Laboratory, Worplesdon, Surrey, England

Many bird species have become closely associated with man and his activities, and, to some extent, dependent on him. In its simplest form this association may merely consist of using man-made structures for perching, roosting or even nesting. At the other extreme his crops may be utilized as food. Two species, the house sparrow *Passer domesticus* and feral pigeon *Columba livia* var., can properly be termed commensals being largely dependent on the food provided accidentally or deliberately by man. Indeed, both these birds probably evolved in close association with man, spreading to northern Europe in the wake of Neolithic husbandmen. These two species are, not surprisingly, responsible for most of the bird problems in built-up areas but, possibly because of the warmth and protection from predators provided by large cities, an increasing number of other species find them attractive as dormitories. In addition, a host of lesser problems may be mentioned, ranging from the fouling of reservoirs by roosting gulls to the emotional impact of a mother duck and young crossing Hammersmith Broadway, but space prohibits their consideration.

Potts (1967), in a recent survey of urban starling *Sturnus vulgaris* roosts in Britain, states that the number of built-up areas with roosts on masonry increased from none in 1896 to fifteen in 1965. The total number of urban roosts has built up steadily since 1845, the birds progressing from using trees to resting on structures such as industrial plant and bridges and finally to roosting on buildings. But although the number of urban roosts is increasing, the numbers of starlings using the well-established ones remains constant and, as yet, only about 5% of the British starling population roosts in urban areas, the contribution from immigrant Continental starlings being negligible. Every morning there is an exodus to suburban and rural feeding grounds, the birds returning at dusk (Cramp *et al.*, 1964; Spencer, 1966). The main damage caused by these birds is fouling and defacing the buildings on which they roost, while nearby pavements can be fouled to the extent that they become dangerous. Large quantities of starling droppings are extremely unpleasant and cleaning the affected areas is expensive.

Many feral pigeons, on the other hand, spend all their lives in close proximity to man in a completely urban environment, roosting and nesting on the ledges of buildings and other man-made structures, and feeding in town streets and squares (Goodwin, 1954, 1960; Gompertz, 1957; Murton and Westwood, 1966). Apart from fouling buildings and streets, feral pigeons cause additional problems by regularly invading and roosting inside buildings. Food stored in warehouses or food processing plants may be eaten or contaminated, and machinery fouled. Dock areas provide particularly good quarters because grain spillage during loading and unloading provides a source of food. In these and other places where much food is stored, the feral pigeon can become a serious problem by transferring its attention from the spilled food to that actually in store.

By virtue of its smaller size, the house sparrow rarely creates problems due to fouling, but infestations in premises such as bakeries and food factories can be serious. Sparrows will sometimes peck holes in bags used for food storage thus creating spillage, and the losses caused in this way can be large. Canteens can be particularly attractive especially when the birds are encouraged by the workers themselves. In fact, one of the biggest problems attached to the control of urban bird pests is the attitude of the general public.

All these species are potential transmitters of disease, either to man or his domestic animals, and local authorities are constantly alert to the possible risks; feral pigeons especially are often considered a reservoir for diseases transmissible to man. There are a number of reviews on the subject of diseases in wild birds (e.g. Keymer, 1958; McDiarmid, 1962) and many have been shown to carry certain diseases or to be capable of carrying them. There is, however, a distinct lack of evidence on the question of whether these diseases are actually transmitted to man or to his stock. Sometimes birds are accused of being mechanical carriers of disease. Thus, Wilson and Matheson (1952) made out a case, on circumstantial evidence, for the starling being responsible for spreading outbreaks of foot and mouth disease, while Murton (1964) produced a convincing argument that the outbreaks were not associated with bird movements. In the United States there is some evidence connecting starling droppings with cases of histoplasmosis, a pulmonary disease, and at least some outbreaks have been shown to have arisen in men working in areas contaminated with starling faeces (Furcolow *et al.*, 1961; Murdock *et al.*, 1962); soil samples taken from under starling roosts were found to contain spores of the causative fungus *Histoplasma capsulatum* (see Emmons, 1961). It has also been shown that pigeon excreta contains spores of *Cryptococcus neoformans* (see Emmons, 1960), a fungus which can cause the disease cryptococcosis (which is primarily a skin disease, although it can affect the lungs and central nervous system). But there is no direct evidence that man has contracted the disease from this source, although the fungus has been isolated from dried faeces in nests and from accumulations in buildings (Emmons, 1955). The chances of man contracting these diseases from bird sources is probably small, but nevertheless the risk remains.

The disease most often quoted as being transmissible from birds to man is ornithosis. Meyer (1959) quotes evidence of transmission from feral pigeons to man in fifteen countries, and Lepine and Sautter (1951) showed that two-thirds of the feral pigeons of Paris were infected with the disease. Hughes (1957) has shown it to be present in both feral and domestic pigeons in Liverpool. Once again, definite proof of transmission from wild birds to man is largely lacking, and the disease is not usually regarded as being particularly serious (unlike the more virulent strain found in psittacine birds). There are a few established cases of ornithosis in Britain among men who have regularly handled domestic pigeons (Ellenbogen and Miller, 1952; Grist, 1960). Ornithosis has also been found in the house sparrow (Keymer, 1958) and this species is capable of carrying Newcastle disease (fowl pest) and of transmitting it to poultry (Gustafson and Moses, 1953). As yet, the house sparrow has not been implicated in the transmission of any diseases to man. Wilson and MacDonald (1967) state that salmonellosis in wild birds is a potential hazard but, although the disease has been isolated from house sparrows, feral pigeons and starlings, its incidence is low. It would seem, therefore, that the case for birds being a public health problem in urban areas has not been proven, although the possibility still exists.

How can the problems created by the three species under discussion be alleviated? One can attempt to remove the birds from the places where they are causing damage; in other words, employ "control" methods to kill them. The traditional methods of control are shooting and trapping, but neither of these is ideal for dealing with birds in an urban environment. Trapping of starlings is not easy and cannot be applied at urban roosts; shooting at such sites is impracticable. Although the feral pigeon can be caught in cage traps, results are not obtained rapidly and the method is not really suitable for use against large numbers of birds. Shooting pigeons at night, using a 0·22 air rifle and with the aid of a torch, can only be effective at a limited number of places. Similarly, the trapping of house sparrows is difficult in urban areas and does not normally produce a large catch (there is a tendency for passers-by to release any birds they see in a trap). But an important technique which has been developed in recent years involves the use of stupefying substances. Under the Protection of Birds Act, 1954, it became legal to lay narcotic baits, under licence, to catch the birds listed in the Second Schedule to the Act, and considerable research was undertaken to devise a technique for controlling birds by this method. The technique evolved for use against feral pigeons has been described by Ridpath *et al.* (1961), and that for wood-pigeons by Murton *et al.* (1963). Work has also been done on the house sparrow (Thearle, unpublished). The method involves laying a suitable bait, coated with a stupefying drug, where and when the species concerned is likely to feed, if necessary after a period of prebaiting. A grain bait is normally used, although bread or cake crumbs can be effective for house sparrows. A stupefying drug is considered preferable to a quick-acting poison because any pro-tected species accidentally feeding on the bait may be revived and released, provided an overdose of the stupefying agent has not been taken. To be successful, it is necessary for the birds to feed close to where they nest or cause damage. Hence, the technique can be applied against the feral pigeon and house sparrow in urban areas, but it is not really suitable for use against the starling which feeds in small groups up to 20 miles from where it causes trouble.

During the developmental stages, it was thought that the two main objections to this method would be the risk to protected species, and the reaction of the general public who are normally averse to any form of killing birds and find the idea of poisoning them most objectionable. The risk to protected species proved to be negligible in urban areas (see below). Adverse public reaction was kept to a minimum, in the case of the feral pigeon, by carrying out treatments at dawn and, at first, by confining treatments to sites which had only limited public access, such as factories and dockyards. Some local authorities have made efforts to "educate" the public and have publicized reasons for reducing the numbers of birds; this has led to treatments at less restricted sites. With the house sparrow it has been possible to restrict baiting to private premises and to do much of it inside buildings, so that treatments have been kept out of the public arena and it has not proved desirable to confine them to the dawn period.

The stupefying substance used in controlling feral pigeons and house sparrows is α-chloralose, a condensation product of chloral hydrate with glucose, which has been described as a cerebrocortical hypnotic (Hariri, 1943). Licences allowing pest-control servicing companies and local authorities to use α-chloralose against feral pigeons were first issued in

1961 and, as reports of operations must be submitted to the Ministry of Agriculture, figures are available for all the licensed treatments carried out in England and Wales since then (Table I). In all, 507 treatments have produced a catch of over 39 000 feral pigeons. It will be seen that

TABLE I

The use of stupefying baits against feral pigeons

Numbers of birds caught by servicing companies and local authorities from the first issue of licences in 1961 to March 1967

(Figures in parentheses give percentages of the total catch)

No. of operations	No. of feral pigeons caught	No. of house sparrows caught	No. of protected species			No. of other species caught
			Caught	Died	Recovered	
			27 greenfinches	15	12	131 starlings
			7 mallard	2	5	31 jackdaws
			6 blackbirds	3	3	27 rooks
			5 collared doves	5	—	21 wood-pigeons
507	39 050	6 532	3 robins	1	2	10 "crows"
			1 song thrush	1	—	3 "gulls"
			1 goldfinch	1	—	
			1 linnet	1	—	
			1 "finch"	1	—	
Totals:	(14%)	52 (0·1%)	30 (0·07%)	22	223 (0·5%)	

the catch of birds belonging to protected species amounts to 0·1% of the total and, as 42% of these survived, the proportion of protected birds actually killed is about 0·07%; it is this figure that can be used as a measure of the risk to protected species. The list of protected birds taken is rather surprising; few people would consider the greenfinch (*Chloris chloris*) to be the protected species most at risk when baiting for feral pigeons. In fact, greenfinches were only caught at six operations; two of these were in a dock area containing some stretches of waste ground and the remainder at sites close to urban parks. The seven mallard (*Anas platyrhynchos*) were taken at a river-side site. House sparrows formed 14% of the total catch of birds.

Similarly, licences to catch house sparrows were first issued in 1963 and the figures for birds taken in operations since then at urban and industrial sites are shown in Table II. The demand for controlling house

TABLE II

The use of stupefying baits against house sparrows

Numbers of birds caught by servicing companies at urban and
industrial sites from the first issue of licences in 1963 to March 1967
(Figures in parentheses give percentages of the total catch)

No. of operations	No. of house sparrows caught	No. of protected species			No. of other species caught
		Caught	Died	Recovered	
		107 blackbirds	19	88	950 starlings
		77 robins	22	55	261 feral pigeons
		23 song thrushes	8	15	20 rooks
		9 dunnocks	5	4	1 magpie
1 002	50 189	8 blue tits	1	7	1 wood-pigeon
		7 pied wagtails	2	5	
		6 chaffinches	2	4	
		1 skylark	—	1	
		6 "doves"	—	6	
	Totals:	244 (0·5%)	59 (0·1%)	185	1 233 (2·4%)

sparrows has proved greater than that for the feral pigeon and over
1 000 operations have been carried out producing a catch of more than
50 000 house sparrows. Some 0·5% of the birds caught have been
protected species, but a recovery rate of 76% has reduced the actual
deaths of these to about 0·1%; a figure which is acceptable, particularly
as many of the protected birds were caught inside food premises.
Blackbirds (*Turdus merula*) and robins (*Erithacus rubecula*) were the
two protected species most at risk and of the "non-protected" birds,
starlings were most frequently caught.

For comparison, Table III and IV give details of the birds caught
when baiting for house sparrows in rural areas. Since November 1965,
servicing companies have been allowed to operate against house sparrows at non-agricultural rural sites and Table III shows the results of
twenty such operations. The number of protected birds killed in these
operations amounts to 1·8% of the total. Table IV gives the results for
twenty-two experimental trials carried out in and around farm buildings;
here again the proportion of protected birds killed is 1·8%. It is clear,
therefore, that the risk to protected species in urban areas is negligible
when compared with that at rural sites.

It is not possible to give an accurate assessment of the success of the operations against feral pigeons and house sparrows, but if an estimate is available of the number of birds present before each treatment, one can express the numbers caught as a percentage of those at risk. Such estimates are contained in the reports on operations, but these figures cannot be considered reliable, and any calculation based on them can only be regarded as a rough guide. Using these figures, the average success against feral pigeons is about 50% and against house sparrows 80%. In spite of the unreliability of these assessments they do at least show that operations against house sparrows have achieved greater success than those against feral pigeons. The figure for house sparrows compares with one of nearly 90% given by Cornwell (1966) in his account of the treatments carried out by one particular servicing company.

Such measurements of success are really meaningless unless one considers what it is hoped to achieve by these operations and has a clear idea of their limitations. The feral pigeon results suggest that their usefulness is somewhat limited. Any attempt to eliminate the vast numbers of feral pigeons living in many towns would probably be futile, and few operations have been carried out with the object of clearing large populations. One such attempt was made in a dock area of Glasgow in the summer of 1963. In 1 month some 7 000 feral pigeons

TABLE III

The use of stupefying baits against house sparrows

Numbers of birds caught by servicing companies at non-agricultural rural sites from extension of licences in November 1965 to March 1967 (Figures in parentheses give percentages of total catch)

No. of operations	No. of house sparrows caught	No. of protected species			No. of other species caught
		Caught	Died	Recovered	
20	1 317	25 blackbirds	13	12	111 starlings
		8 robins	4	4	7 feral pigeons
		6 dunnocks	4	2	5 jackdaws
		5 song thrushes	4	1	2 "crows"
		2 blue tits	—	2	
		2 pied wagtails	1	1	
		1 skylark	1	—	
	Totals:	49 (3·3%)	27 (1·8%)	22	125 (8·4%)

TABLE IV

The use of stupefying baits against house sparrows

Numbers of birds caught in experimental trials at farm sites 1966–67

(Figures in parentheses give percentages of total catch)

No. of operations	No. of house sparrows caught	No. of protected species			No. of other species caught
		Caught	Died	Recovered	
22	1 172	16 robins	7	9	14 starlings
		14 blackbirds	3	11	4 feral pigeons
		12 dunnocks	3	9	2 carrion crows
		9 collared doves	7	2	1 wood pigeon
		3 chaffinches	1	2	
		1 yellow hammer	1	—	
	Totals:	55 (4·4%)	22 (1·8%)	33	21 (1·7%)

were caught, but the effect on the total population was hardly noticeable while the cost was prohibitive (it involved closing some streets to traffic for $2\frac{1}{2}$ h and employed twenty road-sweepers, twenty policemen and forty sanitary inspectors). Against small numbers, stupefying baits can provide a useful tool and, where a discrete population of pigeons is infesting a particular site, good results can be obtained. Even under these circumstances any vacuum caused by the removal of pigeons from a site may be quickly filled by birds from elsewhere, and operations carried out in a particular area may have no apparent effect on the resident population. A population study of the feral pigeon has been in progress in the Salford docks since 1965; regular counts have shown that the population in the study area remains fairly constant at between 2 000 and 3 000 birds. In September, 1966, the count was approximately 2 500, and during the following two weeks two stupefying bait treatments in the study area caught 1 300 pigeons. But 2 weeks after these operations there was still the same total of pigeons in the area. On another occasion numbers increased by over 400 birds in 4 weeks, although more than 600 had been killed in the study area between successive counts. Such results agree with those obtained during some of the original trials reported by Ridpath *et al.* (1961), in which sites cleared of pigeons had bigger populations when visited a year later than they supported before operations began. That this does not always occur is shown by the fact that after a population of some 1 100 pigeons living on a granary in the Birkenhead docks had been almost cleared, the numbers living at the site the following year were still very low, in spite of large populations being present in the surrounding district. It would seem that there was not sufficient pressure from the nearby sites to fill the vacuum that had been created, presumably because food and roosting facilities were adequate at these other sites. In some areas, therefore, a clearance of birds can last for a year or more.

Against house sparrows the technique of using stupefying baits can be applied more successfully. It has been shown by Summers-Smith (1954, 1958, 1963) that house sparrows live and breed in fairly distinct colonies, and although in urban areas these colonies may be less distinct and adjacent to each other, they still exist. Once established in a colony, a bird normally remains attached for the rest of its life (returning to the colony after feeding at the grain fields in summer, or after communal roosting). Most movement of birds between colonies is made by juveniles which do not become permanent members of a group until they have paired. During October and November and from January to March the juveniles spend much time "prospecting" for nest sites, and in the course of this activity may move from one colony to another. If, therefore, the number of birds in a colony is drastically reduced during the breeding season, replacement by other birds is unlikely to occur until juveniles begin prospecting. Consequently, operations against house sparrows can remain effective for some months and it may be a year before the numbers have built up again, provided treatments are done at the right time; Cornwell (1966) reports that sites that have been largely cleared of sparrows remain so for 7–12 months. Operations against house sparrows are most frequently done from March to July and during this period the highest catches are obtained. This is the time when house sparrows are breeding and when it would be expected that they would most easily be caught—first, because the adults have less time to spare for food searching and so will take baits more readily, and second, because the population is being reinforced with juveniles which are less wary than adults. The house sparrow population reaches a peak towards the end of July (Summers-Smith, 1959), when juveniles form about 60% of the total, but then starts to decline steeply. As the maximum natural mortality in adults occurs during the breeding season and as the mortality rate of juveniles is between 70 and 80%, it is worthwhile considering how much effort is being spent during the breeding season in catching birds that would not have survived anyway. During August and September the majority of house sparrows have joined the grain-field feeding flocks, although those living in the centre of large urban areas probably do not do so. From what has been said, it would appear that the best time for controlling house sparrows is at the very start of the breeding season, in late March and April, when the adults are well established in their colonies and the first year birds have mainly become settled, but before a new batch of juveniles has entered the scene. Clearing a site at this time is most likely to ensure that it stays reasonably clear for the longest possible period and that another treatment need not be done for another year (assuming that there is one colony per site). Personal observations have shown that some isolated sites cleared of house sparrows will remain so for over 12 months. Although, as with the feral pigeon, it is not possible, using stupefying baits, completely to eliminate house sparrow populations from urban areas (nor is it necessary or desirable to do so), this technique can be usefully applied in keeping such places as bakeries and food stores relatively clear of birds, provided treatments are carried out regularly. Of all the operations against house sparrows in urban districts, 57% have been in premises handling or storing foodstuffs (26% bakeries, 17% food factories and 14% food warehouses) and 38% in industrial premises. Approximately one-third of the treatments at industrial sites have been to clear sparrows from staff canteens.

The technique of using stupefying baits, as applied to the feral pigeon, introduces a number of factors likely to reduce its efficiency. It has been pointed out that, mainly to avoid public reaction, operations are normally carried out between dawn and 08.00 h. For this reason, most operations have been done during the summer months, when dawn is early, and there is insufficient information to compare baiting success throughout the year. Furthermore, because of this time limitation, only the birds that feed early in the morning will be caught. It has often been observed that only part of the population regularly feeds at this time, the remainder doing so later in the day. This is further complicated by the fact that, during the breeding season, one bird from each pair is likely to be sitting on the nest, so that only a portion of the population is at risk. These problems do not arise with house sparrows because the bait is left down for most of the day.

In all the operations discussed above, α-chloralose was the stupefying agent, and it is necessary to consider why it was selected. When the investigation into the subject of stupefying birds was initiated in 1955, work by Daude (1942) and Giban (1950) in France, and by Borg (1955) in Sweden, had already shown that α-chloralose was effective for catching birds, so this substance was an obvious possibility. Ridpath et al. (1961) tested a small number of other substances, all of which proved inferior to α-chloralose which was therefore adopted as the stupefying agent. It cannot be denied, however, that α-chloralose has its disadvantages and two of these are of some importance: first, it has a rather low safety margin, and second, it is not particularly rapid in action. In the feral pigeon it often takes between 20 and 50 min before a bird is completely immobilized and, because pigeons may fly some distance after feeding, this can cause problems (with house sparrows the drug tends to act more quickly and the birds do not normally move far from where they feed). So although chloralose is currently the stupefying agent in use, some attempt has been made to find more satisfactory chemicals. To be successful, a substance must fulfil a number of conditions: it must act quickly when taken orally and have a wide margin between the hypnotic and lethal dose; it must be in a form (e.g. powdered) that can be applied easily to a grain bait, and it must be readily acceptable to the birds (i.e. have no repellent effect). In a series of experiments, twenty candidate substances were administered to feral pigeons by three different methods: in aviary tests the substances were applied to food as would be done in field operations; in cage tests subjects were force-fed with substances in gelatine capsules, and in further cage tests the substances were presented in the birds' drinking water (Table V). Only pentobarbitone sodium, quinalbarbitone sodium and methyl pentynol carbamate fulfilled most of the conditions and compared favourably with α-chloralose (which was used as a standard in all tests). Tribromoethanol, which showed some promise, was not consistent in its effects.

Field tests with the barbiturates and methyl pentynol carbamate were disappointing and did not support the results obtained in the laboratory. Both laboratory and field tests on house sparrows with these substances showed α-chloralose to be vastly more effective. All the other compounds tested were considered to be of no practical use either because the birds would not accept food treated with them or because very large doses were required to produce an effect; surface application of a substance to a grain bait limits the concentration that can be used. Seven of the substances tested were chloral compounds or derivatives (including chloral hydrate) and none of these approached the efficiency of α-chloralose. Some tests with mixtures of substances have suggested that these might be worthy of further investigation and recently other substances have become available which might prove satisfactory, so the search for a substitute for α-chloralose continues.

This brief outline of some of the bird problems occurring in urban areas has concentrated on one method of control and has mainly served to show the limitations involved. The use of stupefying baits will not, in itself, overcome the problems even if the technique is improved. But the application of this control method does illustrate how necessary it

TABLE V

Tests on feral pigeons with candidate stupefying substances

Substances administered on wheat at 1·5% by weight (free-feeding)

Substance	No. of birds treated	No. affected	Average time to first signs of effect (min)	No. immobilized	Average time to immobilization (min)	No. dying
α-Chloralose	22	20	18	19	37	12
Pentobarbitone sodium	12	10	7	10	17	8
Methyl pentynol carbamate	12	9	8	8	19	2
Tribromoethanol	12	7	10	4	12	—
Quinalbarbitone sodium	6	5	10	4	14	—

Substances administered in gelatine capsules (force-fed)

Substance	Dosage (mg/kg)	No. of birds tested	Average time to first signs of effect (min)	Average time to immobilization (min)	No. dying
α-Chloralose	50	2	28	50	—
	80	2	21	42	—
	125	2	20	34	1
	200	2	16	26	1
	315	2	23	39	1
	500	2	22	30	2
Pentobarbitone sodium	30	8	11	52	—
	40	3	12	21	—
	50	10	15	39	1
	100	2	8	13	2
	200	2	10	15	2
Methyl pentynol carbamate	40	3	14	—	—
	100	2	21	—	—
	200	2	10	15	—
	400	2	12	17	2

Substance	Approx. dosage (mg/kg)	No. of birds tested	Average time to first signs of effect (min)	Average time to immobilization (min)	No. dying	Repellency of solution
Quinalbarbitone sodium	50	2	10	30	—	—
	100	2	12	22	2	
	200	2	7	30	2	
Pentobarbitone sodium + methyl pentynol carbamate (ratio 3:2)	50	8	8	21		—

Substances administered in solution (drinking water)

Substance	Concentration (g/litre)	Approx. dosage (mg/kg)	No. of birds tested	Average time to first signs of effect (min)	Average time to immobilization (min)	No. dying	Repellency of solution
α-Chloralose	4	50	2	12	30	1	Nil
		120	2	10	15	2	
		200	2	7	17	2	
Pentobarbitone sodium	5	50	2	10	50	—	Nil
		80	2	13	25	—	
		200	2	8	12	2	
Pentobarbitone sodium	8	35	2	10	25	—	Nil
		75	2	10	22	—	
		300	2	8	18	1	
	20	100	3	10	20	1	Slight
		600	2	6	16	2	
Methyl pentynol carbamate	12	60	3	20	—	—	Considerable
		300	4	10	—	—	
Quinalbarbitone sodium	8	30	3	18	(would not drink)	—	Strong
		130	2				

H

is to have a knowledge of the life history and population ecology of the species one wishes to control. It is commonly thought, by the layman, that any method of killing birds, if applied indiscriminately and persistently, will have the desired effect of reducing the population. In the case of the feral pigeon and house sparrow this is clearly not the case, just as with the wood pigeon organized shoots in January–March have been shown to have no effect on the population (Murton, 1965). The present knowledge of the life cycle of the house sparrow has helped to improve the use of stupefying baits against it; but more knowledge is required of the house sparrow's habits in urban areas, particularly in the food premises that it so often infests, and on the repopulation of cleared sites. It is surprising how little is known about the life cycle of the feral pigeon; the population study at present in progress in the Salford docks will, it is hoped, fill this gap and help to provide a more effective solution of the associated problems.

It is conceivable that new methods of control, such as the use of reproduction inhibitors, may be developed in the near future, but control measures, however efficient, are unlikely to provide the final answer in the present climate of public opinion. After all there would be no birds in many places if they were not fed by the public. Rather than kill birds, it may be preferable to prevent them from becoming established at places where they can cause a particular nuisance. So far preventive measures have not proved very effective. A sticky substance devised by a servicing company to spread on ledges where birds roost has shown some success, but its application is necessarily limited. To apply it to all suitable buildings at risk in an area is costly and impracticable, so birds are only shifted for a short distance. Similarly the use of recorded distress calls against urban starlings in the United States (Frings and Jumber, 1954; Frings and Frings, 1963) has demonstrated that the birds can be moved to alternative roosts, but that these effects are not necessarily permanent. In many situations buildings could be proofed much more effectively to prevent birds invading them. Many modern buildings are, more by accident than design, unsuitable roosting places for birds; the starling roost that once existed in the centre of Plymouth has not re-established itself since the wartime air raids (Potts, 1967) because the new buildings in the city centre are not suitable for roosting. Although no one would suggest that the many old and beautiful buildings in our towns should be demolished, at least if all the new buildings were roost-proof, the problem might become a gradually decreasing one, instead of increasing as apparently at present, and preventive measures need only be applied to the old buildings where necessary. But although it is desirable to exclude birds from some areas or to reduce their numbers, the idea of urban areas denuded of bird life is not pleasant to contemplate and our towns and cities would be sorrier places without them.

SUMMARY

1. The species mainly responsible for problems in urban areas are the starling, the feral pigeon and the house sparrow. Both the starling and feral pigeon foul and deface buildings; the feral pigeon and house sparrow infest premises associated with food.

2. Although it is possible that these birds are a risk to public health through transmission of disease, the evidence for this is, as yet, insufficient to present a proven case.

3. Traditional control methods such as shooting and trapping are not particularly effective in an urban environment.

4. Baits treated with α-chloralose have been used against feral pigeons and house sparrows with little risk to protected species in urban areas. The method is useful for reducing small, discrete populations of feral pigeons, but is not suitable for large scale control measures. Against house sparrows annual treatments can restrict the numbers of birds infesting food premises; it is suggested that March and April are the best months for such treatments.

5. α-chloralose is not entirely satisfactory as a stupefying agent for feral pigeons. Tests with other substances have not produced a reliable alternative, but some mixtures of chemicals appear promising and details are given.

6. Control methods, however successful, will probably not provide a final solution to the problems of birds in towns. Preventive measures would be preferable if it were possible to apply them successfully.

ACKNOWLEDGEMENTS

I should like to thank Dr. R. K. Murton for advice on the manuscript, Mr. A. Taylor who suggested and obtained a number of candidate stupefying substances, and many other colleagues of the Ministry of Agriculture, Fisheries and Food who assisted in field trials.

REFERENCES

Borg, K. (1955). On chloralose and its use in the capture of crows, gulls and pigeons. *Viltrevy-Jaktbiologisk Tidskrift* **1**, 88–121. (In Swedish.)

Cornwell, P. B. (1966). Control of house sparrows with alphachloralose. *Int. Pest Control* **8**, 10–13.

Cramp, S., Parrinder, E. R. and Richards, B. A. (1964). Roosts and fly-lines. *In* "The Birds of the London Area", pp. 106–117. Rupert Hart-Davis, London.

Daude, J. L. (1942). Capture et destruction des corbeaux, pies et autres oiseaux nuisibles aux récoltes. *Bull. Acad. Méd., Paris* **126**, 452–454.

Ellenbogen, B. K. and Miller, C. M. (1952). Psittacosis in a family. *Br. med. J.* **2**, 189–190.

Emmons, C. W. (1955). Saprophytic sources of *Cryptococcus neoformans* associated with the pigeon (*Columba livia*). *Am. J. Hyg.* **62**, 227–232.

Emmons, C. W. (1960). Prevalence of *Cryptococcus neoformans* in pigeon habitats. *Publ. Hlth Rep., Wash.* **75**, 362–364.

Emmons, C. W. (1961). Isolation of *Histoplasma capsulatum* from soil in Washington D.C. *Publ. Hlth Rep., Wash.* **76**, 591–595.

Frings, H. and Frings, M. (1963). Pest control with sound. Part II. The problems with vertebrates. *Sound* **2**, 39–45.

Frings, H. and Jumber, J. (1954). Preliminary studies on the use of a specific sound to repel starlings (*Sturnus vulgaris*) from objectionable roosts. *Science, N.Y.* **119**, 318–319.

Furcolow, M. L., Tosh, F. E., Larsh, H. W., Lynch, H. J. and Shaw, G. (1961). The emerging pattern of urban histoplasmosis. *New Engl. J. Med.* **264**, 1226–1230.

Giban, J. (1950). Recherches sur l'action du chloralose ou glucochloral chez les oiseaux. *Annls Inst. natn. Rech. agron., Paris*, Ser. C, **1**, 337–366.

Gompertz, T. (1957). Some observations on the feral pigeon in London. *Bird Study* **4**, 2–13.

Goodwin, D. (1954). Notes on feral pigeons. *Avicult. Mag.* **60**, 190–213.

Goodwin, D. (1960). Comparative ecology of pigeons in inner London. *Br. Birds* **53**, 201–212.

Grist, N. R. (1960). Ornithosis and the railway guards (Letter). *Lancet* 1960 (ii) No. 7143, 207.

Gustafson, D. P. and Moses, H. E. (1953). The English sparrow as a natural carrier of Newcastle disease virus. *Am. J. vet. Res.* **14**, 581–585.

Hariri, A. A. K. (1943). Contribution à l'étude toxicologique du chloralose. Thèse docteur en pharmacie, Université de Paris.

Hughes, D. L. (1957). Man and his animals. *Vet. Rec.* **69**, 1061–1065.

Keymer, I. F. (1958). A survey and review of the causes of mortality in British birds and the significance of wild birds as disseminators of disease. *Vet. Rec.* **70**, 713–720, 736–739.

Lepine, M. P. and Sautter, V. (1951). Sur l'infection des pigeons parisiennes par le virus de l'ornithose. *Bull. Acad. natn. Méd.* **135**, 332–338.

McDiarmid, A. (1962). Diseases of free-living wild animals. F.A.O. Agricultural Studies No. 57. F.A.O., Rome.

Meyer, K. F. (1959). Some general remarks and new observations on psittacosis and ornithosis. *Bull. Wld Hlth Org.* **20**, 101–119.

Murdock, W. T., Travis, R. E., Sutliff, W. D. and Ajello, L. (1962). Acute pulmonary histoplasmosis after exposure to soil contaminated by starling excreta. *J. Am. med. Ass.* **179**, 73–75.

Murton, R. K. (1964). Do birds transmit foot and mouth disease? *Ibis* **106**, 289–298.

Murton, R. K. (1965). Natural and artificial population control in the wood-pigeon. *Ann. appl. Biol.* **55**, 177–192.

Murton, R. K. and Westwood, N. J. (1966). The foods of the rock dove and feral pigeon. *Bird Study* **13**, 130–146.

Murton, R. K., Isaacson, A. J. and Westwood, N. J. (1963). The use of baits treated with alpha-chloralose to catch wood-pigeons. *Ann. appl. Biol.* **52**, 271–293.

Potts, G. R. (1967). Urban starling roosts in the British Isles. *Bird Study* **14**, 25–42.

Ridpath, M. G., Thearle, R. J. P., McCowan, D. and Jones, F. J. S. (1961). Experiments on the value of stupefying and lethal substances in the control of harmful birds. *Ann. appl. Biol.* **49**, 77–101.

Spencer, K. G. (1966). Some notes on the roosting behaviour of starlings. *Naturalist*, No. 898, 73–80.

Summers-Smith, D. (1954). Colonial behaviour in the house sparrow. *Br. Birds* **47**, 249–265.

Summers-Smith, D. (1958). Nest-site selection, pair formation and territory in the house-sparrow *Passer domesticus*. *Ibis* **100**, 190–203.

Summers-Smith, D. (1959). The house sparrow *Passer domesticus:* population problems. *Ibis* **101**, 449–454.

Summers-Smith, D. (1963). "The House Sparrow". Collins, London.

Wilson, J. E. and MacDonald, J. W. (1967). Salmonella infection in wild birds. *Br. vet. J.* **123**, 212–219.

Wilson, W. W. and Matheson, R. C. (1952). Bird migration and foot and mouth disease. *Agriculture, Lond.* **59**, 213–228.

Bullfinches and Fruit Buds

I. NEWTON*

Edward Grey Institute of Field Ornithology, Oxford, England

Few English birds have received more publicity in recent years than the bullfinch, *Pyrrhula pyrrhula*. This species now removes the buds of fruit trees on such a scale as to constitute one of the greatest problems with which the fruit growing industry has to contend. The worst affected areas lie in south-east England, but damage is severe locally in parts of East Anglia and the Midlands. It is not a new problem, however, for in Britain the bullfinch had a price on its head for the same offence as long ago as the 16th century. Nevertheless, the bird itself, and the damage it causes, have increased greatly since the 1940s. Compared with the damage caused by bullfinches in orchards, that done by other bird species is negligible (though damage by house sparrows, *Passer domesticus*, may sometimes be severe to trees around human habitation).

Bullfinches eat only the small embryonic centres of flower buds—those parts otherwise destined to become fruit. Buds destroyed are not replaced by the tree in the same year, though with most fruit varieties, the loss is made good the following year by the development of ancillary buds. In some types of plums and gooseberries, however, there is no regeneration of fruiting points, so that damage is cumulative. Occasionally there is also severe damage to leaf buds, making it impossible to train the tree to a good shape, and thus permanently affecting its cropping potential (Wright and Summers, 1960).

The bullfinch prefers the buds of fruit trees to those of native trees (its natural food in spring) and can remove buds at a rate of thirty or more per min (Wright and Summers, 1960; Newton, 1964). Since bullfinches often gather in flocks of twenty or more, they need only a few days to devastate a large orchard. The extent of damage varies greatly from year to year, depending mainly on the month in which the birds begin feeding on buds; in some years they may begin as early as November, in others not until March. Once begun, the attacks continue until blossoming is over (about mid-May); in general, severe damage occurs at most every second year, as explained later.

When feeding in fruit trees in winter, the behaviour of bullfinches is remarkably stereotyped and systematic: alighting at the tip of a

* Current address: The Nature Conservancy, Hope Terrace, Edinburgh.

branch, the bird works towards the trunk taking every bud in turn; on reaching the older wood, which bears fewer buds, it then normally flies out to the tip of another branch and repeats the process. Bullfinches usually enter orchards from adjacent woods and hedgerows, and attack the nearest trees first. As the days go by, they penetrate farther into the orchard, stripping every tree in turn. It is now commonplace, especially in Kent, for an orchard capable of yielding several tons of fruit to be denuded almost completely of buds so that it yields but a few pounds (see, for example, Newton, 1964).

Certain fruit varieties are more vulnerable than others. Among pears, for instance, buds of the varieties Williams, Dr. Jules, and Conference, are preferred; among plums the various gages, and among apples buds of the dessert varieties are generally preferred to those of "cookers". But the least favoured varieties are spared only when the birds have a choice, otherwise they too are eaten. Feeding trials on captive bullfinches have shown that the varieties which the bird prefers are also those on which they can best maintain their weight.

THE RECENT INCREASE IN BULLFINCHES

The bullfinch is found across Europe and Asia. Over most of this area it is restricted to coniferous and mixed forest, which was probably its ancestral habitat, but at the two ends of its range, in Britain and also Japan (Kuroda, *in litt.*), it now inhabits deciduous woods and cultivation as well, and only in these countries has it become a serious problem to the fruit grower.

The cause of the increase in numbers in England is by no means obvious, but it has certainly been accompanied by a behavioural change in the bird itself. During this century the bullfinch has learnt to live-not only in closer association with man, but also in much more open places than formerly. Thus, while old textbooks describe the bullfinch as a "retiring bird", rarely leaving the seclusion of woods and hedges, the species now breeds commonly on farmland and often feeds far out in fields on weed seeds. It is also common now in parks and gardens, both urban and suburban, to which only twenty years ago it was a comparatively rare visitor. Thus, it is possible that the spread from wooded to more open country, and the extra food available there, has been a major factor enabling the bird to increase in numbers. The increase and the spread to other habitats has so far been most evident in the south of England, but has not been restricted only to the main fruit-growing areas.

Once well established in cultivated land, the bullfinch might have been expected to become a major pest in orchards for, although primarily a seed-eater, even in its natural habitat it takes a greater proportion and variety of buds, and for a longer period each year, than does any other European bird (Newton, 1967*b*). Indeed, it is well adapted to do so in bill-structure, feeding technique and digestive system (Eber, 1956; Newton, 1967*a*). All cultivated fruit trees, moreover, have buds of the size most acceptable to bullfinches and are derived from tree-species whose buds are preferred by the bird under natural conditions (Newton, 1967*b*).

Previous Attempts to Reduce the Damage

There are basically two ways of reducing pest-damage to crops: either by protecting the crop (with some sort of enclosure, scaring device or repellent chemical), or by reducing the numbers of the pest. The latter may be achieved simply by killing large numbers of birds each year (by poisoning, shooting or trapping), or "biologically" by adjusting the environment in some way so that the pest's population is held at a permanently reduced level.

Enclosing a fruit crop against bullfinches is feasible in small gardens, but out of the question in large orchards; scaring devices (such as "bangers") are effective only until the birds get used to them—which often takes only a few days—and all chemical deterrents applied so far to buds have achieved little or no lasting success, in part because the bullfinch eats only the small centre from each bud and peels off the outer layers bearing the chemical. Most chemicals also are soon washed off by rain, and when most needed (during cold weather) are difficult to handle as aqueous solutions: a systemic deterrent, that could be sprayed onto the ground and then taken up by the tree into its buds, might be more effective, but has not yet been tried. For reducing the numbers of bullfinches directly, poisoning is undesirable because it is unselective and therefore potentially harmful to other wildlife, while shooting is expensive and time-consuming, and incidentally damages the trees. Credit for the best method of control is due to E. N. Wright and D. D. B. Summers, who on behalf of the Ministry of Agriculture, Fisheries and Food, developed a trap that is not only effective, but also cheap, easy to operate, and harmless to other animals (Wright, 1961). So far, this has proved much the most satisfactory way of coping with the bullfinch problem.

General Biology

It is surprising that, until recently, little was known about a species of such economic importance. It therefore seemed desirable to make a

H*

detailed study of the bird in an attempt to learn what determines the numbers of bullfinches under natural conditions, and also in the hope that it would throw light on the reasons for the attacks on fruit buds and suggest at what time of the year trapping, the best means of control, would be most effective and economically justified. For these reasons, I began in 1961 to study the feeding habits and population ecology of the bullfinches living in an area of woodland and farmland near Oxford, and the rest of this contribution is based mainly on observations made there.

The diet of bullfinches consists mainly of buds for up to one-third of each year, but at other times a great variety of seeds from woody and herbaceous plants; the young are reared on a mixture of seeds and small invertebrates. In southern England, most trees and herbaceous plants fruit between May and September, and after this bullfinches depend almost entirely on seeds remaining on dead plant stems, trees, and shrubs. As such seeds become scarce and their variety restricted, buds become increasingly important in the diet until, in April or May, certain tree-flowers and then fresh seeds become available again. The buds of hawthorn, *Crataegus monogyna*, are the main natural food in spring, but those of the rarer crab apple, *Malus sylvestris*, are preferred. Some other important food-plants and the months in which they are exploited, are shown in Fig. 1. Bullfinches obtain almost all their food directly from the plant and do not normally feed on fallen seeds on the ground.

Bullfinches nest solitarily in shrubs and hedgerows. In most years the first clutches are laid in early May and the last in mid-July, but in years of low population or abundant food eggs may be laid until mid-September, so that the last young of the year fledge in October. A brood normally consists of four to six nestlings and, although each pair would have time to raise three or more broods in a year, few do so because of heavy predation on the eggs and young. Near Oxford, only one-third of all clutches started in woodland, and two-thirds of those in farmland, successfully produce young. The farmland nests are more successful because the chief predators (jays, *Garrulus glandarius*, and weasels, *Mustela nivalis*) are less numerous there than in woodland. It is possible that the protection of predatory animals, such as jays, magpies, *Pica pica*, crows, *Corvus corone*, stoats, *Mustela erminea*, and weasels would reduce further the reproductive output of bullfinches. In this context, it is worth noting that it is so time-consuming for man to find the nests that systematic nest-destruction would be totally impracticable as a means of control. It is also most unlikely that a reduction in reproductive output, caused by man or by natural predators, would bring about any reduction in the size of the winter population.

FIG. 1. The main foods of the bullfinch throughout the year.

Ringing recoveries have shown that, after reaching independence, a bullfinch can expect to live, on average, a little over one year. Some, of course, live much longer, and at least one ringed bird was recovered in its eighth year.

After breeding, adults undergo a complete moult lasting in each individual about 10–12 weeks; at the same time the juveniles have a partial moult lasting 7–9 weeks. It is during the moult that the species is least conspicuous; for the most part it remains in seclusion in woodland and can be found with certainty only at patches of meadowsweet, *Filipendula ulmaria*, whose seeds form the favourite food at this time. After moult, the birds begin to move farther afield again, and from then to the following spring are often seen in parties of five or six, though as mentioned above larger numbers sometimes gather together. The largest flock I have seen in an orchard consisted of fifty to sixty individuals, and the largest flock seen on farmland was at least 150 strong. Woodland flocks rarely exceed twenty individuals, probably because in this habitat food is not normally abundant enough at any one place to support bigger aggregations.

THE FEEDING BEHAVIOUR OF A WOODLAND POPULATION

Although common in cultivated areas, bullfinches are most numerous in deciduous woodland, though they move freely between the two. It was found that in woodland the seed-diet in winter consists almost exclusively of the seeds of two types of herbaceous plants (docks, *Rumex* spp., and nettle, *Urtica dioica*), two shrubs (bramble, *Rubus fruticosus* agg. and privet, *Ligustrum vulgare*) and two trees (birch, *Betula alba*, and ash, *Fraxinus excelsior*). The seed-crops of all these plants are produced in late summer, and thereafter are not replenished in any way during the course of the winter. Thus, the seed-crops available to the birds in October must suffice until the following spring when buds become large enough to provide sufficient nutrients. Seed crops of docks, nettle and bramble are normally fairly constant in size from year to year, but those of privet, birch and ash vary enormously from one year to the next.

The preferred seeds of birch and privet are eaten mainly in autumn, but those of ash become particularly important in late winter, when most other seeds have been eaten. At this time they are often the only source of food available to bullfinches, apart from buds. Bullfinches may include some buds in their diet as early as November, but experiments on captive birds have shown that, at this season, they cannot maintain themselves on buds alone, whether these be of fruit or of woodland trees; they require at least some seeds if they are to survive. Only after about the end of February, when buds are larger and days longer and warmer, can they obtain enough energy from a diet of buds alone (Newton, 1964).

Since captive bullfinches fed on seeds maintained their weight better in midwinter than did birds fed on buds, it seemed to me likely that in the wild they attacked fruit buds mainly when seeds were scarce. Hence, to assess the impact of bullfinches on their winter food-supply, the seasonal decline in seed-availability was measured through several successive winters in Marley Wood, near Oxford. Data for two typical years are given in Fig. 2. The seeds of all six plant-species detailed disappear during winter mainly through the activities of bullfinches, or by falling from the plants, though other bird species also eat birch seeds.

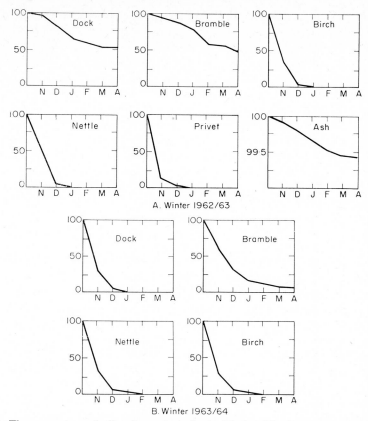

Fig. 2. The percentage decline in seed-stocks in Marley Wood over two successive winters of markedly different food conditions. Note that a different scale is used for ash than for the other food-plants. (For further details see text.)

Figure 2A shows the decline in seed-stocks during the winter of 1962/63, when there was a good ash crop. The entire seed-crops of three of the food-plants had disappeared by January, but by April (when fresh seeds became available again) only half the crops of bramble and the various docks had been eaten. So large was the ash crop that, although bullfinches had fed mainly on these seeds throughout the winter, they made practically no impression on the crop and removed only about 0·5%. In this and other years in which ash trees produced a lot of seeds, bullfinches did not eat out their natural food-supply, and there was always a large quantity of food left over by the following spring, when fresh seeds of other plant-species once more became available. Figure 2B shows the situation in the winter of 1963/64, when there were no ash seeds. All privet seeds had been eaten before mid-October, when measurements were started, as had all seeds of three other plant-species by January. All that remained at the end of the winter was about 7% of the bramble crop. Thus, in this winter, as in all the other years I have examined in which there was no ash crop, bullfinches ate practically all the seeds available to them in woodland.

In the first of the two winters just described (1962/63), in which seeds were plentiful in Marley Wood, the buds of various native trees formed less than one-fifth of the diet from October to April, and were not eaten in appreciable quantities before March; damage on fruit farms was negligible. In the second winter, however, when seeds were scarce, buds formed nearly a half of the total winter diet and were taken in quantity as early as mid-December. This was also an exceptionally bad year for bullfinch damage in the fruit orchards.

THE RELATIONSHIP BETWEEN THE SIZE OF THE ASH CROP AND THE EXTENT OF BUD-DAMAGE

It will be apparent from the fruit-growers' viewpoint that the seeds of ash are the most important winter food of bullfinches as they are often the only source of food available (beside buds) at the end of the winter when other seeds have been eaten. Records of the size of the ash crop in different years show that, since 1956, good crops have occurred about every second year, with little or no seed produced in the intervening years; furthermore, these fluctuations in crop have occurred synchronously over the whole of southern England. Responses to questionnaires sent to fruit-growers in various areas showed that, as expected, most had suffered severe bud-damage in their orchards only in the alternate years since 1956—those years in which the ash crops were poor.

It might be thought that one solution to the bullfinch problem would be to break in some way the biennial pattern of the cropping of ash so that seeds were available every year, or else to supply an alternative supply of seeds in the lean years. However, even if this were feasible, it would not be a satisfactory solution to the problem, for bullfinches are held in check by the winter food-supply and suffer heavy mortality only in years when seeds are scarce (Newton, 1964; and in preparation). As mentioned earlier, they cannot maintain themselves in midwinter on buds alone, and in Marley Wood mortality has been heaviest in those years without an ash crop, for then most seeds had disappeared by January, i.e. before buds were large enough to provide adequate nourishment. Hence, if food were provided artificially in the winters with no ash crop, it is likely that bullfinches would survive these winters in larger numbers than at present and that the population would simply increase to the limit set by this new food-supply.

THE MOST EFFECTIVE MEANS OF CONTROL

The relationship between the ash crops and the pattern of damage to fruit buds at least means that fruit-growers can predict the years in which severe attacks are likely, and as mentioned earlier, a reduction in damage might be achieved then if the birds are destroyed by trapping. However, when traps were first introduced in the late 1950s, most growers, not unnaturally, concentrated their trapping in the spring, when the attacks were actually occurring, and though damage was reduced somewhat in this way it was still severe.

With a knowledge of the natural population changes throughout the year, a more effective trapping programme can be suggested. As mentioned earlier, bullfinches turn to buds mainly when seeds become scarce, and the seed-stocks on which they depend are not replenished in any way during the winter. It follows, therefore, that the more birds there are at the start of the winter, the quicker these seed-stocks will be depleted and the sooner the birds will turn their attention to buds. On theoretical grounds, the greatest potential reduction in damage to fruit buds should be achieved if many birds are killed in autumn, before they can deplete seed-stocks seriously. The natural food-supply should then last longer, and the date in winter when they need to turn to buds in large quantities should be postponed. This method was put into practice on several fruit farms in various areas in autumn 1963, when trapping was concentrated in the period August–November. It has resulted, in the four years since then, in almost complete absence of damage on these farms, all of which prior to 1963 had suffered heavy loss of fruit in the non-ash years. It may be noted that the method has no long-term effect on bullfinch numbers, since it simply brings the main period of mortality forward from midwinter (natural starvation) to early autumn (artificial control). Compared with samples of bullfinches that die naturally, those killed by fruit-growers contain a much higher proportion of first-year birds; evidently these are either easier to catch or they move around more than older birds. For instance, from October to December 1964 the ratio of first-year to older birds netted in Marley Wood was 3:1 (which fits with the reproductive rate), whereas among about 1 600 killed in orchards in the same months, first-year birds outnumbered adults by 38:1.

It is clearly of little use killing bullfinches in an orchard if others continuously move in to replace them. Although this does occur the danger may be comparatively slight, however, for recoveries of bull-

finches marked under the national bird-ringing scheme show that most
move no farther than 2 miles from their birthplace, and that most
movement takes place during their first autumn of life. Elsewhere in
Europe, bullfinches are more migratory, but the suspicions of fruit-
growers on the east coast of England that some come to Britain to
winter alongside the resident population is not supported by the pattern
of ringing recoveries.

In the past, many attempts to deal with pest species have often
begun with use (or misuse) of chemical deterrents and poisons. Most of
these methods achieved little or no lasting success, but have resulted in
considerable wastage of public funds and unnecessary destruction of
other wildlife. Recent studies have adequately demonstrated that any
attempt at pest control must be preceded by a thorough study of the
pest's biology, work that many would consider of academic interest
only. But only with such basic knowledge are we likely to be able to
formulate sound control policies that are economically and morally
justifiable.

Summary

1. The bullfinch is of pest-status because it eats the flower-buds of
fruit trees, thus reducing the subsequent crop. There has been an
enormous increase in damage during the past two decades, owing to an
increase in the numbers of the bird itself, though the reasons for this are
not well known. The problem results because bullfinches prefer the
buds of fruit trees to those of native trees, the natural food in spring.
Also, when given a choice they eat the buds of certain fruit varieties in
preference to those of others.

2. In autumn and winter, bullfinches live on seeds remaining on
certain trees and on the dead stems of herbaceous plants, and when these
become scarce, buds are taken in quantity until fresh seeds become
available again in late April or May. The chief variable in the winter
seed-supply is the ash crop, the size of which varies greatly from year to
year. In years of poor crops, the seeds of all the food-plants of the bird
run out by January, and buds predominate in the diet for the next four
months. In years of good crops, buds are not taken in quantity until
March. It is thus in years when the ash crop fails that bud-damage is
most severe. In southern England, the ash crop tends to fluctuate with
biennial periodicity, years of good and poor crops alternating.

3. Enclosing a fruit crop to protect it from bullfinches is impracticable
in large orchards, and the deterrent effect of distasteful chemicals
sprayed onto buds is slight and temporary. So far, trapping the birds in
the vicinity of the orchards has proved the most satisfactory means of

reducing damage, and this method is most effective if birds are removed in the autumn. In this way, natural seed-stocks are conserved, and the date in winter when intensive bud-feeding begins is delayed. Although autumn trapping will greatly reduce the damage, it is by no means a permanent solution to the problem and for full effect must be carried out in all years without an ash crop.

ACKNOWLEDGEMENTS

The research described herein was financed first by the Department of Scientific and Industrial Research, and latterly by the Agricultural Research Council. I am grateful to Dr. P. R. Evans, Dr. P. Ward and Dr. D. Lack for helpful remarks on the manuscript.

REFERENCES

Eber, G. (1956). Vergleichende untersuchungen über die Ernarhrung einiger Finkenvögel. *Biol. Abh.* **13/14**, 1–60.

Newton, I. (1964). Bud-eating by bullfinches in relation to the natural food-supply. *J. appl. Ecol.* **1**, 265–79.

Newton, I. (1967a). The adaptive radiation and feeding ecology of some British finches. *Ibis* **109**, 33–98.

Newton, I. (1967b). The feeding ecology of the bullfinch *Pyrrhula pyrrhula* in southern England. *J. Anim. Ecol.* **36**, 721–44.

Wright, E. N. (1961). The use of traps to control bullfinches. *Expl. Hort.* **4**, 55–62.

Wright, E. N. and Summers, D. D. B. (1960). The biology and economic importance of the bullfinch. *Ann. appl. Biol.* **48**, 415–418.

The Quelea Problem in Africa

J. H. CROOK and P. WARD*

*Department of Psychology, University of Bristol,
and c/o Edward Grey Institute, Oxford, England*

INTRODUCTION

The Black-faced Dioch, or Quelea *Quelea quelea*, is a sparrow-sized Ploceine weaver notable for being perhaps the most numerous as well as the most destructive bird in the world. It lives exclusively in the semi-arid savanna regions of Africa, from Mauretania in the west across to Ethiopia and Somaliland, thence south through East Africa to South Africa; a northward extension from South West Africa includes much of coastal Angola (Fig. 1). *Quelea* is now known to affect adversely the economies of between twenty and twenty-five nations by its attacks on cereal crops—millet, guinea-corn, wheat and rice.

In view of its present reputation as one of the most serious agricultural pests in Africa, it is curious to find that as late as 1949 Bannerman, in a major faunistic work, was only able to give incidental field notes from West Africa; in South Africa the state of knowledge was a little better in that nesting had been observed (James, 1928). There was no indication, other than vague anecdotes concerning huge roosting flights, that great interest was soon to focus on this species, though, throughout Africa, local farmers had been attempting to protect their crops from Queleas, apparently for centuries (Busnel and Grosmaire, 1955). The alarm was not given until cultivation of large areas by modern methods began in the semi-arid areas, and research organizations were established. In 1947 Wilson published a report on the Quelea situation in the Sudan and in the early 1950s an ornithological research station was founded at Richard-Toll in the Senegal River Valley where new rice growing areas were being created by irrigation, and where *Quelea* was, and still is, a great menace. By 1955 the Colonial Office, London, had commissioned a brief report on weaver-bird pests in West African territories (Crook, 1956) and research had begun in East Africa and South Africa under the auspices of the Agricultural departments concerned. The first detailed ecological studies came from Richard-Toll (Dekeyser, 1955; Morel and Bourlière, 1955, 1956; Morel and Morel, 1957; Morel *et al.*, 1957), and

* Current address: Ministry of Overseas Development, Anti-Locust Research Centre, College House, Wrights Lane, London.

Fig. 1. A map of Africa showing, in black, the approximate area of suitable vegetation for *Quelea quelea* breeding. The regions arrowed are known to harbour large concentrations of breeding birds; many other such concentrations probably occur and there may be small-scale breeding throughout the shaded area in suitable localities. (Modified from Ward, 1966.)

in the same period accounts of Quelea natural history and methods of control were appearing in East Africa and South Africa (Disney and Haylock, 1956; Haylock and Disney, 1956; Haylock, 1959; Naude, 1955). Much of the ensuing literature has appeared in the mimeographed reports of the CCTA/CSA Symposia on *Quelea* at Dakar (1955), Livingstone (1957) and Bamako (1960), and is mostly concerned with methods and costs of killing birds. Special interests soon developed in ecological endocrinology (Disney and Marshall, 1956; Marshall and Disney, 1956, 1957; Disney *et al.*, 1959; Lofts, 1962, 1964) and in sexual and social behaviour (Crook, 1960, 1961, 1964), and in the possibility of using *Quelea* calls in bird-scaring (Busnel and Gramet, 1956).

Following the intensive efforts of the 1950s, a lull in research ensued until the Nigerian government sponsored research in the Lake Chad region of West Africa (Ward, 1965a–c), which was terminated in 1963. At an FAO conference on Quelea bird control (1965), it was noted that little research was currently being carried out, and a request was made for intensive research on the biology and control of this and other bird pests in Africa, under the auspices of FAO.

The Quelea is an extremely difficult pest to deal with because of the enormous numbers of birds and the vast tracts of sparsely populated country they inhabit. Although three races of *Quelea quelea* may be distinguished, they are not separated by geographical barriers and hybrid swarms occupy wide areas of overlap (Ward, 1966). The total area within which Queleas move is probably over 2 million sq. miles (6·5 million km²), though the density is very uneven. The known breeding concentrations are in the areas indicated in Fig. 1, but even here our knowledge is scanty, particularly with regard to Botswana, Somalia and Ethiopia. Over most of the continent, seasonal movements, which involve displacements of hundreds of miles in East Africa and West Africa and over a thousand in southern Africa, are not understood. Even in local movements flocks do not move at random, but are structured according to the social responses of the individuals that comprise them and show diurnal and seasonal changes in relation to feeding and reproductive rhythms.

The relationship between the ecology and social organization of Queleas is briefly reviewed in this paper and an attempt is made to evaluate the problems of Quelea control.

SOCIAL ORGANIZATION AND BEHAVIOUR

In common with other seed-eating Ploceine weavers *Quelea* is a markedly gregarious species. So strong, indeed, is the tendency to remain close to their fellows that in a large aviary birds will concentrate in only one part of it, and an escaped individual will fly up and down outside the wire in co-ordination with movements of the group inside. This extremely sociable disposition is closely linked to the feeding ecology of the species; insectivorous ploceines altogether lack the gregarious behaviour of their granivorous relatives (Crook, 1964). Quelea flocks may range in size from small groups to enormous congregations of millions of birds, and clearly there is no constant membership in their composition apart from the common participation of individuals in roosting behaviour at the local site.

The pattern of Quelea congregation varies diurnally and seasonally. A population is commonly organized into a series of "dispersal systems" (Crook, 1953; Simmons, 1966) located at intervals throughout the occupied habitat. The birds are based upon a roosting site, commonly in a protective place such as a swamp, or dense grove of thorn trees, and every morning the flocks stream away to the feeding grounds. Ward (1965a) considers such a system of direct utility to the participants in that it increases the efficiency with which the population may exploit food supplies in the dispersal area, which may be of the order of hundreds of square kilometres. It seems likely that individuals that have found good feeding one day may return there the next, while less fortunate individuals are likely to select a different direction, possibly joining a group the positively directional behaviour of which indicates a heading for an area rich in food. Flocking itself is likewise primarily a mechanism for increasing feeding efficiency—congregation occurring over locally abundant food sources. The size of Quelea roosts and feeding flocks tends to increase as the dry season progresses and as food availability decreases. Large roosts may last for many weeks, but never long enough to do permanent damage to the vegetation. Nothing is known about the fidelity of individuals to particular sites, but it seems likely that there is a steady turnover in roost membership possibly related to shifts in food supply in the areas exploited. Nomadism probably develops as a continuation of such a pattern, once food resources are seriously depleted. The extent to which local populations are nomadic or migratory is probably a function of the pattern of food availability in particular areas rather than some innate characteristic of the populations concerned.

Marked seasonal movements are recorded in the Lake Chad region (Ward, 1965a), in southern Sudan (Wilson, 1947) and in the Senegal Valley (Morel and Bourlière, 1955), in Kenya and Tanzania (Haylock, 1959), while in southern Africa ringed birds have been found to travel over 1 000 miles from South Africa to Malawi (McLachlan, 1962).

In the wet season the birds congregate into large colonies for breeding. Queleas show no tendency to abandon flocking behaviour during breeding as do certain winter-flocking finches, such as the Chaffinch *Fringilla coelebs* (see Marler, 1956), nor do the spacing relations of flocking individuals appear to change with the seasons. The partial construction of nests goes on throughout the year in roosts and midday resting places, vigorous building at a single site together with its territorial defence by an individual only begins when the birds occupy a definitive breeding colony. The territory is small, consisting of the space immediately around the nest or the area just in front of the entrance.

Territorial aggression at the nest appears to prevent interference from other males in nest construction and courtship sequences, and the attachment to a particular site means that both the male and the female have a precise topographical location at which they meet. Queleas commonly move to and from their nests along regular "routes" between other nests, twigs and branches. The frequency of aggression between neighbours rapidly decreases once territories are established, but strangers continue to be attacked. During nest-burning operations near Lake R'kiz (Mauretania) in 1956 the destruction of nest structures led to a breakdown in the territorial dispersion of males in bushes under observation, and at the same time the pair bonds ceased to exist. The mutual recognition of pair members thus appears contingent upon the presence of the nest structure which defines the site for both sexual and territorial behaviour. Males in the bushes nevertheless continued to show interindividual spacing that approximated to the distances between nests and which resembled an enlarged "individual distance" in that it was maintained as the bird moved about the bush. The birds no longer followed routes through the twigs. In places where a few partially burnt structures remained, a number of males would claim ownership and court any approaching female. A form of temporary promiscuity then developed which finally broke down as the area was deserted. A few pairs with undamaged nests were able to maintain possession and continued to brood their young. The importance of the topographical pattern of nest sites is thus of great importance in the local structuring of the breeding community (Crook, 1960).

Unlike most other savanna Ploceine weavers *Quelea* is monogamous, and this characteristic at first sight appears adaptive to the relatively severe habitat in which the species lives. The long dry season imposes a greater degree of ecological instability than in woodland savannas or the forest fringe areas inhabited by the majority of non-forest ploceines. Also the species diversity of weavers is markedly reduced. Other weavers occur in relatively small demes associated in the breeding season with colonies of limited size. By contrast the Quelea, adapted to a riverine and lacustrine grassland environment in arid areas, occurs in vast numbers as part of a rather simple food chain in a limited ecological community. As with sea-bird colonies (Ashmole, 1963) the areas around the gigantic colonies are liable to overexploitation of food resources and journeys in search of nourishment may be long, but not invariably so (see Ward, 1965b). Under such conditions it appears to be of greater reproductive advantage for the males to assist the females in rearing the brood than to establish several females in a group of nests in the same territory to which the latter then have to bring the greater part of the nourishment for their respective young.

Even though the monogamy of *Quelea* appears beneficial, it could have arisen directly as an effect of the unusual population dynamics of the species. Ward (1965a) found that during the period of least food availability at the onset of the rains females lost weight at about double the rate of males and reached their lowest mean weight a few days before them. The sexes, in fact, appear to be competing severely for the same limited food supply, even though the food preferences of the sexes do not appear completely identical at this season. The sex ratio of nestlings in both Mauretania and northern Nigeria is approximately equal, but the percentage of males in the overall population increases steadily throughout the dry season until males predominate. It now appears certain that more females than males disappear during both the dry season and the critical period at the onset of the rains; this being a result of differential mortality through food shortage (Morel and Bourlière, 1955; Ward, 1965c).

Quelea is a "distance species" in that individuals maintain an individual distance within which approach by a companion is not tolerated (Hediger, 1950). Queleas also rapidly establish dominance hierarchies in captivity in which males rank higher than females. Indeed, females caged in monosexual groups may show so few aggressive responses to approaching birds that hierarchies cannot be observed. Laboratory experiments suggest that both individual distance maintenance and hierarchy formation in males is dependent upon luteinizing hormone secretion from the pituitary. In females this gonadotrophic effect appears to be inhibited by oestrogen (Butterfield and Crook, 1968, and in preparation; Crook, 1961). It follows that males will normally win encounters for limiting commodities whenever they are matched against the opposite sex. Lockie (1956) suggested that social hierarchies in Corvidae function to reduce bodily harm from overt food fighting among members of a population experiencing food shortage. It thereby allows some individuals (the dominants) to survive while, under less critical conditions, subordinates would have the opportunity of searching elsewhere rather than expending energy in fruitless conflict. A parallel situation has been reported from flocks of woodpigeons in winter (Murton *et al.*, 1966). In *Quelea* such behaviour appears to produce a remarkably unequal sex-ratio immediately prior to breeding with males greatly in excess. Monogamy in *Quelea* thus appears to be in part a consequence of this peculiar situation, one that clearly does not exist among polygamous ploceines of less harsh environments. Indeed the large number of unoccupied nests on the peripheries of most colonies testify to abortive attempts by males to obtain non-existent mates (Crook, 1960; Morel and

Bourlière, 1956; Stewart, 1959; Vesey-Fitzgerald, 1958; Ward, 1965b, c). This intriguing phenomenon stands as a warning to theorists who would attribute adaptive significance to species characteristics that appear advantageous, but for which the controlling mechanisms have yet to be worked out. Presumed adaptations may be effects of complex processes involving a species adjustment to its environment and which require analysis at several levels of research.

In the breeding colonies male Queleas are extremely aggressive to all individuals approaching their newly established nests. Courtship consists of sequences in which females showing postures indicative of submissive behaviour repeatedly approach the male and, as he habituates to their presence, sit on twigs near the nest. The male alternates rapidly between aggressive and sexual behaviour. The latter includes a pronounced advertisement display—the "Butterfly Posture" in which he sits on or near the nest with wings raised, tail vertical, beak raised and the body sometimes tilting slowly from one side to the other. This activity appears to attract females who may then hop through the initial ring of the developing nest with the male in close attendance. A variety of precopulatory sequences involving much mutual wing quivering then precedes actual mating (Crook, 1960).

The relations between parent Queleas and their colour-ringed young were studied in a Mauretanian colony (Crook, 1960). After hatching both sexes work hard in obtaining nourishment for the young and territorial behaviour is no longer apparent. Parents regurgitate food to the young in the nest or at the entrance to it. When fledged the young at first hop a little out of the nest but may return to it again at first. The young appear to recognize their parents clearly although it is not known whether this is by visual or auditory means. As a parent arrives in the nesting tree the young rush to it for feeding and as it withdraws the family follows it through the twigs until it flies away. Young birds gradually mix with family parties from neighbouring nests and clump together with them on perches. Then they begin to beg from adults other than their parents and may be driven away by them. In wandering about, the young sometimes enter empty nests and rest there. A parent may then feed part of its family in the original nest and others in neighbouring abandoned ones, clearly distinguishing its own progeny from strangers. From the age of 15 days the young wander more and obtain food more frequently from non-parental adults who now experience difficulty in finding their own young and begin regurgitating to all comers. By day 18 the young begin to explore branch crevices with the beak, to nibble at twigs, and to mandibulate pieces of grass in precocious nest building movements and to pick up fallen seeds below the trees.

The tendency of young Queleas to clump together in parties and to remain in the nest vicinity keeps them safely in the protective cover of the thorn bushes in which the nests (in Mauretania) are normally placed and beyond which there are numerous predators at this time. At between 16 and 19 days the fused family groups start moving about the colony in massed parties showing a marked synchronization of activity. They do not, however, yet show the "individual distance" antagonism of adult birds. Juvenile flocking thus differs considerably from that of adults with its marked spacing of individuals. The transition from juvenile to adult flocking has not been studied but aggressive pecking begins at about 19 days (at the same time as the beak is first used in a variety of other ways including incipient nest-building). It appears that the pituitary—gonad neuroendocrinal mechanism may be established at around this time, even though it is not yet properly operational (cf. Andrew, 1964, on chicks). At around the 20th day, young birds start flying in large parties around and out of the colony area, doubtless confusing any waiting predators by their immense numbers and the already integrated movements of their dense flocks.

FEEDING ECOLOGY

THE NATURAL DIET

Quelea is a typical granivore in having a powerful stout bill which permits it to deal with a wide variety of grass seeds. The conical shape of the bill also serves to minimize the considerable attrition suffered by the beak during the dry season when, for many months, the birds feed by picking seeds off the ground. The principal food of *Quelea* throughout Africa is the seeds of the wild grasses which grow prolifically over most of the species' range (Naude, 1955; Lourens, 1955; Ward, 1965a). The growing season in these semi-arid areas is only a few weeks and the grasses are mainly fast-growing annuals which produce masses of seed, such as *Panicum, Echinochloa, Digitaria* and *Pennisetum*. The only detailed study of the diet has been made in the Lake Chad region of Nigeria where marked seasonal changes in the food were found (Ward, 1965a). Although the birds were found to eat the seeds of over forty species of grasses, only ten of these were important. Two-thirds of their annual diet was composed of the seeds from only three species (wild rice *Oryza barthii*, wild sorghum *Sorghum purpureo-castaneum*, and *Echinochloa colonum*). At certain times of year insects and spiders are eaten in large numbers, but constitute only a small fraction of the annual diet.

The pattern of seasonal dietary changes given below was recorded in Nigeria (Ward, 1965a), but there are indications that it may be typical of other areas in Africa (see, for example, Plowes, 1955; Stewart, 1959; Morel *et al.*, 1957).

During the wet season grasses grow to maturity, flower, and seed in a few weeks. As the seeds ripen, or when the grasses dry out following the wet season, all the seeds are shed. Thus, seeds are available on the plants for only a few weeks; for the rest of the year the birds must find the seeds on the ground. The density of seeds on the ground has not been assessed, but it is evident that areas of low-lying, rich alluvial soil, which are frequently inundated to shallow depth during the rains, have a far greater seed productivity than do areas of sandy or rocky ground.

Once the rains have ceased, and the ground begins to dry out under the fierce sun, no more seeds (apart from cultivated cereals grown under irrigation) are produced for 9 months or more. The abundance of seeds on the ground must be steadily depleted by many animals including, besides *Quelea*, other birds, rodents and insects. The rate at which the supply is reduced has not been measured, but must depend on both the initial production and the numbers of animals exploiting it; the rate must vary considerably annually and regionally. One result of the decline in food during the dry season is a change in the feeding behaviour of *Quelea*. At first, when seeds are most abundant, Queleas may be seen feeding everywhere, on sand dunes, farmland, and open plains, often in small flocks numbering only hundreds of birds, and often in places where other species of birds are feeding on (presumably the same) seeds. Moreover, their feeding appears leisurely, birds within a flock hopping about in all directions picking up seeds. As the dry season advances, Queleas concentrate more and more on the extensive alluvial plains where seeds are most plentiful, and the flocks swell into thousands or tens of thousands. No longer do the members of a flock feed as before; instead the whole flock moves forward over the ground, all individuals hopping in the same direction, picking up any seeds they chance upon, then finding themselves at the rear of the advancing horde, fly over the flock and land at the front. From a distance the general impression is of a great black cloud rolling steadily forward across the plain. Yet another indication of the gradually worsening food situation is the birds' acceptance of a wider variety of seeds, including some not eaten at other times. In the early dry season the food is almost entirely grass seeds of about 1 mg each, but the proportions of very small ($0 \cdot 3$–$0 \cdot 5$ mg) and larger (14–30 mg) seeds in the diet increase markedly as the dry season advances.

Throughout *Quelea's* range, the greatest dry season concentrations of birds are in river valleys (Rivers Senegal, Niger, Nile, Zambezi, and countless smaller water-courses) and on ground inundated during the wet season around lakes, or in seasonal swamps (inundation zone of the Niger, Lake Chad, Lake Rukwa, Okovango Basin, etc.).

Although, in at least some years, the birds' food situation may become serious in the latter part of the dry season, it is the beginning of the rains which is the most crucial time. As the ground is wetted by the first heavy rain, all the viable seeds suddenly germinate and within a few days there is no longer any food available, other than the termites which swarm at this time and offer abundant food for a few days. The Queleas must then migrate to areas where seeds are available, either because rain has not yet fallen, or because it began weeks earlier and fresh green seeds are already forming on the grasses. In Nigeria, the Lake Chad population moves some 200–300 km south to areas which have been receiving rain for several weeks and feed there on the seeds of wild grasses and on cultivated millet to which they do very great damage. After a few weeks they move back north again; by this time there is abundant fresh seed to be had in the Lake Chad area, and the birds can breed. This southerly displacement of the Quelea population may occur right across West Africa, from Mauritania to Tchad Republic, where the rain front always advances steadily northward. In eastern and southern Africa, however, the rainfall pattern is more complicated, and the migrations of *Quelea* can be expected to be similarly complex. There are some indications that displacements of Quelea populations, at the onset of the local rains, occur here also. Long (1961) has noted that although Queleas were common during the breeding season near Port Herald (Malawi) and occurred in variable numbers during the dry season, they disappeared entirely for a few weeks at the beginning of the rains. Lamm (1955) noted a similar departure at the onset of the rains in southern Moçambique, and the birds' return to breed after an absence of a month or so (see also Plowes, 1955; Disney, 1957).

QUELEA DAMAGE TO CEREAL CROPS

The only agricultural crops which Quelea are known to eat are cereals, though they occasionally do serious mechanical damage to trees, cotton and other crops, by sheer weight of their combined numbers. The most serious losses are probably suffered by African farmers growing millet and guinea-corn, though far more attention has been paid to the birds' depredations on rice (Senegal and Mauritania) and wheat (Kenya, Tanzania, Rhodesia and South Africa), in part because these crops are often grown on government schemes or other areas where sophisticated farming is practised and research on pests is promoted.

It is often asserted by agriculturalists that Queleas prefer cultivated cereals to their natural food, though there is no experimental evidence of this and strong indications that it is not true, the birds preferring the small seeds of wild grasses to the much larger cereal grains. In the Lake Chad region, for example, in a year when wild seeds were abundant at the time of the guinea-corn harvest, Queleas were roosting in vast numbers close to the crops, yet ignored them almost completely—even to the extent of feeding on grass seeds at the base of ripe guinea-corn plants which they left untouched.

Another factor which is of great significance when considering control measures, is the birds' ability to live independently of man's crops. Very large numbers of Queleas must live their entire lives in regions where no agriculture is practised at all. Even where there are crops of cereals, these are only available to the birds for a few weeks each year and then the Quelea population—while doing damage—may not be relying on the crops for all its food. In January and February 1961 and 1962, many random samples, each of fifty birds, were obtained from roosts destroyed with explosives in Bornu, Nigeria, in an area of intense guinea-corn cultivation; the fields were at this time full of ripening grain. In 1961, damage to the guinea-corn was considered serious, yet in only fifteen of the twenty-five samples did the birds have any guinea-corn in their crops (*Quelea* goes to roost every evening with its capacious crop in the neck packed full of seeds); the average percentage by weight of guinea-corn in the crop contents of all birds was only 20%, the rest being seeds of wild grasses. Thus, even in an area of intense farming, in a year when losses of guinea-corn were rated serious, the birds were relying on the cereal grains for only one-fifth of their food intake during the harvest period. In none of the roosts sampled did the birds have more than 62% of guinea-corn in their crops. In the next year, 1962, when damage was said to be unusually light, a mere 3% of the crop contents of 1 350 birds (belonging to twenty-seven roosts sampled) was guinea-corn (Ward, 1965a).

It is a relatively safe guess that, in most parts of Africa, Queleas are relying on natural grass seeds for 90–100% of their annual food requirements. Nevertheless, when the birds do take to raiding the crops, they are able to inflict very serious losses by virtue of the enormous numbers of birds involved.

Breeding Ecology

Queleas breed during the wet season after rain has been falling for some weeks. By this time there is abundant green grass for nest-construction, unripe seeds and water for both adults and nestlings, and a plentiful supply of insects which are required by both nestlings and adult females (Villiers, 1955; Ward, 1965b).

The nesting colonies, which may be very large, are established in groves of *Acacia* or other thorn trees (often in flooded areas), or in reeds and aquatic grasses. The daunting task of counting the nests in a colony has never been attempted, but some estimates are given for colonies in Senegal (Morel and Bourlière, 1955; Morel *et al.*, 1957). These authors found that small trees held about 500 nests each and the few tall trees in a site each held 5 000–6 000 nests. In a 50 hectare site, which they rank as average in size, there could be about half-a-million nests, while 200 hectare sites (which they say are not rare) could hold 10 million nests or more. Equally large colonies are reported from Kenya (Haylock, 1959), Nigeria (Hitchcock, 1960), Tanzania (Vesey-Fitzgerald, 1958) and several other countries, and probably occur throughout the species' range. In particularly favourable habitats, such as the shore-line of Lake Chad, several such enormous colonies may be separated from one another by only a few kilometres (Ward, 1965b). It will surprise people unfamiliar with the difficulties of travelling in such areas during the wet season, that even the large colonies of *Quelea* are hard to locate, and small ones are usually discovered by accident. We have, thus, no idea how prevalent are small sites harbouring hundreds or thousands of nests, though some have been found in Nigeria, Senegal and elsewhere. This is significant in that although at present most Queleas probably nest in large assemblages, selective destruction of these could result in the birds' breeding increasingly in small colonies, impossible to destroy in any number.

Part of the difficulty in locating *Quelea* nesting colonies is their ephemeral nature. The roughly spherical nests of woven grass strips can be built in a few days, eggs laid and hatched within 2 weeks, and the young birds able to quit the nest after a further 2 weeks (though they must remain in the site for some little time more). The activities of the members of a colony are, as a rule, highly synchronized, so that within 5 or 6 weeks millions of birds can have settled in a few hectares of trees, nested, and departed with their young. The adults never raise a second brood in the site.

Most nests contain two or three eggs, three being the commonest clutch-size all over the species' range. Egg and nestling mortality has been found to be low in most colonies examined (but see Vesey-Fitzgerald, 1958), there being too few predators to make any real impact on the large number of birds in a period of a few weeks. At one colony studied in north-east Nigeria, 87% of the eggs laid gave rise to young able to leave the nest (Ward, 1965b). This study and one by Morel and Bourlière (1955) indicate that a pair of Queleas can, on average, produce two young able to leave the site. There is no evidence that *Quelea* can breed twice in the same year, although they could conceivably do so by moving between areas which receive rain at different times of year; this is more likely in East Africa than in West Africa where the rainfall pattern is very uniform.

The total area of Africa within which breeding may occur, wherever local conditions permit, is probably over 2 million sq. miles and is much greater than the area that can support permanent populations of *Quelea*. Many breeding colonies have been discovered in places which could not harbour Queleas in the dry season, because of insufficient water or food.

PROTECTION OF CROPS FROM QUELEA DAMAGE

Before considering how our knowledge of *Quelea* biology could possibly be applied to the problem of crop protection, it is well to realize how little we know about this pest. No figures for Quelea damage can be found which are in any way reliable; all one can say at present is that over most of its range Queleas cause considerable damage to crops, and in some areas probably make cereal cultivation impossible. Wherever the birds are numerous the crops must be guarded constantly by men, women and children perched on high platforms built at close intervals in the fields; this vigilance must be maintained for many weeks, as Queleas readily take unripe grain. A constant clamour is made with rattles, strings of tins, and the like, but if the situation becomes really desperate, the whole village turns out, and patrols the rows of millet or guinea-corn with everyone shouting or beating on drums. In fact, the African farmer is powerless to stop the birds feeding on his grain; at best he can only ensure that he does not bear a disproportionate share of the losses in an area, by keeping the birds on the move.

Practically nothing is known of the distribution of breeding concentrations in half of the twenty or more countries included in the species' total range. Some aerial surveys have been carried out within relatively small areas, but it would be extremely difficult to survey large areas by this means. Only when the birds are at the breeding sites can they be located easily from the air; in any region this is only a month or two each year, and ground conditions then—at the height of the rains—often make it impossible to transport fuel, etc. to the areas being surveyed. During the rest of the year, Queleas are highly nomadic; and their roosts may be abandoned after only a few weeks occupancy. Thus, we have no real idea of the total numbers of *Quelea* in any area, though the numbers killed by control units give us some scale to work with. Two teams working along the River Senegal valley were able to destroy, with explosives, sixty-eight roosts—and kill an estimated 80 million Queleas—in 5 months (Mallamaire, 1960); it is not known what proportion of the total population of the valley this represented. Equally fantastic numbers have been accounted for elsewhere (see later), and suggest that the total Quelea population of Africa might be between 10^9 and 10^{11}.

The best way to study Queleas' movements probably will be by ringing, though possibly biotelemetry could be used in some areas. Some ringing has already been carried out, notably in southern Africa (Ashton, 1950–60; McLachlan, 1961–65), but the results are somewhat disheartening. Of 58 957 birds ringed, 143 (0.2%) were recovered, and only 20 (0.03%) from distances greater than 200 miles away; much the same recovery rates were obtained in East Africa where 54 000 birds were ringed (Disney, 1960). Despite such low recovery rates, many records could be obtained by greatly increasing the number of birds ringed. This is feasible, but there is great danger of getting biased results, the majority of recoveries coming from those areas where Quelea control is being practised. Despite these difficulties there are good reasons to carry out ringing in order to obtain information on population dynamics, long-distance returns being regarded as bonuses. One short study of this kind has been made (Morel and Bourlière, 1955), but long-term studies in various parts of Africa are badly needed.

Without a fuller knowledge of Queleas' numbers, natural fluctuations in numbers, and movements, there is great risk of spending large sums of money on control measures aimed at permanently reducing the population size, and finding, after some time, that the campaign has coincided with a natural decline following which the birds reappear in their former numbers. This may have happened in South Africa where, between 1956 and 1960, 400 million Queleas were destroyed by aerial spraying; by 1961 the Quelea problem was seemingly under control. Then, in the 1962/63 season the spraying programme had to be extended over a greater area than ever before because of massive invasions of the farmlands. In the 1966/67 season, over 6 000 acres had to be sprayed and a record 112 million birds killed (*Landbounuus*, 1967). It is possible that invasions have occurred for a long time; for example, Rowan (personal communication) finds evidence for mass invasions in 1910, 1917, 1925 and 1929. Although there now exist many practicable ways of destroying Queleas (poisons, explosives, flame-throwers, etc.), we believe it is impossible permanently to reduce the bird population anywhere. The reasons for this assertion have been given elsewhere (Ward,

1964, 1965d) and may be summarized as follows. The total range of the species is very large and in many parts of it the birds do no damage to crops and are inaccessible. Any temporary local reduction in the numbers of Queleas effected by control operations would be rapidly followed by re-invasion from such "reservoirs". Apart from this, their annual breeding probably results in a temporary doubling of the pre-breeding population size. From the little evidence we have, it appears that the numbers of Quelea are limited by the supply of natural food (Ward, 1965a). It is quite possible that the birds killed by man constitute only a (small) part of the "doomed excess" which is bound to die each year. In other words, attempts to reduce the population size may be no more than culling operations which, if anything, have the result of keeping the Quelea population closer to a permanently healthy level!

If this is the case, is there any point in killing Queleas? The answer to this depends on the local situation. If, by killing them, a temporary respite can be obtained and the harvest gathered with reduced losses, the operation may be economically sound. This is only likely to be the case where the crops are concentrated. In the Senegal Valley the annual destruction of large numbers of Queleas living close to the new rice schemes is felt to be worthwhile, the cost per bird (0·19 CFA francs) being far less than the amount of rice it would have eaten over the subsequent weeks (Mallamaire, 1960). Over most of Africa, however, there seems little point in mass destruction of Queleas, and other ways of protecting the crops must be found. Modern bird-scaring devices are little better than traditional methods and the breeding of "bird-proof" varieties of cereals has not yet met with any success. Indeed, there are reasons for thinking that, even if such varieties can be produced, they will not provide the answer everywhere; in some areas the crops are probably being raided by starving birds which would not easily be deterred. In certain places, such as Lake Chad, it may be possible to avoid trouble by planting crops which ripen when the birds' natural food is plentiful and not, as is done now, so that they ripen as Queleas natural food supply is becoming short. Like all other possible remedies, the utility of such "Quelea avoidance" tactics is limited to specific areas. Over the continent as a whole, many methods of crop protection will need to be developed. While this is being done, much research is required into the ecology and behaviour of *Quelea* and other weaver-bird pests.

SUMMARY

1. Quelea birds have apparently been causing serious damage to grain crops in the drier parts of Africa for a long time, but the problem has

I

only recently been recognized. *Quelea quelea* has a range of some two million square miles and in places is exceedingly numerous. In all their activities queleas are highly gregarious; the ethological basis of their gregariousness is discussed.

2. The natural diet of Queleas consists of small grass seeds; where this food supply is abundant—in areas of fertile soil—dense populations of queleas can exist. At certain times of year the birds raid crops of millet, wheat, guinea-corn, or rice, and can do enormous damage. In some areas at least, these depredations result from seasonal shortage of the birds' preferred wild food supply.

3. Breeding colonies are established in well-protected sites and may contain millions of nests. As a result of breeding the population can be approximately doubled, so that a natural annual mortality of around 50 per cent is to be expected.

4. Highly efficient methods of killing queleas have been devised and hundreds of millions of birds can be destroyed each year within a single country. However, the birds killed probably constitute only part of the "doomed excess" produced by breeding. Also, losses can be made up by immigration from remote areas where the birds cannot be attacked.

5. We believe that, except where it is done to give immediate relief to an area of concentrated farming where the birds are currently doing damage, massive destruction of queleas is excessively expensive and, at most, can only bring about temporary, local reductions in the population of the pest.

6. In specific areas it may be possible to avoid quelea damage by changes in agricultural procedure. Elsewhere much research will have to be done before any solution to the problem can be found.

Acknowledgements

We wish to thank Dr. I. Newton for his criticism of the manuscript and Miss Waina Cheng for her help in the preparation of Fig. 1.

References

Andrew, R. J. (1964). The development of adult responses from responses given during imprinting by the domestic chick. *Anim. Behav.* **12**, 542–548.

Ashmole, P. (1963). The regulation of numbers of tropical oceanic birds. *Ibis* **103B**, 458–473.

Ashton, H. (1950–60). First to sixth ringing reports. *Ostrich* **21**, 106–111; **23**, 56–61; **25**, 2–12; **25**, 130–138; **27**, 5–13; **28**, 98–115.

Bannerman, D. A. (1949). "The Birds of Tropical West Africa." Crown Agents, London.

Busnel, R. G. and Gramet, P. (1956). Recherches préliminaires sur le comporte-
ment acoustique de *Quelea quelea quelea* Latham en captivité. *Bull. Inst. fr.
Afr. noire* **18** Ser. A. No. 1, 280–325.

Busnel, R. G. and Grosmaire, P. (1955) [The traditional method of campaigning
against Quelea. An enquiry among the people of the Senegal valley.] *C.C.T.A./
C.S.A. Africa* (55). Joint Secretariat. Bukavu. Original report in French,
partial translation in Crook (1956).

Butterfield, P. A. and Crook, J. H. (1968). The annual cycle of nest-building and
agonistic behaviour in captive *Quelea quelea* with reference to endocrine factors.
Anim. Behav. (in press).

Crook, J. H. (1953). An observational study of the gulls of Southampton Water.
Br. Birds **46**, 386–397.

Crook, J. H. (1956). "Bird Damage and Crop Protection in West Africa." Report
to Colonial Office. Ref. D 46/1/58 100 3/57 R. 6 pp. London.

Crook, J. H. (1960). Studies on the social behaviour of *Quelea q. quelea* (Linn.) in
French West Africa. *Behaviour* **16**, 1–55.

Crook, J. H. (1961). The basis of flock organisation in birds. *In* "Current
Problems in Animal Behaviour" (W. H. Thorpe and O. L. Zangwill, eds.),
chap. 5. Cambridge University Press.

Crook, J. H. (1964). The evolution of social organisation and visual communication in the weaver birds (Ploceinae). *Behaviour Suppl.* **10**, 1–178.

Crook, J. H. (1965). The adaptive significance of avian social organisations.
Symp. zool. Soc. Lond. No. 14, 181–218.

Dekeyser, P. L. (1955). Recherches sur la biologie du Travailleur à bec rouge.
Quelea quelea (Latham) en AOF (1951–1954). *Bull. Inst. fr. Afr. noire* **17**, Ser.
A, No. 2, 592–615.

Disney, H. J. de S. (1957). *Quelea quelea* in Tanganyika. Notes on plumage skull
and food. *C.C.T.A./C.S.A.* (57)8. Joint Secretariat, Bukavu.

Disney, H. J. de S. (1960). Ringing and marking of Quelea in Tanganyika.
C.C.T.A./C.S.A. (60) 9. Joint Secretariat, Lagos.

Disney, H. J. de S. and Haylock, J. W. (1956). The distribution and breeding
behaviour of the Sudan Dioch (*Quelea q. aethiopica*) in Tanganyika. *E. Afr.
agric. J.* **21**, 141–156.

Disney, H. J. de S. and Marshall, A. J. (1956). A contribution to the breeding
biology of the weaver finch *Quelea quelea* (Linnaeus) in E. Africa. *Proc. zool.
Soc. Lond.* **127**, 379–387.

Disney, H. J. de S., Lofts, B. and Marshall, A. J. (1959). Duration of the
regeneration period of the internal reproductive rhythm in a xerophilous
equatorial bird, *Quelea quelea. Nature, Lond.* **184**, 1659–1660.

F.A.O. (1965). Report of the F.A.O. conference on Quelea bird and water hyacinth
control in Africa. F.A.O., Rome.

Haylock, J. W. (1959). "Investigations on the Habits of Quelea Birds and their
Control." Govt. Printer, Nairobi.

Haylock, J. W. and Disney, H. J. de S. (1956). Control of the Sudan dioch or red
billed finch in Tanganyika. *E. Afr. agric. J.* **21**, 210–217.

Hediger, H. (1950). Wild Animals in Captivity. London.

Hitchcock, R. (1960). Quelea control in northern Nigeria. *C.C.T.A./C.S.A.*
Quelea. (60) 10. Joint Secretariat, Bukavu.

James, H. W. (1928). Nesting of the southern pink-billed weaver (*Quelea quelea
lathami*). *Ool. Rec.* **8**, 84–85.

Lamm, D. W. (1955). Local migratory movements in southern Mozambique. *Ostrich* **26**, 32–37.

Landbounuus (1967). [Queleas still give much trouble]. **498**, 9. (In Africaans.)

Lockie, J. D. (1956). Winter fighting in feeding flocks of rooks, jackdaws and carrion crows. *Bird Study* **3**, 180–190.

Lofts, B. (1962). The effects of exogenous androgen on the testicular cycle of the weaver finch, *Quelea quelea. Gen. comp. Endocr.* **2**, 394–406.

Lofts, B. (1964). Evidence of an autonomous reproductive rhythm in an equatorial bird. *Nature, Lond.* **201**, 523–524.

Long, C. (1961). The birds of Port Herald district (Part III). *Ostrich* **32**, 147–173.

Lourens, D. C. (1955). Biology of *Quelea quelea lathami. C.C.T.A./C.S.A.* (55) 124 Joint Secretariat, Bukavu.

McLachlan, G. L. (1961–67). Seventh to twelfth ringing reports. *Ostrich* **32**, 36–47; **33**, 29–34; **34**, 102–109; **35**, 101–110; **36**, 214–223; **38**, 17–26.

Mallamaire, L. (1960). "La Lutte Contre les Oiseaux Granivores." Dakar (mineograph).

Marler, P. (1956). Territory and individual distance in the chaffinch, *Fringilla coelebs. Ibis* **98**, 496–501.

Marshall, A. J. and Disney, H. J. de S. (1956). Photostimulation of an equatorial bird (*Quelea quelea*, Linnaeus). *Nature, Lond.* **177**, 143–144.

Marshall, A. J. and Disney, H. J. de S. (1957). Experimental induction of the breeding season in a xerophilous bird. *Nature, Lond.* **180**, 647–649.

Morel, G. and Bourlière, F. (1955). Recherches écologiques sur *Quelea quelea quelea* (L.) de la basse vallée du Sénégal. I. Données quantitatives sur le cycle annuel. *Bull. Inst. fr. Afr. noire* **17**, Ser. A, No. 2, 618–663.

Morel, G. and Bourlière, F. (1956). Recherches écologiques sur les *Quelea quelea quelea* (L.) de la basse vallée du Sénégal. II. La reproduction. *Alauda* **24**, 97–122.

Morel, M. Y. and Morel, G. (1957). Notes complémentaires sur l'écologie et l'éthologie du *Quelea quelea quelea* (L.). *Alauda* **25**, 6–93.

Morel, G., Morel, M. Y. and Bourlière, F. (1957). The black-faced weaver bird or dioch in West Africa. *J. Bombay nat. Hist. Soc.* **54**, 812–825.

Murton, R. K., Isaacson, A. J. and Westwood, N. J. (1966). The relationships between woodpigeons and their clover food supply and the mechanism of population control. *J. appl. Ecol.* **3**, 55–96.

Naude, T. J. (1955), The red-billed weaver and its control. *Fmg. S. Afr.* October. Reprint no. 69, pp. 1–4.

Plowes, D. C. H. (1955). Queleas in Southern Rhodesia. *C.C.T.A./C.S.A.* (55) 121. Joint Secretariat, Bukavu.

Simmons, K. E. L. (1966) Pattern of dispersion of the white wagtail and other birds outside the breeding season. *Bull. Br. Orn. Club* **85**, 161–168.

Stewart, D. R. M. (1959). The red-billed quelea in Northern Rhodesia. *Nth. Rhod. Jl.*, 55–62.

Vesey-Fitzgerald, D. F. (1958). Notes on breeding colonies of the red billed *Quelea* in southwest Tanganyika. *Ibis* **100**, 167–174.

Villiers, A. (1955). L'entomophagie de *Quelea quelea quelea* latham. C.C.T.A./ C.S.A. (55). Joint Secretariat, Bukavu.

Ward, P. (1964). The war against the Quelea bird. *New Scient.* **22**, 736–738.

Ward, P. (1965a). Feeding ecology of the black-faced dioch *Quelea quelea* in Nigeria. *Ibis* **107**, 173–214.

Ward, P. (1965b). The breeding biology of the black-faced dioch *Quelea quelea* in Nigeria. *Ibis* **107**, 326–349.

Ward, P. (1965c). Seasonal changes in the sex ratio of *Quelea quelea* (Ploceinae). *Ibis* **107**, 397–399.

Ward, P. (1965d). Biological implications of Quelea control in West Africa. Compte-rendu, Congrès de Protection des Cultures tropicales, Marseilles, pp. 661–665.

Ward, P. (1966). Distribution, systematics, and polymorphism of the African weaver-bird *Quelea quelea*. *Ibis* **108**, 34–40.

Wilson, C. E. (1947). The Sudan dioch in grain growing areas. *Sudan Notes Rec.* **28**, 151–156.

Discussion

Professor Wynne-Edwards opened the final session by commenting on the high standard of objective discussion that had been maintained even though many points at issue roused strong emotional feelings. Only by free and open discussion of this kind could we expect to reach sound and rational decisions about important wildlife matters whether in terms of pest control or conservation.

THOMPSON: I have some comments to make, which follow from Professor Wynne-Edwards' opening remarks about rational decisions. We are pleased to have a number of non-biologists at this Symposium, but this is primarily a meeting of biologists so do not let us forget that there are many biologists in government departments (it will be difficult to do this after looking at the conference agenda). Whether a biologist is concerned with the protection of crops, livestock or fisheries, with conservation, or with general ecological research, he has been and is subject to the same discipline as his professional colleagues in other institutions. The results of his work are published and available for criticism and discussion. It is easy to become over emotional about animals, especially birds and mammals, but only by reasonable discussion will rational decisions be reached.

PRESTT: What damage do feral pigeons cause and what is its cost?

THEARLE: Apart from generally fouling our towns and giving cause for concern on grounds of hygiene, they may locally invade food storage and processing plants, where the damage caused in terms of fouling and food loss may become extremely severe. For example, in the Liverpool docks it was estimated that feral pigeons removed several hundred tons of stored grain and grain products from a single warehouse in one year.

CORNWELL: It may be of interest if I comment on the results obtained by a pest control servicing company in the use of traps to deplete populations of feral pigeons in towns. It has proved possible over a period of 7–8 weeks, including time for pre-baiting, to remove 75% of a population of feral pigeons in towns containing 50 000–100 000 people, and in certain places the pigeon population has by no means recovered to its original size within a period of a year. This has been achieved without antagonizing the public and without putting protected species at risk.

Could Mr. Thearle please state whether the Ministry is currently undertaking field trials with sterilizing chemicals as a means of pigeon population management?

THEARLE: We are not currently undertaking field trials with sterilants though we are interested in the subject and have followed developments.*

* Laboratory experiments have been conducted in the Infestation Control Laboratory of the Ministry of Agriculture, Fisheries and Food and field trials are scheduled to begin in late 1968. Eds.

Proper understanding of the effectiveness of these methods requires a full knowledge of the population dynamics of the species concerned and this has been a major aim of our Salford studies. Moreover, the problems involved in introducing chemicals selectively to birds are fundamentally the same as those we are tackling in our field research into the use of stupefying baits.

I wonder if Dr. Cornwell can tell us what trapping effort was needed in the towns he mentioned where successful control was achieved.

CORNWELL: We mapped all the feeding sites in the area and then used twelve traps over 7–8 weeks.

PALFREMAN: How good is your ability to count feral pigeons in your study area because in my experience only 50% of the birds are visible at any one time.

THEARLE: We accept this drawback and have checked our counts by making them at different times of day and by making several counts in succession. Furthermore, we can estimate our accuracy by comparing data from visual counts with figures derived using Lincoln Index techniques on several sub-populations which are marked with numbered rings and plastic wing-tags. Provided our counts are an accurate index of population changes it does not matter that they may not be absolute. This can be checked.

BOURNE: Just now I asked a former Assistant Secretary to the Medical Research Council whether he thought birds were important carriers of disease, and he observed that anyone who caught diseases from birds deserved what they got. This may be the case with one ringer I know who caught a fairly severe fever, though it seems more doubtful with the child of another ringer who had one. Parrots are well known carriers of psittacosis, and their importation is restricted accordingly; and the fact that the fulmars of the Faroes caught psittacosis from parrot carcases and infected the local human population is also well-known. There has also recently been another medical report of a fairly considerable epidemic of ornithosis among pigeon-fanciers in Cambridgeshire. These are merely the detected cases of birds carrying human disease amongst us; the salmonellosis mentioned by Mr. Thearle involves the group of bacteria causing one of the more important forms of food poisoning (and also typhoid fever), and we do not know how much of that is caused by birds.

I am not clear if the Newcastle virus which seems fairly widespread among our seabirds is the same as the fowl pest one, but in any case it seems very worthy of more attention. Thus a virus antigenically similar to one causing an infection of chickens in Scotland in 1959 was discovered causing an epidemic among Common Terns (including some probably originating in Scotland) in South Africa in 1961 (Uys and Becker, 1966). The capacity of birds for spreading disease is frightening; large sums are already being spent on research into migration in the Middle and Far East, largely in connection with birds capacity for spreading various arthropod-born diseases including some obscure human encephalitises. This work could also be developed for warlike purposes; whatever may be the position with foot and mouth disease, nothing would be easier than to get birds to carry a disease like anthrax from one continent to another to give rise to serious epidemics of untraceable origin. The whole subject of bird-transmitted disease deserves continuous watchful scrutiny.

ELLIOTT: In our field experiments throughout the country, damage from small birds, mainly sparrows, is a serious problem. I am one of those who believe that sparrow damage to farm cereal crops leads to greater economic loss than is generally recognized. I was therefore very interested when I heard that the Institute of Biology was to arrange a symposium on "The problems of birds as pests" but disappointed to find that in the programme there was no paper nor any reference at all to this important subject. This seems to confirm what some of us have felt for a long time which is that insufficient priority is being given to solving this serious problem.

I have two questions:
1. Could we please be told what work is being undertaken or is planned for the future at the Infestation Control Laboratory or elsewhere?
2. Can any of the assembled experts suggest any novel control method to try as none of the present methods available, e.g. bangers, shooting, trapping, narcotics, balloons etc. are wholly successful.

THOMPSON: Many problems posed by birds in urban areas are made by man and perpetuated by him. An agricultural research station near to, or engulfed by, urban sprawl is bound to suffer. Scaring devices, no matter how elaborate, are of limited use and complete physical protection of experimental plots is perhaps the cheapest solution in the long run. However, large-scale live-trapping trials are currently being carried out and the results are awaited with interest.

It must be emphasized that the study of urban birds is a large subject, and one of increasing importance as the human population rises and increasingly aggregates in towns and cities. The problems that arise are not likely to respond to *ad hoc* solutions, but merit and require thorough study by biologists.

NORRIS: The real solution to the sparrow problem at the N.I.A.B. is to put the Institute in the middle of Dartmoor or to have everything caged in.

However, we, like Dr. Ward, have concluded that in this situation the only possible time when killing birds is likely to stop damage is to try to get the sparrows immediately before damage is expected, and this we hope to try next year by what might be called neolithic trapping methods.

HARRISON: In view of the fact that damage by bullfinches to orchards has increased significantly in recent times, is it not possible that this is correlated with modern farming practice which may have reduced the amount of weeds such as dock and nettles which are available as food?

NEWTON: There is good evidence that the upper limit to the size of a bullfinch population is set by the amount of seed available in winter. If more seeds were available in the past, there would therefore have been correspond-

ingly more bullfinches and damage should still have been severe in the years
of scarcity. But in any case, as I mentioned earlier, it is doubtful whether
farmland was formerly colonized by bullfinches to the extent that it is now,
so that even if food were more plentiful then, the birds would not have been
there to take advantage of it.

DUNNET: You give a list of four staple items in the diet of bullfinches
during winter, and related bud damage to the abundance of the ash crop only.
Could you give us some idea of the relative importance of the various seed
sources to bullfinches?

NEWTON: The weight of ash seed eaten greatly exceeds that of all other
items added together.

BOURNE: The relation between bullfinch damage to fruit buds and the
preceding ash seed crop seems very interesting. If one understands it rightly,
in the years when the ash seed crop is good, the fruit buds are spared the
following spring and the fruit crop is good the following autumn. That year
the ashes are exhausted, the bullfinches turn to fruit buds the next spring,
and the fruit crop is poor the next autumn, when the ash crop is good again
because the trees have recovered. Thus the fruit crop is liable to be inversely
proportional to the ash crop in the same autumn. Of course, one might expect
the fruit trees also to have alternate poor years from exhaustion anyway, but
presumably the farmers must be right in attributing their years of failure to
bullfinches rather than exhaustion of the trees? In any case, the whole system
provides an interesting demonstration of the way in which the existence of
secondary foods will tend to damp down fluctuations resulting from a variable
production of primary ones before they are reflected on a large scale throughout natural communities. One might think that the moral of all this is that
the farmer who catches his bullfinches and gets his fruit crop on the same
two-year-cycle as the ash, instead of its reciprocal, will have fruit when there
is a scarcity rather than when there is a glut. But then, if there are local
variations, perhaps in the end everything is evened out?

NEWTON: Many fruit trees do tend to crop biennially, as Dr. Bourne
suggests, but one of the aims of cultivation is to even out this inherent
periodicity, by appropriate pruning and manuring, so that at least a moderate
crop is produced every year. Bullfinch damage is very easily recognized and
there is no possibility that growers are attributing a natural rhythm to the
actions of bullfinches. Before the bullfinch became a major pest, good crops
were obtained most years, as indeed they are today in places where the bird
is effectively controlled.

The problem of why ash trees tend to crop biennially raises two separate
questions: why individual trees have this periodicity, and why different trees
fruit in phase with one another. To take the first point, it seems that in
southern England, two years are required by an ash tree to accumulate enough
food-reserves (stored in the twigs and branches) to produce a seed-crop. (In
northern Britain, where the growing season is shorter, three years may be

required for this and in southern Sweden four.) Different trees tend to crop in phase with one another because certain environmental factors, such as a late frost, may destroy all the flowers in one year, thus bringing all the trees into phase the next. The trees will then tend to crop in parallel for a number of years, gradually getting out of phase with one another, until some external agent again destroys the flowers of one year to restore the rhythm. This is a common explanation offered by botanists of synchronous fruiting in trees, though no doubt other factors are involved, too; in some tree-species, the weather in late summer is supposed to be important in influencing cropping.

SUMMERS: It is worth stressing the difficulties involved in estimating the damage caused by bullfinches. To avoid the biases due to the accumulation of damage and the concentration of damage near to hedgerows, very large counts must be made to obtain a reliable estimate of bud damage. Even then the percentage bud loss does not have a direct bearing on the loss in yield as some types of fruit tree are more tolerant of bud damage than others. For example, in an orchard where individual Conference pear trees suffered bud losses of between 6 and 90% it was not possible to detect any loss in the subsequent yields of trees having less than 70% bud damage. On the other hand Leveller gooseberry bushes situated near to a hedgerow which had suffered slight to moderate amounts of damage over a period of about five years produced less than one third as much fruit as similar bushes situated in the centre of the plantations which had never suffered bud damage.

Referring to the discrepancy between the age structure of Dr. Newton's woodland population and the orchard population as shown by samples received from fruit growers, I believe this to be due to the methods used to catch the birds and not any difference in the behaviour of bullfinches in two habitats. My own experience suggests that young birds are more easily attracted by decoys than are older birds and I am assuming that Dr. Newton's growers were using traps employing a decoy while he himself was using mist nets. Using baited Chardonneret traps I have obtained first-year to adult ratios of from 2·2:1 to 2·7:1 corresponding figures of my own and some growers using a decoy range from 5·3:1 to 12:1 (see Table I). It is also true that bullfinches move slightly farther in their first autumn than in subsequent years but presumably this holds equally for woodland and orchard populations.

TABLE I

County	1st year : adult	Total number	Time	Method of trapping
Kent	2·7 : 1	138	Nov. 1960	Baited Chardonneret (M.A.F.F.)
Sussex	2·2 : 1	51	Dec.–Mar. 1962–63	Baited Chardonneret (M.A.F.F.)
Kent	5·3 : 1	76	Nov.–Dec. 1962	Decoys (growers)
Sussex	12·0 : 1	13	Dec.–Mar. 1962–63	Decoys (M.A.F.F.)

NEWTON: I fully agree with Mr. Summers' remarks on the difficulties of assessing bud-loss and its effect on the subsequent crop. But in cases where there has been almost complete removal of buds by bullfinches, there is no question that they have thereby reduced the crop.

In the winter of 1963–64, I recorded the age of over 1 700 bullfinches trapped by fruit growers in orchards (with the aid of baited traps and decoys), for comparison with birds netted from a "natural" population in Marley Wood. The results were as follows:

TABLE II

Sample size		Number of first-year birds per adult		
		Oct.–Dec.	Jan.–Feb.	Mar.–April
Marley Wood	242	3	2	2
Orchards	1761	38	4	21

The autumn ratio from the wood fits with the reproductive rate of the species and the decline in proportion of first-year birds during the winter is consistent with findings on other species. In the orchards, on the other hand, for much of the year, growers trapped proportionately many more first-year birds than one would expect to be present in a population. Only in January–February, the months when food was scarcest, did they catch a near-random sample of birds. The bias towards young birds may result because, for much of the year, these are less wary and easier to catch than older birds, or because they move around more (so that more come into the trapping area), or to a combination of both factors. But although for much of the year, growers catch a non-random sample of birds, this does not prevent them from achieving their aim, which is to hold the total population below the level at which seed-stocks are eaten out early in the winter. This can be achieved, as I said earlier, if trapping is intensive in autumn.

NORBURY: A neighbour of mine, Mr. Joe Dance, has for 20 or 30 years used lime wash with Jeyes fluid flicked on to a redcurrant bush put on at the end of November; this has effectively kept off bullfinches for many years.

A certain amount of work has been done using lime wash and fish oil. Few details are available. People who used lime wash in the early 1920's say this did not discourage bullfinches, but perhaps if something was found to mix with lime wash this might act as a remedy against bullfinch damage.

MILSTEIN: My knowledge of the red-billed quelea is comparatively limited, but a close former colleague, D. C. Lourens, has done considerable research. This is being worked up for a D.Sc.(Agric.) thesis. In South Africa the quelea is no longer considered a research problem, but more a routine, highly successful control operation. Aerial surveys are practicable over large areas. Assessments of crop damage have been made. Movements are probably food search in varying degrees of magnitude. Monogamy may have been relatively over-emphasized. The 0·02% recovery rate involved superseded rings with a number outside and an address *inside*. Field experience with bird-proof sorghums resembles Dr. Ward's aviary trials.

WARD: We are aware that research on quelea has been in progress in South Africa for about 15 years. We have not been able to refer to this work in our paper as, unfortunately, few detailed results have been published so far. It may be that, as Mr. Milstein claims, there is little need for further research on quelea in South Africa. If so, there must be an explanation for the dramatic increase in the numbers of queleas which have been invading South Africa in recent years despite the routine control operations. As far as the rest of Africa is concerned, a considerable amount of work has already been done in several countries, but we must admit that a tremendous research effort will be required before the quelea problem can be tackled effectively and economically.

Dr. J. H. Crook commented on the remark that monogamy may have been over-emphasized and drew attention to his paper (Crook, 1964) "The evolution of social organization and visual communication in the weaver birds (Ploceinae)". *Behav. Suppl.* 10, 1964.

SEUBERT: Is it true that overgrazing contributed to the quelea problem in Africa?

WARD: I know this has often been suggested, but I doubt if there is any real information on which to base such an assertion. If overgrazing leads to a change in the grass cover, such that annual grasses (which produce the seeds on which the birds feed) replace perennial grasses, then the area may be able to support more birds than it could formerly. Other activities of man, such as shifting-cultivation, burning, deforestation, and irrigation may also be extending the areas suitable for queleas. It would be wrong, however, to think that queleas have only recently become a menace; vast numbers were seen by early explorers of Africa. The serious damage being done by birds in many isolated regions was treated everywhere as a local problem until about twenty years ago, when it was realized that the main culprit was the same species all over the drier parts of the continent.

YAPP: In most of the problems that we have heard about today there is the common factor that the chief damage is done by the birds between breeding seasons, so that the reduction in numbers, by starvation or predation, that occurs during this period, can reduce the damage only to the extent that it can be shifted earlier in the season. The breeding population of most birds probably depends on the available habitat, and the best way of reducing the population would seem to be to reduce the area of suitable habitat in the neighbourhood of the places where damage occurs. Even then, some species may manage to change their habits and occupy a new environment, as has happened to some extent with the wood-pigeon.

MURTON: It is difficult to understand how in many circumstances habitat control can be a feasible proposition. Wood-pigeon numbers appear to be determined by the availability of certain field crops and they breed in any convenient woods and hedgerows adjacent to the feeding grounds. It would be quite unrealistic, as well as detrimental to many other forms of wild-life, to advocate cutting down hedgerows. In the Orkney Islands, where suitable woods are absent, wood-pigeons nest in the long heather while at times of high population density in southern England I have found them nesting in fields of corn. It is impossible to see how the winter habitat of the oyster-catcher could be altered without detriment to cockle stocks. Natural popula-tions are not in practice controlled by their reproductive rate; a one-third reduction in the number of breeding pigeons would only increase the survival chances for the progeny of the remainder and very doubtfully influence the incidence of damage. Hence, anything but complete success in interfering with breeding potential could not be considered as beneficial—threshold effects are manifest in this connection.

Some people have advocated controlling pigeons by introducing the goshawk. This neglects the question of why goshawks have always been scarce in Britain even though the occasional breeding pair has been given every opportunity to become established in recent years. But goshawks mostly take wood-pigeons when the population is swollen by a post-breeding peak of young, and all the indications are that they, like man, crop the pigeon population without causing any regulatory influence.

NEWTON: In recent years another European finch, the Redpoll *Carduelis flammea*, has started to cause serious damage to the partly open buds of apricots and pears in New Zealand. The bird was introduced there last century, had become common by the start of the present century and began attacking fruit blossoms in 1951–53; since then, damage has increased steadily (Sten-house, 1962). This is apparently a new habit for the species, and the damage done is often serious, but unlike the Bullfinch, the Redpoll gets little or no food from the buds, as gut analyses have shown. The reason for their attacks is thus unknown, but the birds are apparently attracted into the orchards by the presence of weed seeds below the trees. In April 1965, similar behaviour was noted for the first time in England on a large fruit farm near Canterbury, Kent (Newton, 1967). About a thousand Redpolls were involved in damaging pear trees, some of which had nearly half their buds destroyed. Similar, though less extensive, damage has occurred on the same farm each year since. In all years, however, the Redpolls left the orchard as soon as the ground was ploughed and the Fat-hen *Chenopodium album* seeds on which the birds had fed beneath the trees were removed.

If this habit spreads among English Redpolls, it could pose a serious problem, for large numbers pass through the southeast each spring on migra-tion between the Continent and their breeding grounds in northern Britain. On the other hand, there is hope that damage by Redpolls (unlike that by other bud-eating species) can be prevented easily by ensuring that no small weed seeds are available in the orchards in April when the birds pass through, and this is most easily achieved either by ploughing or establishing a per-manent grass sward below the trees.

REFERENCES

Crook, J. H. (1964). The evolution of social organization and visual communication in the weaver birds (*Ploceinea*). *Behaviour* (Suppl.) **10**.

Newton, I. (1967). Attacks on fruit buds by Redpolls *Carduelis flammea*. *Ibis* **109**, 440–441.

Stenhouse, D. (1962). A new habit of the Redpoll *Carduelis flammea* in New Zealand. *Ibis* **104**, 250–252.

Uys, C. J. and Becker, W. B. (1966). Studies on tern virus infection in chickens. *Ostrich* (Suppl.) **6**, 443–451.

Chairman's Conclusion

V. C. WYNNE-EDWARDS

"Birds as Pests" has proved a successful and rewarding subject for a symposium, and the gratitude of everyone concerned must go to Dr. I. Thomas for originating it. We are greatly indebted also to Dr. R. K. Murton and Mr. E. N. Wright who have acted as organizers and editors, and to all the contributors, not forgetting to mention those who travelled from overseas to participate. We would like to express special thanks, too, to the Institute of Biology for sponsoring the symposium, and to the Royal Geographical Society for their generous hospitality in making available the use of their rooms.

Birds can become pests to man in any highly developed and populous part of the world, as well as in a good many remoter places where human enterprises are less advanced. It is clear that the papers presented in the symposium ought to be regarded simply as examples of the kind of trouble that man encounters from birds. A few of the problems are world wide, for example the bird-strike hazard on airfields; and some of the incriminated species, including the domestic pigeons and house sparrows, have become widely established in sea-ports and cities in parts of the world where they were not originally native.

Usually only a small minority of species present in a region assume the status of pests; but the minority often includes those that are individually among the most abundant members of the local avifauna, for example starlings, house sparrows or red-billed queleas. The symposium contributors have made it clear that it is usually impossible to make any permanent reduction in the stocks of such species as these, so that control measures have to be accepted as a regular and persistent feature of management. In the case of abundant bird pests there may be little if any aesthetic objection to humane control; but in our own country, whenever an ornamental and attractive species is involved, the public tend to get up in arms about bird killing, and passions are aroused.

Some larger species that have been or are now regarded as pests, including many birds of prey and, locally in Britain, oystercatchers, are potentially long-lived and do not have so high a reproductive potential as many of the smaller birds; and here it is necessary to move with more caution in attempting to control their numbers, because in the past, lasting and regrettable results have sometimes been produced culminating in local extinction instead of control.

239

It is desirable to act in every case on as full a knowledge as possible of the biology of the species concerned. Given enough knowledge, rational decisions can be taken. But if people blindly take sides on questions of bird control as a matter of principle, and insist on forcing the issue one way or the other by a trial of strength, the decisions reached must necessarily be political decisions, and they may do quite unnecessary harm or injustice to the less appreciated interests on the other side. Perhaps the most encouraging feature of the whole symposium has been to show what a tremendous advance there has been in our knowledge and thinking on problems of avian population ecology in the last ten years. Even so, the more intractable of the pest problems with which our speakers have dealt look like being with us for a good many years yet.

Author Index

(Numbers in italics refer to the references at the end of each article)

A

Adams, F. R., 30, *38*
Aden, A. L., 62, *84*
Ajollo, L., 182, *196*
Andreasen, M. G., 68, *84*
Andrew, R. J., 218, *226*
Ashmole, P., 215, *226*
Ashton, H., 224, *226*
Atlas, D., 54, 79, 80, *84, 85*

B

Bannerman, D. A., 211, *226*
Becker, W. B., 231, *238*
Blacksmith, P., 60, 69, 73, *84*
Blokpoel, H., 47, *50*
Borg, K., 190, *195*
Bourliere, F., 211, 214, 216, 217, 219, 222, 223, 224, *228*
Boudreau, G. W., *28*
Bremond, J. C., 19, 21, *26, 27*
Bridgman, C. J., 99, *105*
Brough, T., 21, *26*
Busnel, R. G., 17, *26, 27, 28,* 31, 32, *38,* 211, 213, *227*
Busse, P., 129, *139*
Butterfield, P. A., 216, *227*
Buxton, E. J. M., 153, *155*

C

Chapin, J. P., 47, *50*
Clark, S. P., 161, *169*
Cook, H. F., 58, *84*
Coombes, C. J. F., 129, 134, 137, *139*
Coultas, F. W., 58, *84*
Cox, B., 17, 18, *26, 28*
Cornwell, P. B., 187, 189, *195*
Cramp, S., 181, *195*
Crawford, A. B., 54, *84*

C

Crisp, D. J., 142, *155*
Crook, J. H., 211, 213, 214, 215, 216, 217, *227,* 236, *238*

D

Dare, P. J., 143, 152, *155,* 178, *180*
Daude, J. L., 190, *196*
Davidson, P. E., 141, *155*
Deam, A. P., 69, 80, *85*
De Jong, A. P., 47, *50*
Dekeyser, P. L., 211, *227*
Disney, H. J. de S., 212, 220, 224, *227, 228*
Drinnan, R. E., 146, 149, *155*
Drury, W. H., 64, *85*

E

Eastwood, E., 54, 64, 72, 79, 80, *85*
Eber, G., 201, *209*
Edwards, J., 60, 69, 70, 71, 73, *85*
Ellenbogen, B. K., 183, *196*
Emmons, C. W., 183, *196*
Errington, P. L., 178, *180*

F

Falls, J. B., 19, *26, 27*
F.A.O., 213, *227*
Farner, D. S., 83, *85*
Fisher, H. I., 47, *50*
Franz, W., 65, *85*
Frings, H., 17, 18, *26, 27, 28,* 31, *38,* 194, *196*
Frings, M., 17, 18, *26, 28,* 194, *196*
Furcolow, M. L., 182, *196*

G

Gause, G. F., 158, *169*
Gere, B. H., 66, *85*

Scientific Names of species mentioned in the text

Acanthis cannabina	Linnet
Accipiter gentilis	Goshawk
Anas platyrhynchos	Mallard
Anser anser	Greylag goose
Anser brachyrhynchus	Pink-footed goose
Anser caerulescens	Snow goose
Apus apus	Swift
Aquila chrysaetos	Golden eagle
Asio flammeus	Short-eared owl
Buteo buteo	Buzzard
Carduelis flammea	Redpoll
Carthartes aura	Turkey vulture
Charadrius apricarius	Golden plover
Chloris chloris	Greenfinch
Circus cyaneus	Hen harrier
Colinus virginianus	Bobwhite
Columba livia	Rock dove
Columba livia var.	Feral pigion
Columba palumbus	Wood pigeon
Corvus corax	Raven
Corvus corone corone	Carrion crow
Corvus corone cornix	Hooded crow
Corvus frugilegus	Rook
Corvus monedula	Jackdaw
Cygnus columbianus	Whistling swan
Diomedea immutabilis	Laysan albatross
Diomedea nigripes	Black-footed albatross
Erithicus rubecula	Robin
Falco peregrinus	Peregrine falcon
Falco tinnunculus	Kestrel
Fregata spp.	Frigate birds
Fringilla coelebs	Chaffinch
Fulmarus glacialis	Fulmar
Gallus spp.	Chicken
Garrulus glandarius	Jay
Gyps fulvus	Griffon vulture
Haematopus ostralegus	Oystercatcher
Lagopus lagopus	Red grouse
Larus argentatus	Herring gull
Larus canus	Common gull
Larus delawarensis	Ring-billed gull
Larus ridibundus	Black-headed gull

Lyrurus tetrix	Black grouse
Melospiza georgiana	Swamp sparrow
Mergus merganser	Goosander
Mergus serrator	Red-breasted merganser
Motacilla spp.	Wagtails
Passer domesticus	House sparrow
Pica pica	Magpie
Pyrrhula pyrrhula	Bullfinch
Quelea quelea	Quelea
Regulus regulus	Goldcrest
Somateria mollissima	Eider duck
Sterna fuscata	Sooty tern
Sterna hirundo	Common tern
Sturnus vulgaris	Starling
Tetrao urogallus	Capercaillie
Turdus merula	Blackbird
Turdus philomelos	Song thrush
Tyto alba	Barn owl
Vanellus vanellus	Lapwing

Subject Index

A

Aberdeenshire, 119–139, 170, 171
Acacia, 222
Acetylene guns, 30
Aerial spraying, 224
Africa, 211–229, 236
  East, 211, 212, 213, 223, 224
  South, 211, 212, 214, 231, 235
  Southern, 213, 220, 224
  South West, 211
  West, 213, 220, 223
Agriculture, 18, 171
Agricultural Research Council, 118
Agriotes, 100
Agropyron, 172
Air Canada, 103
Aircraft,
  civil, 3, 6, 7, 11, 42, 43, 50, 87
  design, 8, 39, 42, 50, 96
  engines, loss of power of, 3, 4, 9, 39,
    44, 87, 89
  hanger, 112
  low flying, 6, 43, 89
  military, 3, 6, 7, 8, 11, 14, 43, 87, 89,
    90
  radio controlled model, 30
  small, 4
  speed, 9–10, 43, 89
  structure testing, 6, 11, 12, 50–51
  supersonic, 7, 42
  tail plane, 3, 10
  vertical take-off, 11, 96
  windscreens, 4, 6, 8, 11, 42, 50, 51,
    87
Airfields, 18, 29–38, 40, 48, 88, 97 *et seq*,
  116
  activities of birds on, 29, 102
  birds grazing on, 101
  location of, 46, 98
Airports, *see* airfields
Air Registration Board, 11, 14

Airspeed,
  species identification from, 77–78
  of birds, 53, 75, 79
  of insects, 79
Air traffic control, 87, 95
Airworthiness regulations, 11, 13
Aix-en-Provence, 94
Akrotin,
Albatross, 46 47, 103
  Black-footed, 104
  Laysan, 104
Alberta, 93
Aldabra, 47, 113
Altitude, 7–8, 9, 11, 50, 89, 90
Alternative sites, 49, 98, 167
America, North, 178
Amphibia, 39
Anatidae, *see* ducks, geese and swans
Anchovy, South American, 141
Angels, 53, 54, 72, 77, 79–81
  avian, 79–81
  entomological, 54, 64, 79
  meteorological, 54, 79–81
Angola, 211
Anthrax, 231
Apples, 200
Apricots, 237
Arctic, 95, 158
Arnage Castle, 137
Ascension, 47
Ash, 204, 205, 206–207, 233
Asia, 200
Auchmacoy, 119
Auckland, N.Z., 98
Auditory memory, 20
Australasia, 42, 100

B

Bamako, 212
Barking Creek, The Battle of, 106

247